MW00576076

THE BEST SMALL FICTIONS

2021

RION AMIL *guest editor* CAR SCOTT

NATHAN *series editor* LESLIE

MICHELLE *assistant editor* ELVY

CLAIRE *assistant editor* GUYTON

SONDER PRESS

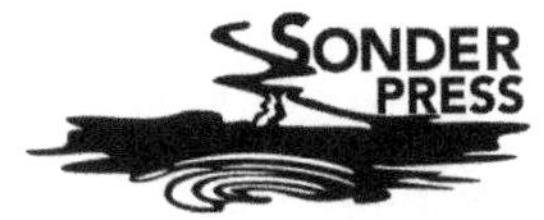

Sonder Press
New York
www.thesonderpress.com

ISBN 978-0-9997501-5-5

First U.S. Edition 2021
Printed in the USA

Best Small Fictions Founding Series Editor: Tara Lynn Masih.

Cover Design by Chad Miller
Distribution via Ingram

THE
BEST SMALL
FICTIONS
2021

CONT *contents* ENTS

SPOTLIGHTED STORIES

MAIN CONTENTS

ESSAY INCLUSION

SPOTLIGHTED JOURNALS

A YEAR AGO AT this point I was in the midst of drafting my introduction for *Best Small Fictions* 2020 in a state of utter confusion and with an accompanying sense of dread and anxiety about the state of the world. The Trump administration continued to make a mockery of American democracy; police brutality seemed to worsen on a weekly basis. The economy seemed in imminent collapse. The global pandemic expanded outward, landing on American shores and devastating communities along the way. Hundreds thousands of people perished. The mood of the country was apocalyptic. Do I seem traumatized? I guess we all are a bit, still. Maybe we always will be.

The works within this year's *Best Small Fictions* 2021 anthology were published, if not written, during 2020--in what might seem an inauspicious time for literature. As Covid-19 raged, literature seemed to some a kind of triviality. How can words on the page or on the screen matter when a plague is striking down three dimensional human beings in the real world? To some, it could not, did not. Many writers on social media complained of complete writer's block. How can one focus on writing fiction or poetry when the real world was in the midst of collapsing? However, as the pandemic deepened and became a kind of fixture in our lives, to many literature took on the role as a source of consolation—a solace, a way of understanding. Many of us stayed at home, isolated in lockdowns or quarantines or otherwise huddling away from a pandemic which, at first, we barely understood.

And yet here we still are, betwixt and between--vaccinations on the horizon or already received. Is 2021 the year of purgatory? Are we stuck in between the new normal and some kind of resurrected old normal? What does the future hold for our world, our country? By the time you have this anthology in your hand perhaps some of these questions will be resolved.

2021 seems to be a year of questions and yet the most pressing one regarding flash fiction for the past year and beyond seems to be: Does literature reflect or shape reality? This is, of course, the age-old aesthetic conundrum. Regarding small fictions, I would say it is a bit of both. In *Best Small Fictions* 2021 some of the work is clearly implicitly reflective of the horrific troubles of 2020. Yet, at the same time, the works that stood out to me were not necessarily the pieces which captured mask-wearing and pandemic isolation and job dislocation and political turmoil. Rather, a certain 2020 *mood* seemed to ribbon throughout most of the selected small fictions in this anthology. The work captured a gloomy menace, a kind of rage and anxiety different even from that of just a few years earlier. We confronted something completely new--and the small fictions within this anthology are the product of that attempt to understand. The work within these pages processes the pandemic; it digests it--even if indirectly, by mirrors and shadows.

The small fictions selected for this anthology, however, also has helped shape my understanding of what we experienced last year--and the individual lives and experiences within it. The internalization of turmoil is perhaps the dominant strain within this book. There is a darkness at the very surface of many of these pieces--I can't even refer to an "underbelly," since it is so often readily apparent at the very forefront of many of the small fictions within this year's anthology.

The state of the world may be troubled, at best; the state of small fictions, by contrast, is robust. There are more and more online and print magazines that publish flash and short prose pieces; more and more literary magazines are nominating work for inclusion; more and more authors who perhaps in years past would have only focused on longer forms now also try their hand at small fictions. And the work itself continues to surprise us, enlighten us, transport us, and emotionally move us. And the creativity and imagination employed within the works in this year's anthology astounds. These are all clearly positive developments which capture the sense that the still-young form continues to evolve. And how!

I am grateful for Rion Amilcar Scott for his wise and insightful guest editing, Elena Stiehler from Sonder Press for publishing this volume yet again and for being a great team player week by week month by month. Thank you also to the globetrotting and ever-astute assistant editor Michelle Elvy, newly-added assistant editor extraordinaire Claire Guyton, the crucially helpful interns April Stettner and Gisele Gehre Bomfim and to all the others on the extensive volunteer staff for their perspicacity and for lending a hand at scouring, tipping and nudging. I hope you find much to revel in here in this year's Best Small Fictions. 2020 may have been a horror show, but we have emerged on the other side to 2021 and beyond. I can't wait to see where small fictions go from here. As the late great Prince might say: *take me with you!*

Nathan Leslie
Series Editor, *Best Small Fictions*
Spring, 2021

RION AMILCAR SCOTT

an introduction

1.

GO OUTSIDE AND LOOK upon the land these days, you can almost see the spirit of death and disease spreading like a shadow of smoke. It's been like this for roughly a year. *Roughly* is an accidentally well-chosen word. Shut-in, cut off from loved ones, taking ill, losing people—it's been *rough* for everybody. I've never had more sympathy for the Egyptians in Pharaoh Ramses II's Egypt. They endured plagues of insects, watched their river water turn to blood, and mourned the deaths of their first-born sons. It feels as if we are in a modern re-telling of Exodus. Stories are where I go for solace, but I take no comfort in watching Dr. Fauci as Moses growing exasperated at the rebellious Israelites who, worshipping the false idols of disinformation, ignore his simple commandments to wash thy hands and wear thy mask.

2.

Sometime early in the pandemic I found my brain scrambled. I read, but the words took no shape. I understood the sentences as sentences and knew the meanings of most of the words, but my brain refused to pull it all together. I learned soon that I was not alone; this was a common secondary plague passing along the pandemic-scarred world. We were all beset by the sudden onset of extreme anxiety, fearful for ourselves and our family members. Everyone took losses as suddenly trips were cancelled, schools and offices shuttered, and the realities of isolation set in. Not most alarming, but certainly alarming, was that my place of comfort, the well-told story, felt nearly unavailable to me. At the same time, I felt the need to write as I usually do. Perhaps it was my ego who assigned me the task of writing something that captured how the pandemic world feels. A craftsman alienated from his tools, words in this case, is indeed a sad thing, and I soon found that I wasn't up to the task of capturing the pandemic in story form.

The tiny narrative, the flash form, has been a balm to me when I previously felt too scattered or emotionally-wrecked to read or write and it was that again in this moment. There's something about the way good short narratives capture the world briefly, yet profoundly, that can shake up the soul. Perhaps it's that the form is inherently experimental, and thus inherently disturbing (in a good way, one hopes). A story of a couple hundred to a thousand words has the power to quickly shift our perspective. We see the full scope in minutes, as opposed to the weeks, or even months it might take to see the full scope of a grand, operatic work. In a flash narrative there often isn't space to take on every element of fiction, so a tiny story might be fat with poeticism, fat with character, fat with setting, fat with symbols, but not fat with all of them. Flash fictions offer us depth over breadth. Fat with substance, as playwright August Wilson used to describe his plays. Fat with substance, even while being made of less substance.

Consider "Walnuts" by Jenna Heller, the rare work in this anthology that takes the pandemic head on. A divorcing couple postpones their separation because they are now shuttered together. In their shared quarantine, they find something like a new rapport, a new connection that springs from gathering fallen walnuts. I don't want to give away everything—and indeed, I can't; the beauty in the story is in experiencing the lovely way Heller arranges her words—but the cracking of an eponymous walnut leads to a new understanding. It's often said it's too soon to take on the pandemic in fiction, our emotions are too raw and the situation is still evolving like new covid strains. That may be true for other forms of fiction—the epic novel may need some time and space—but Heller taking a slice of the moment is just the balm I needed.

Venita Blackburn's "Smoothies" takes place in line at the mall waiting on the drink of the title. The narrator is told she "looks like a man." A mundane moment and a cast off, thoughtless comment, in the hands of a master writer like Blackburn become the basis for profound musings about gender, definition and self-definition. It's also a reminder that even our most staid moments are full of meaning.

Elsewhere, we meet a woman who goes on living after her death, menstrual blood clots who speak, live and dry up, an abrasive union guy undone by his love of cigars, and of course we meet dazzling sentence after dazzling sentence.

3.

It's tempting, when I'm looking out onto the world, watching the spirit of death and disease pass, to say that in addition to a vaccine it's new stories that we need. A new epic narrative to shift understanding. One of the stories I never asked my grandmother to tell when I had the chance was what it was like during the flu pandemic of 1918. I didn't even know I was supposed to ask and she didn't know she needed to tell me. There were anti-maskers then as there are anti-maskers now. We stopped telling of their fate, of their damage. But it's probably not true that a grand story is all we need. What narrative could I tell to stop a man, a cop, from kneeling on a black man's neck? We need stories, of course. The stories contained in this volume show that they need not be grand to move us. They can be short and powerful punches or hugs. My hope is that by the time you read this volume, the pandemic is a recent memory and all that is left is our bruises and our trauma and these brief gems can be part of our healing from that and from so much more.

SPOTLIGHTED STORIES

I AM NOT ALWAYS small, somebody's little sister, somebody's baby girl born with pneumonia. i guess that makes me a miracle & on god's green earth how can any miracle be small? we moved to harlem after mommy didn't like the way the landlord was looking at my legs. i don't know what mommy means by that. she looks at my legs every day & say how skinny they is, like chicken legs when they still alive & pecking ground for rocks or worms or whatever fills they tummy best. i never been to a farm only seen a chicken on black 'n white tv & picture books. most chicken i see come dead in plastic wrap down at the supermarket.

mommy often cusses me for not having more meat on my bones like my sister. my sister is what mommy like to call *healthy* so healthy for halloween we dress her up as a fat boy, stuff her front with pillows to make her gut round enough to really pass. i'm a ghost—one giant white sheet pulled over my plaits down to the ankle right above my white sneaks. being small & all the sheet almost swallows me whole.

sissy's fat boy disguise is so good the neighbor boys stop us right in front of miss mable's stoop. they circle around us like ants on a cheese cracker but sissy naturally don't scare easy. i seen her beat up at least one of them boys the last time they tried to mess with her so i know sissy ain't about to let them whup our butts & steal our trickortreats. the tallest most ashy one come forward, say *sara that you? almost didn't recognize you in that get-up. i always knowed you was some kinda bulldagger. guess today you tryin out your true form.* sara say back, *why you worried bout what i'm doin? wit them rusty knees. who you sposed to be—the tin man?* tall & ashy ain't like that remark one bit. his friends liked to keel over, laughing & whooping like it's the best thing they heard since last wednesday.

it look like she really hurt tall & ashy's feelings & i ain't think he had much in the way of feelings since his mama died last week on accident. he ain't cry not once. she was giving birth to his sixth baby brother which meant another kid he was gonna have to look after while no one was gonna look after him. they daddy still around not like our daddy so they all will get to stay together for now but it look like tall & ashy gonna have to stock full time down at the woolworth. he gonna miss the 7th grade which seem like he'd be ok with since he never went to school all like that anyway.

didn't seem like nothing really hurt him until today when sara call him tin man & his eyes flash something ugly. sara went for them knees to cut him down right there but i remember the tin man ain't got no heart & that's what the elders been saying about tall & ashy, they been asking about his heart. shoot, even his daddy cried a bit while they took the mama's body out the house. i try tugging at the rope pretending to be a belt at sara's waist, hoping she get the hint it's time to go. i says to sara, *my feet hurt & i'm scared for you.* sara turns to me quick, *well go on in the house then. i ain't got no problem beatin all they narrow behinds. boys don't scare me none.* tall & ashy sees that as a greenlight to haul off & punch sara square in the chest. me, sara & the other boys ain't see none of it coming but when sara goes down on the concrete she take tall & ashy with her. i can't stand here & watch so i run. i run past the pink house with no shutters & the brown house missing steps. i run pass ms. patty in her housecoat call herself raking the leaves meanwhile she busy being nosy, on her way inside to tell somebody's mama what was what. the ghost sheet trips me up so i wrap it in a wad & carry it like a baby in my arms. i leap over the old tire that never found its way off the middle of the sidewalk. my heart racing but my mind clear: *a bat. get that bat.* i run home to get the biggest bat i can find & come back swinging.

Nefertiti Asanti is a poet born and raised in the Bronx and a recipient of fellowships and residencies from the Watering Hole, Lambda Literary, Anaphora Arts, Winter Tangerine, and the Hurston/Wright Foundation. Nefertiti's work can be found at *AfroPunk, Foglifter, Santa Clara Review,* and elsewhere. Currently, Nefertiti serves as prose poetry editor of *Stellium Literary Magazine.*

THE FIRST TIME A guy said I look like a man was at the Jamba Juice stand in the mall. He was still a boy, probably my age and sticky from adolescence. *You look like a man.* He said it as if he had the right to say anything to me. As if it was important for his survival, an echo of his ancestors who were my ancestors, long and black and muscled, though we were two strangers holding smoothies. His phone was three generations older than mine. I had superior sneakers, a designer sweatshirt, better moisturizer, and even my drink held more protein and complexity, but he wielded his right to possess them all in one note of disgust. I took a sip as a man in a suit too tall to have a head in my sightline jingled the change in his pocket.

You look like a man. It took a few seconds before I knew it wasn't a compliment, that it was a lesson, an exchange, that he was learning too, how to be a man by not being a girl. In Sunday school we were learning about the first man and first woman and how Adam must've been closer to God because God made him first, and pretty much all the problems of all time thereafter came about because of Eve and a snack. I chewed a hunk of ice that hadn't broken down properly, and a woman hit the headless man in a suit in the heel with her stroller.

The boy could've said the words like he'd say hello or nice to meet you or where did you get that watch or what a wonderful day it is to be upright and breathing here together. But he said them in a different way, the way we tell strangers your shoes are untied or you have toilet paper on your ass. He saw himself in me and felt ashamed. He saw himself in me and felt proud, but pride wasn't supposed to live inside of women, so he had to walk it back and cut its throat till the blood ringed around my neck.

You look like a man. Years later it would become *You eat like a man. You walk like a man. You sound like a man.* My chromosomes had not yet been tested. My birth certificate says female, live birth, seven pounds and three ounces.

I didn't think I wanted to be loved by boys until that boy told me it was not possible. I don't remember what I looked like then, a few years ago, but I remember him, his dirty Chucks, ashy corners of his mouth, and dry scalp. Back then I stared deeply at people the way children do, still curious. He existed. I didn't expect him to look back though. Children are rarely seen, but I wasn't a child anymore and had not fully realized that. Now strangers could assert their judgments on my whole body, my whole story without permission.

You look like a man. I was three sips into the smoothie before it hit. To be a woman seemed a terrible thing to have happen, and it happened at 3:54 on a Friday when I was fourteen to the sound of a blender jolted to life. Women have to be small, give birth, wear makeup. I could see all the women, the court reporters, the accountants, psychics and secretaries, biologists and senators, important but nameless with inconvenient hairstyles and morning routines. Men got to invent women over and over one generation after another by the grace of God.

The woman's stroller spit out a toy from what must've been a child tucked inside. The mother cooed, then retrieved the toy and fed it back to the stroller. The mall was not a place to fall apart. It happened anyway. When I get hurt, usually the universe opens up a little like a bullet through a watermelon. Things separate and scatter. It feels like this is how we really are all the time and everything else is just pretend. We pretend to have legs and skin and penises and milk ducts. We pretend some skin looks one way while other skin is different. We pretend to have green eyes and brown eyes and yellow teeth and gray teeth, and the sky is blue to us in the day and black at night. We pretend lots of things that are only sort of true when we are the sky and time and memory and the center of the earth and destiny and gods and gravity and salted oceans and children of the gods who ate their mothers and birthed the constellations and nebulas and death is a myth because everything goes into itself to begin again. There was fear and doubt on the boy's face when I finally turned away. The condemnation dissolved. I, a girl, would grow to be a better man than he and still be a woman.

The sugar pooled like acid on my tongue when the feeling passed. All the other customers departed, and it was just us under the fluorescent lights together again. There seemed nothing left to prove and a whole new point was born between us that we had not yet named.

Works by Venita Blackburn have appeared or are forthcoming in *Ploughshares, McSweeney's, The Paris Review* and others. She received the Prairie Schooner book prize in fiction for her collected stories, *Black Jesus and Other Superheroes* in 2017. She is founder of the literary nonprofit Live, Write (livewriteworkshop.com), which provides free creative writing workshops for communities of color. Blackburn's second collection of stories, *How to Wrestle a Girl,* will be published fall of 2021. She is an Assistant Professor of creative writing at California State University, Fresno

WHEN SHE SEES EDNA'S boy in the grocery store, she doesn't feel at all strange walking right up to him and asking him to reach up and get down that soup can from the top shelf. He gets it for her, just as a young man should when an old lady asks for help, but afterward, he won't let go of the can, and when she tries to pull it from him, he strokes the top of her hand with his thumb.

Startled, she lets go and takes a step back. Maybe this isn't Edna's boy after all—he didn't have those green eyes, did he?

"You live in that big yellow house all by yourself?" he asks though it isn't a real question. Of course, she lives in the yellow house, and alone too—everyone knows that—after her husband of thirty-five years had died suddenly, foaming at the mouth and shaking at a picnic last spring. He was dead by the time she'd called the paramedics. The doctor told her later it hadn't been a heart attack but the red-bellied newt that had crawled into the pitcher of lemonade and died after its body released enough neurotoxin to kill a horse. "You're lucky you didn't drink any yet," he'd told her.

She makes up her mind to reprimand the young man for being nosy and impertinent with an old lady, but right as she opens her mouth, he sets the can in her basket, leaning down as he does, and putting his lips right next to her ear. His wet breath makes her tremble in a way she's forgotten is still possible. "I'll tell you what I'm going to do," he says, "I'm going to pay you a visit and make sure there's nothing that needs fixing in your old yellow house." He straightens up just as a young mother comes down the aisle, two blonde children riding in her cart. Examining a sale on pinto beans, he doesn't turn around until her squeaky wheels have turned the corner, then he faces the old woman again.

She's stunned and waiting, half horrified and half delighted by the young man, who really couldn't be Edna's boy, could he? He smiles, seeing her still standing there, and she notices that his two front teeth are chipped. He gets close again and she waits to feel his breath. "Now you go on ahead and pay, sweetheart," he tells her, "then get in your car." His fingers touch the small of her back. "I'll follow you home."

At his touch, something electrifies her, and she nods one too many times. "Of course," she says, breath coming fast. The rest of her list abandoned, she wanders down the aisle to the cash register. The checker asks twice how her day is, but all she can do is smile, not hearing a single word he says.

She doesn't see Edna's boy in the parking lot, and a pink wave of worry washes over her, but when he pulls his pickup behind her on the road, she takes a shuddery breath and settles. On the fifteen-minute drive home, she sees that the willow outside the old green church is festooned for Easter again, the pastel ribbons proclaiming, "He Has Risen." Daffodils push their heads out of the mud by the side of the road, and the whole world seems remade on this day, separated from the dingy old skin it usually wears.

When he shuts her front door behind them, he locks it. She turns to look, but he's beside her again, with his fingers on her jawline now, turning her head from the lock to his face. "Come on now, sweetheart." He sets down the groceries and takes her hand, gently, though she knows somehow that if she tries to pull away, he'll break her arm.

She follows him through the hall to the kitchen, glad, for a moment, that she took the time to clean it that morning. He sits her at the round table in the center of the room and turns slowly, taking in the apron-front sink, her breakfast plate drying in the rack, the magnetic strip of knives.

"Bet you didn't think someone like me was going to come into your life," Edna's boy says, cracking his knuckles as if his fingers are impatient for something.

"No," she says, her heart thumping.

He smiles that chipped smile and walks towards the knives, examining a cleaver before selecting the boning knife.

"Can I fix you a drink, dear?" she asks, trying to keep her words from tumbling out too quickly, "before we get started? I have some fresh lemonade in the fridge."

He blinks languorously like a cat, like he can't believe the audacity of this old woman, but he nods and then smiles. "You go right on ahead, sweetheart. I'd like that."

"Hand me a glass?" she asks, before turning to the fridge to retrieve the blue pitcher. It is filled to the brim with lemonade, even though that had hardly been necessary--she'd planned on being the only one to drink any that evening, after her dinner, until she met Edna's boy in the grocery store, of course. Now it seems almost too heavy, and the weight of it makes her hand shake so badly that he sets down the boning knife to help her. He pours himself a glass, and without sitting, drinks the whole thing, smacks his lips and fills it again.

Sitting very still at the table, she is sure she sees a veil of something pass over his eyes. In the hallway, her groceries wait, abandoned, and beside her--the perfectly sliced lemons inside hiding the motionless body of a red-bellied newt, the wet pitcher is staining the kitchen table, but she does not move, just counts the seconds as he finishes his second lemonade. She has all the time in the world.

Julie Cadman-Kim lives in Ann Arbor while she pursues her MFA at the University of Michigan's Helen Zell Writers' Program. Her work has been published or is forthcoming in *Black Warrior Review, Fairy Tale Review, Barren Magazine, Passages North,* and elsewhere. You can follow her on Twitter @julieloukim or see more of her writing at juliecadman-kim.com.

FOR MANY OF US, the substitute teacher was the first white person we'd ever seen outside of television. Before this, for us, white men fell into two camps: Leonardo DiCaprio—youthful floppy-haired, desirable; or Prince Charles—wrinkled, dog-like, horrifying.

Mr. Gardiner was different. He was older than Leo, but maintained a similar, though less successful middle-parted hairstyle that stuck to his forehead like an oily curtain. His face, ruddy like the Prince's, shone with sweat from the humid classroom, pink as the whole chickens our mothers would defrost in the kitchen. And he mispronounced everyone's name. After an unfortunate incident where he called Lee Pooi Kee, "Lee PU-KI" (puki, being the word for cunt), he appointed Laila, whose name he could pronounce, class monitor, to help him take attendance.

My mother did not approve. What business, she asked, did the school have hiring a gweilo during an economic downturn? "Can't find someone local?" she raged. She listened every day to Radio 4, as Prime Minister Mahathir blamed the 1998 financial crash on an American Jewish conspiracy.

My father took issue with something quite different. "The English are so smelly. Why is it with them, the soap budget is the first to go?"

He doesn't smell too bad, I countered, and besides, it's too hot for them here.

Undeterred, my father asked, "How do you know? Have you sniffed his bum?"

My older sister wanted to know, "Is he cute?" And to be honest, I wasn't sure.

Mr. Gardiner taught history. It was an unfortunate incongruence, a white man hired to educate 13-year-olds on the impact of colonialism in their country, yet the syllabus, unlike the tropical weather or the pronunciation of girls' names, was the one thing that Mr. Gardiner did not seem uncomfortable with.

Each day, he learned three new Malay words, then he would teach the rest of the class in English. For example, he might ask, in English, "What positive impacts did British colonization have on Malaysia?"

Then he would turn to the blackboard, scratching his three new Malay words in chalk.

Agama. *Religion.*

Pendidikan. *Education.*

Tamadun. *Civilization.*

In the years that followed, we learned to be appalled by this unapologetic Eurocentrism. But at the time, we were preoccupied with something more ridiculous – when he finished scribing, Mr. Gardiner would wipe the chalk dust off his fingers and onto the back of the dark polyester slacks he wore. The white chalk stains looked like ghost fingers grabbing his bum.

Laila, the class monitor, detested him. Her parents, like my mother, were angered by the influx of foreigners, "taking jobs from locals."

Kalaiselvi felt sorry for him. "He has no wife, and no friends, and he's hot, all the time!"

And I, as I watched the chalky fingers flex on his bum, felt a curious spaciousness fill the area below my stomach and above my pelvis. Much later, I would identify the feeling as desire, but at 13, it just made me feel like peeing.

Vanessa Chan is a Malaysian writer preoccupied with identity, colonization, and women who don't toe the line. She has been published in *Conjunctions, Electric Lit, Porter House Review,* and more. Her writing has received support from Tin House, Disquiet International, and the Mendocino Coast Writers' Conference, and has been included in and nominated for multiple anthologies. She is a fiction editor at *TriQuarterly,* a former tech worker.

I'LL ALLOW IT, MAYBE JUST THIS ONCE

OKAY DONKEY

jeff chon

BRETT LAMONICA HAD LONG feathered hair like Bon Jovi. He was three years older than me and his black denim jacket smelled like baby powder and Lucky Strikes. I used to see him smoking with the other metal kids off school grounds, spitting brown tobacco flakes off his tongue.

He wasn't the first person to call me a Chink and far from the last, but he was definitely the only one who'd made it matter. It might have been the way he smiled, like he wanted me to think he was joking, even though he wasn't. He'd put his arm around me when he said it, pulling me into a headlock, or he'd slap me on the back like it was supposed to be good-natured. But he wasn't fooling anyone—not even himself. I'd once asked him to stop, and then he asked me what I was going to do about it, and that was the last time I asked him to stop.

I used to see him after school, bent over the boy's room sink, making sure all the eyeliner was gone before he went home. He'd clench his eyes shut and scrub pink powdered soap into his eyelids. It looked so painful, the way he'd squint at the mirror, his bangs sticking to his cheeks.

He once came over with his dad so he could apologize for squeezing a ketchup bottle down my shirt. He said he was sorry and then went home, and his dad and my dad smoked on the porch. I don't know what they talked about, but I do remember getting hassled for making another boy's father feel sorry for me. A couple days later, I was enrolled in Taekwondo, where a stocky, middle-aged man yelled at me in Korean and told my dad how sensitive I was. Other than that, nothing much changed. Brett kept hooking his arm around my shoulder, and the little fourth and fifth-graders never tired of snickering at my pathetic front kicks.

Brett was the lead singer of Vendetta, a hair metal band he'd formed with these guys who were always telling him to lay off of me. I'd once heard them perform "When the Children Cry" in his garage. It was one of two times I'd ever thought about fighting back, about rising from the bicycle seat and pumping the pedals harder and harder as I barreled toward his bewildered bandmates, about leaping off the bike, crashing into him as my ten-speed crashed into one of the amps. But instead, we locked eyes as he held the mic against his lips and sang about a world healed by tears, and I rode away.

Looking back, Vendetta was a pretty good name for a band.

The only other time I thought about fighting back was when he crimped his hair. The only reason I didn't was because he'd changed it back to normal the next day—at least that's what I told myself. He also had a fat lip, which at the time looked really funny. I remember laughing at how dumb he looked, his eyes bloodshot from the pink soap, the water sliding off his overhanging bottom lip like some kind of drooling idiot.

Sometimes, you realize your hands aren't clean and you tell yourself it makes you sick, but that thing you're feeling isn't anything like sickness. It's something else you can't name, even though not naming it means you're either stupid or cruel. And then you shrug and tell yourself there's nothing else to really say about it, but you know that's a lie.

Brett graduated and I didn't see him again until my senior year, a couple months after he'd been kicked out of the Navy. He asked if my parents were home, and I told him they weren't. Then he told me he was here to fix the sink, and I told him I knew that.

So you're working for your dad now? I asked. He didn't say anything.

We walked into the kitchen so I could show him what needed work. You look different, he said. I told him I'd been working out, and he gave me a weird look because how else do you respond to that? He crawled under the kitchen sink, and I went back to the living room to unpause *Road Rash 2*.

He finished up, and I gave him the money my mom had left. I stood on the porch and watched him walk to the van.

Remember when you crimped your hair? I said.

He stopped and chuckled, asked why the hell I'd bring that up, so I told him he looked like a fag. He took a breath and shook his head.

Yeah man, he smiled. My dad said the same thing.

He slammed the door and turned the ignition. Guns N' Roses was in the tape deck. We locked eyes as he backed out of the driveway, and I wanted him to call me a Chink again, just one last time, like maybe he'd be the only person I'd make an exception for.

Jeff Chon's novel, *Hashtag Good Guy with a Gun* (Sagging Meniscus Press 2021) is available in bookstores everywhere. His work has appeared in *3AM Magazine, Maudlin House, Excuse Me Magazine,* and *The North American Review,* among many other fine places. He is a contributing editor at *Heavy Feather Review.*

57 WAYS TO TALK ABOUT YOUR TIME

kanya d'almeida

YOU DID NOT WANT it. When it came you'd have to enter that veiled, silent place where the women lived, and the things you loved—the bicycle, your school, even laughter—were considered improper. Obscene.

In Sinhalese they call it The Cleaning of the Body. In Tigrinya it is That Thing Belonging to Our Mothers.

Halfway to the mountain summit is a village of goatherds who make the most wonderful cheese, pungent, creamy spheres wrapped in wax paper. When their daughters are in bloom, the villagers tie their animals outside and shut the girls up in the goat sheds. Even the little ones, eight or nine years old. Sometimes they have to drag them, screaming, away from their mothers and into those hovels full of straw and shit.

Flamingos are migrating, cardinals are mating, the rooster is molting.

Headline from the frontlines: They Didn't Have Napkins So They Used Sand and Bread.

It came. Your mother called it Your Time and showed you how to extract the sodden cotton from its plastic wrapper, shred it between your fingers and flush the bits away, an exercise that left stringy-clingy traces of membranes on your skin.

In some cultures they say the hive is dripping with honey. Or, she's tapping maple trees. In Sweden the girls say they're "having jam with the waffle."

Describe it in one word: Gold.

Chico Mendez was killed. He was a rubber tapper. Yes, they shot that gentle forest guardian and his blood stained the floor of the Amazon. Now, when their insides come out, when the blood congeals in the forest between their legs, some women say, "Estou com Chico," *I'm with Chico.*

Is the strawberry patch fruiting, did the peach tart explode in the oven, has the pomegranate ripened on the tree? Is the cherry soaking in the sherry?

There were some perks. Your father and brothers refused to eat a meal prepared by a woman under the curse. Released from your duties in the kitchen you invented games that required no playmates: tossing a marble into a broken coconut shell, folding old bank chits into birds.

A feminist once said, "Frida Kahlo is painting in my studio." A Hungarian hairdresser announced, "There are communists in the funhouse."

Somewhere in the world a little boy is playing Growing Up. He drapes himself in his mother's clothes, lamenting the absence of fleshy lumps on his chest and a mysterious cave between his legs. Most of all he covets the secret his sisters hide from him—their season that comes with the moon and sends them, in tears and whispers, to the outhouse at all hours. Spellbound, he follows them, observes their ritual through a crack in the door. In a fever of curiosity he salvages their discards, unwrapping old newspapers to discover musty headlines. He puts the parcel in his own underpants as an act of mourning.

The lotus opened last night. I'm shedding poppy petals. The bougainvillea is in full flower.

She told no one she was going through menopause. She went to work as usual, returned to her flat, ate, passed wind and bought the newspaper from the same kiosk every morning. But she felt a hard emptiness inside her, a small round stone of sorrow that grew and grew until she could barely breathe. She stood naked before the mirror and examined her parts: a belly free of stretch marks. Two lovely breasts that never fed a child.

Dawra. Mahina. Haiyz.

Mine smells like? Rust. Vinegar. Rot. Earth. Nails. Booze. Damp, like the grass after the rain. Foul, like a freezer full of meat.

When it was time to make the pilgrimage, you lied. Women in your condition were not allowed in the holy city and you didn't want to be left behind. You carried your little secret everywhere. As you circled the shrine on the final day, you felt big, silky clots slipping out of you, and it made you smile.

Cost of supplies: A day's wages. A carton of cigarettes. More than rice. A sexual favor. I pawned my wedding ring.

First they came in twos and threes, then by the dozen, all with guts in their hands. Months of soiled napkins, bucketsful of menses.

A priest with an oil-barrel belly and prayer beads around his neck accosted them at the temple's threshold.

A young protestor with a braid as thick as a python led the charge.

"You dare to stand between us and our goddess? You refuse our offerings of flowers and incense? Take *that* and *that*. Let us in, or drown in our pollution."

Suggested group nouns: a rage, a clot, a flow. A hysteria of power. A sisterhood of lamentation.

Instructions from the United Nations: Don't let the girls drop out of school. Let them use cloth, leaves, coconut husks. They may stink and scrape, never mind. They must learn to read or they will end up like their mothers, grandmothers—forever squatting over holes instead of sitting on a throne.

The man they chose was older by a generation, a respected figure in the community. Throughout the ceremony you prayed for your pangs to come early and spare you the wedding night, but they didn't. Nor did he.

Worst places to be unprepared: In the bus, squashed between men with ripe armpits and hungry eyes. On a lifeboat. In a camp full of hopeless waiting.

In Chile they call it *La Regla*, the Rule. Then there is the Bloody Baron, the Maroon Marquis, the Crimson King. But in South Africa matriarchy trumps monarchy: Granny's stuck in traffic, they say. The Auntie with the red car is parked outside.

In one word? Relief.

Nowadays you welcome it. Released from your duties in the bedroom, you sleep alone on a mat in the hall. Your mother was right to call it Yours—this is the only time of the month you can escape him. The only time of the month you can come.

Kanya D'Almeida is a fiction writer based in Colombo, Sri Lanka. Her stories have appeared on *Jaggery* and *The Bangalore Review.* She is the host of The Darkest Light, a podcast exploring the untold stories of birth and motherhood in Sri Lanka. She holds an MFA in Fiction Writing from Columbia University's School of the Arts.

LATE ONE NIGHT, ALFONSO crept to the manager's cabin and stole a box of twelve prime cigars. He returned to the bunkhouse and sat on the edge of his stinking pallet, smoking these pungent cigars one after the other. Alfonso was an ancient cannery worker, disdained alike by his fellow canning union men and the seasonal city kids. "It's more than criminal for us not to have a nice cigar when we're the ones doing all the work," said Alfonso. He and I were alone in the squat bunkhouse. The cold room already reeked of fish and bodies, but the thick smoke of the cigars ran up my nose and died there. I hid in my filthy blankets, feeling ill. I knew if I peeked back at Alfonso, the scales stuck to his ruddy arms would be winking in the glow of the cigar's tip.

Out on the beach, the moon rolled its big belly among the rest of the cannery workers, all of them blind drunk on grain liquor. The canning union men staggered on the wet dark sand and traded each other meaty punches. The seasonal city kids guzzled while perched on logs at the high-tide mark.

"I smoke this for Jack Buenavista," said Alfonso. "I smoke this for Trinidad Rojo." Alfonso was always swearing fealty to the bygone heroes of the canneries. I was the only one who listened. I was up from the city, muddling through my first miserable cannery summer, not a union man but not yet accepted by the seasonal city kids. Over the dark sea, another trawler came our way, engorged with glistening fish.

The next afternoon, the manager pulled all the city kids off the canning line. The manager's gut clung like a baby to his middle, and his legs plunged into waders slick with blood and fish grease. He stuffed us into the hot little canteen. "I do not blame you kids," he said, "You're up here earning your dollars for an education, a house, a lover back in the lower states." He dripped syrup over us until we preened. "If you find out who of the canning union stole my cigars," he said, "You tell me." He rustled his hand in his waders. He produced a foul one-hundred dollar bill, which he fluttered like a handkerchief. "For your troubles," he said, "now get back on the line." We scurried out, and he called in the canning union.

Rain came in fat gouts. Without the guidance of the canning union men, we clogged the slime table and jammed the feeder machine. We ran around mewling and shaking, covered in guts. When the union men returned, they cleaned up our mess with a fine sustained rage burning in their eyes. They were steeped in year after year of seething fishmeat, while the city kids came and went, dabbling.

That night in the bunkhouse, boots squelched, fists hit palms, and there was the terrible rasp of something being sharpened. Ivan, a fat union man with glittering earrings, stood up near the door. "So, you bitches, you little runty milk-feeders, who stole the cigars? The manager is docking pay," he said. I writhed in my blankets. From among the folds of the odorous wool I peered at Alfonso. He lay on his back, staring at the weathered wood above him with drowned eyes. No one said a word. Ivan stomped back to his bunk. Bottles clinked. I dozed.

Shouting woke me. Ivan and another union guy stood over Alfonso's bunk, screaming into his face. Alfonso said nothing. They ripped him from his bunk and shook him. Ivan waved the wooden cigar box over his head, shouting Wake up, betrayal, wake up. The bunkhouse disgorged its filthy tenants into the mud and the rain. The canning union men held Alfonso in their midst, while around them the city kids yipped and yelled. "Stop, stop," I sobbed. I tried to fight my way to Alfonso but was repelled by a dozen fetid, muscled backs. Someone shoved me and I fell into the mud.

The crowd bore Alfonso up the muddy path to the manager's cabin. A single sodium bulb burned over the door. Ivan banged on the door until the manager emerged, still wearing his waders, congealed hate upon his face. Ivan and the others brought Alfonso forward, and kicked him behind the knees. The manager stood on the concrete stoop above Alfonso. Ivan offered him the cigar box, which he turned over in his hands. "Well, old man?" said the manager.

Alfonso opened his mouth. Stubs of rotten teeth marched in weary formation. His weathered tongue lolled out of his mouth like a sea cucumber. "Nyah," he said. He waggled the tongue back and forth, shining in the rain. The manager's face squirmed and bucked. He raised the box up high, and swung it down. He broke the little wooden box over Alfonso's head with a wild crack.

Alfonso fell forward into the mud. The crowd roared and drew back. "Take him away," said the manager. Ivan and three others said they would haul him to the infirmary. I followed them, toiling through the mud, believing they would pitch Alfonso from the docks and into the frothing oily water. At the infirmary Ivan said he'd fallen from his bunk. "Liar," I said.

"I'll drown you," hissed Ivan. Alfonso came back to work a week later, addled and weak. He died in his sleep a week after that.

That was how we lost Alfonso. I was heartbroken, for Alfonso and I were interested in the same things. We talked some nights of putting the manager into the canning machine, and of the fishermen who braved winter seas on boats rhimed with ice. We both knew a woman in Pioneer Square who would serve you lunch and charge you nothing, so long as you promised to kiss her old neck when you finished, and tell her of the beauty that was still in Alaska.

Sam Dunnington lives in Missoula, Montana, and is an MFA candidate in fiction at the University of Montana. He has previously lived in Philadelphia and Seattle, and his writing appears in the *Missouri Review* and *Narratively Magazine*. He loves hiking, cooking, and watching movies.

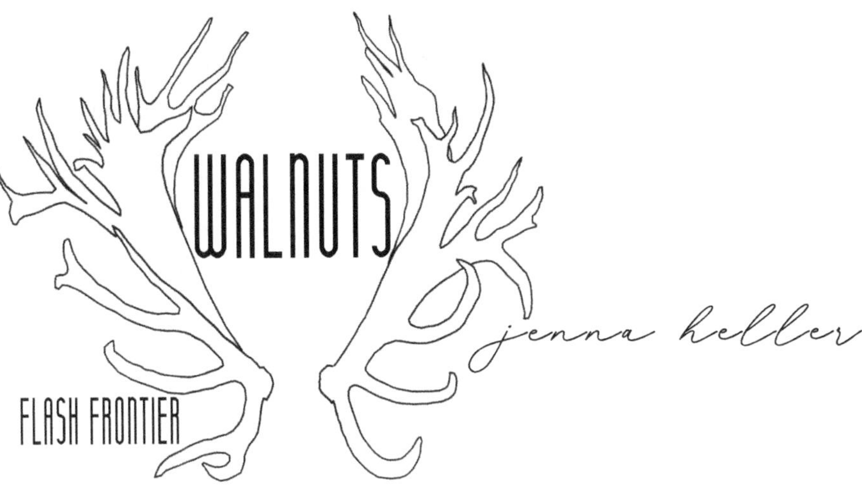

NOT LONG AFTER WE agreed to separate and you'd already packed up half your things, we found ourselves stuck because of the lockdown. Remember that? Remember how the wind howled for two days straight and blew all the walnuts from the trees? How we heard them pelting the fence, pummeling the lawn, cracking on the deck? How we spent the better part of a whole day collecting the stone fruit from the wet lawn and autumn leaves? It took so much longer than we expected. But what else did we have to do?

Secretly, I reveled in the time outdoors, the time to achieve something, the time to do something in concert with you. It felt so different from being cooped up inside where all we seemed to do was sigh and move into separate rooms.

So there we were, the two of us stooped over, sweeping the yard like spoonbills sweep the estuary. Back and forth, filling our hands before filling our buckets. And while our backs were killing us, our hands got a sort of massage from the wrinkled shells swirling in our palms.

After we'd picked them all up, we sat on the deck and each held a couple, moved them around like Chinese medicine balls. Feeling familiar and warm. The rhythm comforting. And we saw each other again. I mean, we really saw each other. For the first time in months. Like when we were young and we could look into each other's eyes forever without saying a word.

Then you grabbed the mallet and smashed one. Broke the spell. Offered me half.

Jenna Heller is an American-New Zealander whose small fictions can be found in *Flash Frontier,*

Landfall, Love in the Time of COVID, Hot Flash Fiction, Ghost Parachute, Bending Genres, North & South, and *Meniscus.* In 2020, she won the New Zealand National Flash Fiction Day competition—'Walnuts' was shortlisted—and she was shortlisted for the New Zealand Society of Authors' Heritage Awards (single poem category) and the takahē Monica Taylor Poetry Prize. She is currently seeking a publisher for her debut poetry collection and is working on a short and small fictions collection as well as a novel-in-flash.

CYNTHIA B. HURLEY, KNOWN online as @iBrake4Corgis17, was a well-connected woman visible across the social media landscape. Her beloved Instagram feed totaled 12,574 posts, and she amassed 836 followers after more than twenty-five years of daily engagement with the app. Cindy's all-time, most-liked post was a photo from October 2031 of her wearing a Davy Crockett raccoon-skin cap, pretending to strangle the eight-foot-tall stuffed grizzly bear in the lobby of the Fern Creek Lodge which garnered 529 likes and spawned dozens of comments, including the expected accolades from her dear friends @tango4one and @winediva77. This post's popularity surpassed her previous record for the selfie she took in front of copulating zebras during her well-documented safari trip to the Serengeti back in the winter of 2029.

Cindy's YouTube channel was a hallowed storehouse for her personal concert recordings, including a third-row video capture of nearly all of Neil Diamond's "Cracklin' Rosie" live from the Hollywood Bowl that, to date, has been viewed more than 8,200 times. She also leaves behind a nine-part series of how-to videos for removing stubborn stains from a variety of fabrics. Cindy's upload demonstrating how baking soda and vinegar can be used to get a dark roast coffee stain out of a hand-tufted wool rug has gotten nearly 5,000 views, and it ultimately earned her an invitation for a featured segment on household cleaning tips and tricks on *Wake Up Bakersfield!*

While a perilous allergy to pet dander rendered Cindy incapable of keeping a dog in her apartment, she nonetheless maintained an active Tumblr account where she collected innumerable photographs of dressed-up Corgis. Her favorite was of a Pembroke Welsh outfitted with a deerstalker hat and wool tweed jacket to which she added the caption, "the Corgi of Baskerville."

On Twitter, Cindy only followed celebrity chefs. She liked their weeknight recipe links, and appreciated their reluctance to discuss politics in public forums. Cindy had registered accounts on Linkedin, Pinterest, Snapchat, Pastiche, Splay, among others, however, it was her Facebook presence that most endeared Cindy to hundreds of family and friends throughout the world. Her profile picture—a brown-and-white cartoon face of a pointy-eared Corgi, sporting a top hat and monocle—became iconic among her followers. This tiny portrait was framed next to each of her comments, linked Instagram photos, and witty status updates. "I forgot to workout today; that's nine years in a row!" was posted at 8:52am on the day she passed.

On Facebook, Cindy was known for her tenacious commitment to celebrating birthdays within her vast circle of friends. She developed something of a trademark for the occasion, writing "Feliz Cumpleaños" squeezed between two maracas emojis for each friend on their special day. On her own birthday, Cindy would respond to each of her well-wishers with personalized GIF reactions and emoji sequences tailored to their particular connection.

Although she could be playful, Cindy did not shy away from important global issues. She received 345 likes and 97 sad-face reactions for the article she shared about the devastating flooding and refugee crisis in Cambodia and South Vietnam. Her powerful post that simply displayed the block-lettered phrase "dog fighting" within a red circle and backslash had a similar kind of impact on her followers.

While Cindy's passing is sorrowful, she did opt-in for Facebook's Posthumous Content Generator, so it is comforting to know that her spirit will live on with posts authored in her likeness, originating from her account forevermore. The first such post, Cindy's *Life Retrospective,* is now live and can be viewed at her profile page, or at her memorial tablet onsite at Hillcrest Cemetery.

#pour1forCin #CorgisRpeople2 #mother_of_4

Michael Hendery is a clinical psychologist and professor who lives with his wife and two daughters in New Hampshire. He completed the Mountainview MFA program in fiction at Southern NH University. This is his first published short fiction. He has a boutique Twitter presence @psychmych and has opted out of Facebook's Posthumous Content Generator.

THE FIRST TIME I birthed a blood baby it plopped to the tub floor and slid to the drain, trail of red staining the porcelain. I didn't know what it was. It looked like a chunk of canned cranberry sauce. It wobbled in the shower spray, too big to be washed away. I pressed my big toe against its smoothness and smashed it down the drain in pieces.

The third time it happened, I picked up the thing to examine it, turning it around in my hands, soft and squishy like an overripe plum. "Keep me," a voice said. I slipped and almost dropped it. I turned off the shower thinking the water was playing tricks on me. Trevor wasn't home, so it couldn't be him. "Keep me," the squeaky voice said again. There was only this bloody blob in my hands. Sitting naked on the tub's edge, I looked for a mouth. No arms or legs, no mouth or face, but its voice vibrated in my hands; it was all heart. "Keep me," it pleaded.

I grabbed a towel, raced to the kitchen, and got a dessert bowl from the china hutch. I'd been saving the silver basket weave patterned dishes for a special occasion. After 12 years of marriage, I thought we'd have more things to celebrate. I thought there'd be children and chipped china. I wiped dust from the bowl with my towel and placed the blood baby gently in. I set the bowl on the windowsill that got the most sun.

Every month a new blood baby came to join her sisters. The oldest lost her luster and shriveled to a burgundy-black pea. The youngest was silken, wet. I organized them around the bowl by birth date, a blood-baby-stages-of-metamorphosis clock. Trevor shunned the window, passing it with eyes focused on the floor or body glued to the opposite wall. Avoidance was his coping strategy.

I found joy in sitting by the window talking to my blood babies as they aged and withered. Sometimes we sat in silence. Sometimes they said sorry on behalf of my uterus. Sometimes I'd teach them songs we'd sing together in harmony, but I loved hearing them call me

Mama most. Once they became crisp pebbles, I returned them to the earth, buried in our small backyard beneath a circle of smooth stones.

The doctor said I had abnormal growths called fibroids, but I heard fruit. One, a plum, another a grape. My uterus became a small orchard. I gave thanks to its inhospitable environment for sustaining fruit. I signed up for Your Baby's Fruit Size This Week emails and learned a plum is the size of a 12-week-old fetus. I'd never made it past the blueberry stage with my pregnancies, but my fruit continued to grow. Plum became orange, grape became plum. They drained me as they grew. I craved blood, going from well done to medium rare red meat. I told the staff at the steakhouse near my job, "The baby likes steak!" Then grapefruit, then orange again. Out of breath walking up the stairs, stars in my eyes when I stood up too fast. Then honeydew melon, then mango. Strangers gave me their seats on the subway. I gladly sat down while rubbing my belly.

My weekly baby-size email said I had heartburn, frequent urination, trouble sleeping, and my internal organs were being squished. It also said my baby could hear and its kidneys and liver should be fully functional. I wondered if Honeydew and Mango heard me when I groaned in pain. Did they feel responsible? My doctor said they were dangerous and had to be taken out. I woke from surgery with a flatter stomach, a new scar above my pubic hair, but no fruit, no babies. In online groups, no amount of calling fibroids fruit made people like them—they were always monsters. But I miss my little monsters and how they showed me what a pregnant body would look like on me.

My mother used to say to me, "Never throw your hair in the garbage because birds will find it, use it in their nests, and you'll have headaches for the rest of your life." As a child, I'd picture pigeons pecking my brain like worms. After cornrowing my hair, she'd put the little bundles of shed hair in an ashtray and light it. I'd watch, mesmerized by how the hair sizzled, quickly becoming ash.

After the doctor said I couldn't have babies, I began leaving gifts for the birds in our backyard. It feels good to have my own ritual now. My hair is perfect for nests, soft and coily, dark brown to easily blend with other nest materials, a few wiry grays for strength. During the week, I gather hair from my brush or finger detangling. I put the strands in the same bowl by the window my blood babies spent their short lives in; Trevor still avoids that window. By the end of the week, the bowl has sprouted. On Saturdays, after Trevor leaves to coach football, I scatter hair mixed with twigs and birdseed on the grassy section of our small yard.

After the hair is spread, I sit in a lounge chair on the patio, sip chamomile from a silver-lined teacup, and wait. Two tiny birds I call Kiwi and Tan have been coming for birdseed for a long time. They like the hair, taking pieces in their beaks and flying up to the top of our towering London planetree. Their nest is hidden by leaves and branches, but I know they're pleased with my gifts because they leave me trinkets near the feeder: feathers, ribbon, small colorful beads, a keychain in the shape of a house. It feels good to know that something beautiful can be made with my body. When the pain comes, it's not a headache, but sharp beaks at my belly, pecking at my already mangled uterus. There's still life inside me.

LaToya Jordan is a writer from Brooklyn, New York. She is a fiction writer, poet, and occasional essayist and journalist. She is the author of a poetry chapbook *Thick-Skinned Sugar* (Finishing Line Press). Her essay "The Zig Zag Mother," appears in *My Caesarean: Twenty-One Mothers on the C-Section Experience and After* (The Experiment) and another essay, "After Striking a Fixed Object," published by *The Manifest-Station,* was listed as "notable" in Best American Essays 2016. Her writing has appeared in *Anomaly, Literary Mama, Mom Egg Review, Poets & Writers, The Rumpus,* and more. LaToya received an MFA in Creative Writing from Antioch University, Los Angeles. She is a mother to two amazing kids and wife to an English teacher. Follow her on Twitter @latoyadjordany.

LUCY WILL SWIM OUT too far. Just three weeks after she becomes a certified lifeguard. She won't want to be a lifeguard, but her parents argue it will look good on her college applications.

She will ignore the lessons she learned in her training to impress a boy named Rick. He has a brother in college who sells Adderall. He also has a Jeep, so she thinks she just might date him, or at least let him feel her up.

They will have a sandy kiss on the beach one night. She'll strip to her bra and panties and prance into the sea. She'll swim the illuminated lane laid out by the moon. She'll expect Rick to follow, but he won't.

The undertow will bully her. Her skinny arms will tire. Her kicks will become more spread out as fatigue overtakes her. Waves will slap her face just as she inhales. Salt will burn her throat. Make it raw. She'll no longer see the shore when a buoy bell tolls nearby. If she could just get ahold of it, then she might stay afloat. The last thing she will see is the blinking lights of two planes flying toward each other in the cloudless sky. For a moment, she thinks they will collide, but they don't.

Two days later, a crab fisher will find her floating face down. Knots of seaweed in her hair and the straps of her B cup. Her skin like pristine ice. He'll place two fingers on her wrist, just in case, but will find no beat. So preserved by the salt she'll be, he'll want to wrap her in a blanket to warm her.

But Lucy will ignore her death. Will go on living as if it never happened, ticking all the boxes of life.

There will be a wild phase. She'll wake up in the apartments of guys whose names could be Jim or Steve or Jay. Who almost always sleep on mattresses on the floor. She does ecstasy for a year. Gets a tattoo of a swallow on her hip. She thinks about taking part in

protests, but never finds the time.

She'll graduate from Baruch, not at the top of her class, but respectably. She stays afloat as a financial analyst. Her friends will ask what a financial analyst does time and time again but can never seem to remember. She'll never need to look at prices at Whole Foods. Or wonder whether she can afford gas for her Land Cruiser. She'll hear people say things like *the struggle is real* and she'll respond, *I hear that,* even though she doesn't relate.

She'll marry a man named Ben who she meets at a farmer's market. She'll be a dollar short on a jar of honey, and he will offer up his last. Ben will be an engineer. She'll tell her friends he has an eye for detail, which is weird to say since he won't notice that she's already passed away. He'll give her his mother's engagement ring. A sapphire, not a diamond. On their wedding day, he'll say she looks breathtaking. His voice will shake. As she walks down the aisle, she'll think her bouquet smells like a funeral parlour. Their marriage will be considered a harmonious one, exemplary even. People will not only invite them to dinner parties, birthdays, weddings, but will be disappointed if they can't come.

Even children become part of their plan—two girls—Rory and Charlotte. Rory will never think that there's something wrong with her mother. She's inherited her green eyes and cold hands. But Charlotte suspects something. A feeling that's always dancing on the tip of her tongue. When Lucy hugs her little girls, she feels Charlotte go rigid all over. They will never discuss what's wrong. The words refuse to form the idea.

The family will vacation every year. Greece and Scotland and Belize and the Maldives. There will be photo albums, lots and lots of photo albums. When the need for a nostalgic remedy strikes, they'll take them out and point at the moments they house and say, *do you remember that day? I can't believe we made that boat*! And when she enters a different country, its immigration officers will stamp her passport, never noticing they are granting a dead person permission to enter their borders.

It will be a day well into her seventies when she finally remembers. Ben will have already died of a heart attack. Rory will live in London with her husband and two kids, and Charlotte lives only an hour away but hardly visits. Lucy will be at the sink washing dishes. She'll suddenly want to submerge her hands in the sudsy water. Squeeze the sponge until it's wrung dry. Her death will be reflected back at her on the surface of the water—that illuminated lunar path. There will be no sadness or anger. Maybe a feeling of foolishness for having not noticed up until now. She won't dwell on the realization for long because a drip in the faucet will distract her. I should call the plumber, she'll think, but below this, existing but unspoken, she'll know that it would be more satisfying to fix it herself.

L. Soviero was born and raised in Queens, New York but has made her way around the world, currently laying her hat in Sydney. She has an MSc in Creative Writing from the University of Edinburgh. When she is not writing flash, she works as a Learning Designer. You can check out her work and nominations at lsoviero.com.

MAIN CONTENTS

YOUR GRANDMOTHER'S ANTIQUE

adedayo agarau

THE WAKING

HOW DO YOU KIIL a shadow that stays when the light goes off? You sit at the edge of your bed in the stillness of the young night and count the number of times this dream has replayed itself. Your grandmother stands at the shore of a familiar beach and calls you to come. Her voice, lifting the voracious sea in its depth, says *maa bo, Ola*.

Today, you wake up from the dream breathing heavily, your heart racing as if it will leap out of your mouth. This is the same way every one of your fears leaps out of your body. The fear of heights, the fear of water, the fear of staying. Today, this dream came to take a chunk of your peace away. Your bed drenched in sweat, you must have bodied so much water to have rained this heavily. You tried to cry in the bathroom the night before but the stars in your eyes stood heavily, unshaken, unmovable.

You bring out your journal to note this dream down. It's the 23rd entry this year. Maami died two years ago. You remember the way the winds took ownership of the room where you slept, how they whistled angrily. Your father as he walks in, decked in his jalabiya, his shadow standing taller than him in your room, his eyes searching for meaning in yours. Your mother's voice now rising like a whirlwind, calling your grandmother's names, *Arike, Olanike, Adégbolá, Arike*...while yours settles into her growing absence the way birds digest whole wheat.

When someone dies, everyone talks about how pleasant they were. How they were once the sun rising in the east of their problems, how they were someone"s saving grace. But you say nothing. What do you say when you carry a mouthful of salt in a wounded mouth? Your throat slowly thawing the reality of someone's absence.

This dream is never complete, you know. You wonder why someone, even in the death of their conscience, still deeply wants to bring you close. The fan in your room comes on, power has been restored. The candle you lit before you dies silently. Your grandmother, whose mouth you know so well, once told you the body will listen when the earth speaks. In May, you woke from this dream and tried to overdose on a sleeping tab. You say you wanted to sleep for a long time.

You know it is not just this dream that haunts you. You know that this house, this room, the shadows and the way they form on the walls, the bed and the way it creaks, everything brings you close to someone"s grave. You have always wanted to say it but who do you tell? How do you say it?

Your mother comes through the open door of your dark room and you begin to cry. She hastens towards you and puts your head on her chest. She does not ask what it was. You do not say a word.

I know, Ola. She finally says.

You do not think she does. She unwraps the edge of her old ankara to wipe your tears.

The spirit of your mothers are with you, Ola. I know you miss her so much. Your father and I heard you call her name out of your sleep moments ago.

She does not know your grandmother, one evening when you were seven, walked into your room and asked you to undress. She placed her lips over yours and sucked your lips into her mouth. *This ritual is sacred,* she said. She asked you to pack your books away from your bed and lay. You laid. She walked her mouth over your young body. You ached. You shivered. *Calm, calm, Ola,* she said, this ritual is sacred.

That was only the beginning of a life that you lived pleasing a now dead woman.

I know, Ola, I know, your mother says. She does not. *Thank you, mummy,* you mutter, from your heavy mouth.

Adedayo Agarau is the third-place winner of the Frontier Industry Prize, 2020. His chapbook, *Origin of Names,* was selected by Chris Abani and Kwame Dawes for New Generation African Poet (African Poetry Book Fund), 2020. He is the author of *The Arrival of Rain* chapbook. His works have appeared in *Agbowo, Frontier Poetry, Glass, Perhappenned,* and elsewhere. Adedayo curated and edited *Memento: An Anthology of Contemporary Nigerian Poetry.* He is an Editor at *IceFloe* and Assistant Editor at Animal Heart Press. Adedayo is a member of the Unserious Collective. You can find him on Twitter @adedayo_agarau or agarauadedayo.com.

A POTTER'S FIELD HELD unwanted bodies. Some Puritans did not mark their graves, viewing their dead as blessed to have transcended their sinful husks, to have achieved perfection without the weight of flesh holding them to earth.

The dead girls can float, but they still sin.

Where are the bodies of the dead girls? In the basements of houses and trunks of abandoned cars. In the woods, mostly, covered over with leaves or under a few flimsy inches of earth. In pieces in an oil drum, cinderblocked to a riverbed, dumped off embankments on nights with no moon. The dead girls don't see this as transcendence. The dead girls want their bodies back.

What do the dead girls see? Milk-film over their blinking eyes. A world gone on without them, a thousand petty dramas playing to an audience of the not-bereft. A wave endlessly arguing with the shoreline, stealing a few grains of sand every time.

The living dare each other to walk through the field of dead girls, though of course they can't see anything but air. Only the sense that something is wrong, air charged with grief like a storm is always coming. The field where no grass grows, only patches of low bramble with fat, untouched berries. The kind of quiet that hums danger into your ears, fills them with a warning you can't parse. At night it's never quite dark, even when the Pizza Hut's lights shut off and the nail techs are counting their tips in their cars. Anyone alive who walks through that place feels claustrophobic even out in the open, their skin seeming to tighten over their bones. And anyone who isn't would see how the dead girls follow them in a glowing swarm, pressing from all sides, desperate for warmth.

Most of the dead girls are cold. They can feel the rush of the polluted river, the snow promising itself to the mountainside, the wet of the pine needles' slow, sympathetic rot. The chill of their urgent loneliness even surrounded by the only others who understand their not-life. It's no wonder the grass refuses to grow.

The dead girls whose bones are buried unmarked claim to be colder than the rest of them. They have new names in the living world, called for the landscape their body was plucked from—Juniper Mountain Doe, Horseshoe Creek—or the human trappings that still clung to it—Cerulean Jacket, Twin Rose Tattoo. These girls make incantations of their true names, pace the perimeter whispering: *Lucinda. Lucinda. Lucinda. Maria. Maria. Maria. I was. I was. I am.* Some of them are afraid they'll forget. Others are imagining their voices as radio waves, arcing over the miles until they reach what remains of their source.

Some of the dead girls know they'll never be found. There will be no cemetery plot, no epitaph – no one who would think to compose one, no human alive up late agonizing over a lost friend. The way the found blink out of the field, some of the forever-missing blinked out of life. No one mourns.

The lucky girls only stay a few days. Barely have time to turn around, see the spot that could be eternity, make a few friends and they're gone. A car pulled from the quarry like a bad tooth. A door broken open into a bloody room. No one knows where they go next, only that it must be better than here. There is no sense in missing them, now that they've been found.

The oldest dead girls remember when the building's foundation was dug, watching the men lift their dirty shirts to wipe sweat from their foreheads. And before that, when the road was paved in stinking asphalt, and before that, when the cart-tamped dirt was covered in broken stone. And before that, when it was only a few of them and sky and pine in every direction, when they still could have thought this might be paradise.

Cassandra de Alba is a poet living in Massachusetts. Her chapbooks are *Habitats* (Horse Less Press, 2016), *Ugly/Sad* (Glass Poetry Press, 2020) and Cryptids (Ginger Bug Press, 2020). Her work has appeared in *The Shallow Ends*, *Big Lucks*, and *Wax Nine*, among other publications. She is a poetry reader for *Underblong*, an instructor at the Redbud Writing Project, and tweets about *Cats* (2019) at @cassandraintroy.

I DIDN'T NOTICE MY neighbor until I caught her wearing a pair of red shoes. I live down the hall and don't dare to wear my own red shoes anymore. I see her red shoes often now, almost every day in fact. She wears them with the cruel disregard of a bird taking over another's nest, leaving no room for what used to exist in her place. They are an unrulier shade of red than mine; they have the bite of the flesh of a blood orange while mine are a pair of overripe, softly bruised cherries. I've had mine first, for many years, ever since a lost friend's wedding, and they used to kindle in me some soft feeling, a pleasant opposite of pride. Now their sight offends me, and I pretend to have forgotten where I've hid them from myself.

Some days I think of the long-ago wedding: being made to stand in a neat row and to wear identical red shoes under identical dust-colored gowns, two tall steps below the bride, like uniformed schoolgirls each waiting in vain for her name to be called. On those days I hate my neighbor's red shoes, and I want to steal them and bake them in the oven and only open the door when they've charred black, or maybe never. Other times I feel in love with the shoes, and on those days I lie on top of my bed and fantasize about stealing the shoes and wearing them every day, never taking them off until I've grown them onto my body, trained them to be a part of me. I would stay inside forever, safe and alone with my secret. And there are days when I'm sure I've fallen in love with my neighbor, and I imagine peeling those shoes off her feet and throwing them hard under the bed never to be looked at again, keeping only the neighbor for myself. But those times are rare and brief, and I soon turn my mind back to the shoes.

My neighbor wears a kind face when we cross paths in the dim hallway, down by the letter slots, on the blind curve of stairs. Time ravels around itself; anger and hunger become indistinguishable. She keeps her eyes on me for long moments, and we watch each other as through a window, or the bars of a cage. She smiles and her teeth are the bones of stars, bright and picked clean and too far away to possibly be real.

I've kept the dress, and every year on the anniversary of the wedding I sway myself in it through my silent rooms, barefoot and with all my lights turned on, and in the bright dining room I keep clean in case an old friend should ever come by unannounced I dance around the too-big table and then, grabbing greedy handfuls of fabric to pull up and away from me, I step onto a chair and then the table, and up here I dance a wilder dance, stomping my feet and throwing my limbs at the far-away ceiling, and I think there is no way they've ever done anything even remotely so outrageous, and I bare my teeth in a careless laugh as I jab at the pain of comparison and wish that for just one night I were the only one dancing in the world.

.

Layla Al-Bedawi writes fiction, nonfiction, and experimental hybrid work. English is her third language, but she's been dreaming in it for years. Born in Germany, she now lives in the greater Houston area, where she co-founded Fuente Collective, an organization focused on experimentation, collaboration, and hybridity in writing and other arts. Her work has been published in *Wigleaf, Juked, Bayou Magazine, Winter Tangerine, Strange Horizons,* and elsewhere. Find her on Twitter under @frauleinlayla and at laylaalbedawi.com.

TURKISH GOLD CIGARETTES IN your glove box. Beside you, me. Sixteen, we cruised the Main Street strip every Saturday night. I was a glammed-up rodeo queen with a hair-do like Slash. You, you had hands like a rope and every Monday, after a Sunday spent apart at church, you lassoed me back to you. Under the bleachers, behind the cafeteria tables, as my mother slept with a bottle of Jim Beam in our trailer's kitchenette. I never got whiplash, only rope burn.

A Parliament between your fingers. We screamed at each other beneath the burning bright lights of the football field. You told me to go to college. I told you to go to hell. You crossed your arms, trying to look mean in your graduation gown, but I knew better. You picked up glass in parking lots, kissed your mother like it mattered. I shuffled toward you, cowpoke slow. For you, I said, I stay. Then, your lean arms roped me. I went wild, I knew what it meant. The house under the overpass was ours.

Lucky Strike cigarettes on your breath. It was a baby the size of a fist. I curled up in the bathtub, bled it out like rain. You paced hard boot steps. Sweat broke a bead on your brow. It was Texas, it was hot as hell, but it was also you and me, and you were worried, calling out my name. *Susanna.* I had never heard your voice sound like that before. A storm cloud. One that rumbled. Right before it broke.

A patch on your right bicep. My arm looped around your waist. The Harley burning up interstate blacktop. Vegas. We're gonna maul a buffet, renew our vows, make love beneath neon light. I'll bust you up and then some, your lip between my teeth, my hands on your chest, calling out your name in spades. *Townes.* Man, we used to drive around thinking about how we were the rodeo king and queen of Johnson County, but this. This. We never had a clue how good this all got.

Jules Archer is the author of the short story collection, *Little Feasts* (Thirty West Publishing, 2020) and the chapbook, *All the Ghosts We've Always Had* (Thirty West Publishing, 2018). Her writing has appeared in various journals, including *SmokeLong Quarterly*, *Wigleaf*, *PANK*, *Okay Donkey*, *Maudlin House*, and elsewhere. She lives in Arizona and looks for monsters in strange places. Find her @julesjustwrite or julesjustwrite.com.

MA'I MALIU (I)

I LIE ON THE floor in corpse pose. I have been dead for three weeks now. Audrey and Ben enter their house to find me on their floor.

I measure myself against 23-kilometre races that I'm not running. Up Mt Vaea with a TV crew at my back—all the amazing stories I'm not talking about, the selfies I'm not jostling to be in, set against a Samoan sunset. See look, I'm not there. See look, I'm not telling the stories, I'm not winning this or writing that. I don't even know if I'm writing this poem. Maybe I'll write this poem and then I'll forget.

I lie on the floor in corpse pose. I find myself on a hotel bathroom floor just before the book awards. I ring my cousin in Christchurch to ask where I am. I ring Catherine to come and get me. I ring Selina to stand behind me on the stage just in case. The next morning they find me dead in the breakfast bar. Catherine's face looms over me as the ambulance arrives. I get all death-bed on her and tell her I love her. I touch her cheek and afterwards don't know why. I guess that's what you do when you are dying.

Perhaps I'm getting deader all the time or perhaps I want to use this poem to explain to you why I'm not writing. Why I shuffle through the day from death pose to death pose. The bits in between are not marathons, they're not novels or poems, they're not even driving a car. Dead people aren't allowed to drive cars. I wake up with dead people pulling me down the hall. I fight my girl into her clothes, cut toast, forget I'm in the kitchen. Brush my girl's hair. She gets angry because I'm not specific, I say 'thingy' all the time.

The doctor told me the pills would ruin my word recall—and he wanted to double the dose. You can't do that, I said, I'm writing a book. OK, then, I'll triple them, he said.

I show the pills to my daughter and explain why I say 'thingy' all the time. *But I can't see it happening, Mummy*, she says. I nag her to get her thingys on and then she's gone. I sit on the couch. Forget my father is dead. Then remember. Then I cry. This is called jamais vu. It's not dying – it's the opposite of déjà vu. Déjà vu feels like having memories before you have them. Jamais vu feels like forgetting your father is dead and then remembering and then crying.

MA'I MALIU (II)

It starts with losing my footing—the way a person does in an earthquake, when the floor becomes the sea. I fall and slide headlong into the corner, where the linen cupboard meets the bathroom. I am face up, pulled along by the torpedo of my head.

A pile of coat hangers pierce the top of my head, my forehead and the top of my face and narrowly miss my eyes. Perhaps they stake out an area of my brain, the punctures like stitching, like a diagram in a 1950s neurology text.

My handsome untouchable father walks up the hallway. He beams above me and I beg him, I cry and cry for fifty years. But he is thirty, and he looks somewhere above me, smiling and talking to someone else.

I've had a seizure, Dad. I choke this out, but I am speaking into space. When I am on my feet I turn back to the corner and there is my blood halo on the wall.

If I look at myself in the bathroom mirror I am there. There are my wounds, not gory, just there. And there is my face, paler than I've seen it, thinner, so I don't look as much like me as I should.

My mother has been watching quietly but is gone. I try to track her, making my way past the old chicken farm that used to be behind the house, then the big tree, the rope swing hanging from it.

She is sitting there. I see her in three-quarter profile. She is crying. My mother's tears come only three times a lifetime and they are silent and strike me hard in the chest. I step back into the shadow but I am forty or fifty years old so I step forward again.

I don't look or speak but I sit down beside her. I hook my arm through hers and press my knee against her knee. I exist and I can help.

Tusiata Avia is an internationally acclaimed poet, performer and writer. She has four collections of poetry: *Wild Dogs Under My Skirt, Bloodclot, Fale Aitu/ Spirit House and The Savage Coloniser Book* (finalist for 2021 Ockham NZ Book Awards). She has published 4 children's books and her poems, stories and essays have been published in over 100 anthologies and literary journals. *Wild Dogs Under My Skirt*, is also a multi-award-winning theatre production for 6 women; most recently garnering The Fringe Outstanding Production of the Year at Off-Broadway theatre, Soho Playhouse in New York City. The recipient of a number of awards, Tusiata is a current Arts Foundation Laureate and in 2020 was made a Member of the New Zealand Order of Merit for services to poetry and the arts.

GET BENT

a. a. balaskovits

HOW DOES A GIRL dance when her legs are bent at the knee? This is a riddle my grandmother once asked. At the time, I had no answer. My legs were as still as the two beams of the cross, and I dared not do anything but stand as straight as corn.

"You'll have to bend sooner or later," she told me. "All girls get on their knees."

She crushed rose petals in her palm until the red dripped down her arm like a wound. She did this for many weeks, each morning and evening, until her skin was a gnarl of stains. She collected the droplets into a silver bowl. When the liquid neared the brim, she bade me bring her my white shoes and dipped the leather in.

"When you're up there with your head bowed with the rest of them," she told me, a wink creasing her eye, "they'll only be looking at you."

Red shoes needs black stockings and black stockings need a white dress to cover them, but I had no white dress except the one I was to wear on my knees, and so I put it on. I twirled and plied and pirouetted as well as I could, though I had never been trained to do more than lower my eyes. None of us girls were trained beyond the smallest of movements. An eyelash flutter there. A curl of the finger here. Anything more and you'd have green eyes on you.

Green eyes on red shoes was another sort of riddle, but there was a simple answer to that.

The other girls were already on their knees when I arrived at our little church, so the only eyes on me were the priest with the buttoned-up cassock. When he woke up that morning his eyes were blue, like bird eggs, but when they changed the other girls saw—such magic, after all, is only possible through our Lord—they began to weep, for nothing they wore inspired a miracle.

But a miracle is not a miracle unless it spreads as dandelions do in the wind. I bent my legs where bone meets bone and leaped into the air, so high that the girls could see my body over the pews, and more so, they could see my shoes, as bright as rubies, tipped to a point at the toe.

I knew better, but how could I stop, now that I knew all the ways my body could move?

Later, one night after dancing well into starlight, I awoke to my grandmother weeping in the other room, and the hands of my sister-cousins holding me down. The moon was only half full through my window, but it was enough light to see the edges of green in their eyes, and the glint of silver on the dull blades they grasped.

How does a girl dance with only shoes? They asked this to one another that evening. One by one they put my red shoes on over their stockings, but they had never considered bending their knees for anything other than kneeling, and no matter which way they swayed back and forth, they could not dance.

If their hands were not covering my mouth, I could have told them: shoes were not enough, not for twisting, not for crouching, not for leaping. They realized this on their own soon enough, but they did not solve the riddle of how to bend.

They took my legs as well.

Grandmother wept but she did not weep long, not even when, over the small fence around our house, we saw my legs propped in the air, my red shoes bright in the sun, swaying back and forth in a macabre parade. Even with these parts of me, those girls did not know how to dance.

Later, my grandmother would tell me she did not mean me any pain. Later, she would say that a girl with legs as long as I should have been born in a place where girls were not discouraged from knowing what their bodies were capable of. Later, she stood far enough away from me so I could not touch her, and her grimace pulled at her chapped lips until they bled.

Then she brought me another pair of bright red shoes.

"How does a girl get out of bed?" she asked me. "Will you bend again?"

I moved what I could at first. A twist of my neck. The curl of my thumb. Blinked both eyes. My belly could curve inward.

My hands slid into the shoes as easily as my feet. An elbow is not so different from a knee, and mine curved into a fine edge. I could swish. I could reach. I could lift myself into the air.

How does a girl dance with red shoes and no legs? The answer is me.

A.A. Balaskovits is the author of *Strange Folk You'll Never Meet* and *Magic for Unlucky Girls.* Her work has appeared in *Kenyon Review Online, Story, Indiana Review* and many others. She is the co-editor-in-chief at *Cartridge Lit.* On Twitter @aabalaskovits and online at aabalaskovits.com.

WHAT HAPPENS FIRST IS he kisses you, licks your neck, then your tit, then he's like a snake charmer calling up something slick and flickering, a lit coil sparked alive inside you. Joined now, you breathe together then buckle, then he's gone, and something dries up like the tide drawing in, you're dry like bone littered with pine needle, crackling. Hammer and batten down the hatches. There's something new here and it needs everything. A lodging, a burrowing, a hollowing out until you hold a new planet, a whole world turning on its axis within you, the unwanted multitudes are multiplying, you place your hand on your own belly and it rumbles hard against your palm and digs in deeper. Your father and mother call you down for dinner. She smells like ground beef and talcum powder and your father, he's always been a quiet man of knuckle and bruise. You sit with them like you should but you can't stand to hear them chew. You wish they'd turn the light off. You've gone feral. You prefer to eat alone, in the dark, tiny morsels touch your lips over and over because what's born inside you can't tolerate much at once but then again it never gets enough, it's voracious, it's famished, like a black hole it will swallow everything, until it stops.

You didn't tell it to stop, just like you didn't call it forth, you didn't ask for it, you never ask for anything. You couldn't wish it away hard enough if you wanted to, that magic was lost in your bloodline long ago. The stillness, you tell yourself, isn't your fault. The black blood comes first in daylight, stains the sheets from your childhood, patterned with princesses once pink now rust. Your window is open, curtains pulled apart to reveal the merciless sky of Ohio, a blue dome shredded by cirrus, and always, so much corn, corn standing tall at the periphery of your father's property, cloaked in the withered husks of autumn, like a warlock's circle parted for a true-green lawn, meanwhile your mother's thirsty browning mums clamor at the pink brick along with a seasonal display of shellacked gourds. You manage to pull the blind down on it all.

Dusk falls. You lurch to the bathroom and wait. Your parents come and go but don't look for you, your actions and your absences are no longer strange to them, you've been there/not there so long.

You lower your body into the empty bath. It holds you like an egg. Your body cracks and your self seeps out, you watch from above as your body is strung out on the rack but not you, not you, you're dangling from the pink light that frames the bathroom mirror, a dozen polka-dot light bulbs, you comb your hair and apply lip gloss and make fish lips. You're a girl, you're a daughter. You're not the one in the bathtub with screams stuffed like wet rags down her throat, the girl who eats herself inside out with silence, who so desperately needs some help right about now but does not want to be a bother.

And then, after such long pain, she comes, a perfect curl peeled out of you, purple-blue, and already breathless, here but never here, arrived but already gone, revered in stillness more than you will ever be loved in life. Oh how oh hollow moon: you will be damned for this. Bend low, girl, and clean yourself up, then stand and carry the burden.

Melissa Benton Barker is a graduate of the MFA program at Antioch University-Los Angeles. Her fiction appears in *Wigleaf, Moon City Review, Heavy Feather Review,* and elsewhere. She lives in Ohio with her family.

EAGLE SWALLOWING GIRL

kate bernheimer

ADROIT JOURNAL

I WENT OUT TO my carport. A man stood in the gravel beside his white pick-up truck. He told me he was there to fix the crack on my windshield. I hadn't called him to do this, so I was surprised. He said he wanted to do it between the hours of X and Y, which was a one-hour time slot, something to do with it being Friday and tomorrow was Saturday and thus and therefore. He repeated, "Tomorrow's *Saturday*, man," like somehow, not repairing my windshield on Friday between the hours of X and Y had something to do with tomorrow being Saturday. I consented, though I was confused. Still, I remained cheerful in the face of it. "Oh yes, yes, tomorrow's going to be Saturday, that's for sure!"

I noticed something in the sky. An enormous eagle—way bigger than eagles are in real life. I told the mechanic, "That's an eagle." I began a conversation with him about how the eagle was was a national symbol. Soon I became insecure that the eagle was a national symbol. I pointed to where the gigantic eagle was perched, on top of the Aleppo pine in my backyard. "There's usually an owl on the tree, where the eagle now is." This was and was not untrue. Sometimes, an owl was there. But not usually. The eagle was bigger than a truck, yet the pine tree did not show any sign of distress. The pine tree was very upright. It held at least three nests of which I was aware: hummingbird, mourning dove, goldfinch.

Then the eagle took off in a beautiful angle of flight. It quickly swooped down—in fact it was on the hunt for a hawk who had begun to fly above my house at that time. The hawk headed from west to east. The eagle was swooping down toward it. I said, "I didn't know eagles ate hawks." The repairman showed no sign of curiosity.

I saw that the way the eagle would eat the hawk was that it would swallow it whole, as a snake swallows a mouse. There is a snake living under my yard shed and I have never seen it eat anything. In fact, even the small rabbits sit and stare at the snake, who sometimes comes out to sun herself on the pool concrete. She shows no interest in them. The rabbits have a puzzled expression as they sit and look at the snake. Sometimes they seem to exchange glances with one another. It is possible the snake isn't normal in some way, but who wants to be normal?

I stood on the hot gravel and wrung my hands. The eagle headed up into the sky and then dove for the hawk, over and over again. The hawk seems entirely unaware of the eagle. I very much wanted to know whether eagles were hawks, and thought to pose this question to the hawk herself, because the repairman clearly would be of no assistance, but the hawk disappeared. In her place, but not having transformed from the hawk, there was now a girl in the sky. A long and narrow girl. I had the thought, "She looks like a pencil though she is life-size." I chose not to tell the repairman about this thought, for while so far he had only revealed zero interest in my commentary, I suspected his disinterest could quickly turn into something more difficult for me, if I gave him reason to take notice of me.

The girl in the sky had fine, long, straight, brown hair. She flew, or rather floated, with her arms by her sides and her legs held together, so she made a tidy line through the air, angled with her head tilted slightly to the west and up toward the sky. And the eagle was now hunting her, I realized – he swooped down toward her again and again. At this point he was enormous. Yes, he had been the size of a truck. Yet now he was maybe the size of something larger than a pick-up truck. The eagle was the size of a garbage truck now, but more elegant. He was going to swallow the girl whole, I realized. Girls and eagles, were both protected, I wondered? Surely both were. This would not be a good question to pose to the repairman, who had made no motions toward repairing my windshield, but was just leaning on my white stucco wall in white overalls, smoking a white cigarette. Puffs of smoke rose past the brim of a tan baseball cap. I could not quite discern the words on the baseball cap at first, and then I wished that I couldn't at all. It read:

I ♥ INTERCOURSE

Up in the fine blue sky, the eagle continued to dive toward the girl with his beak open, but he continued to miss the girl every time. This was unlikely, for she was making herself as easy to swallow as could be imagined, up there in a straight, angled line, fresh for the taking. It should be no surprise that I realized the eagle was going to hunt for me next. Though this was no surprise, I was terrified. Finally, I turned to the man next to me. I said, "He's going to get me next." I tried to hide under the car but I couldn't get all the way under it. The eagle was going to swallow me whole. The repairman stood there, watching the sky. Though I was to be hunted, I felt protective somehow. Protective and hunted.

Kate Bernheimer is the author of two story collections, including *How a Mother Weaned Her Girl from Fairy Tales* and *Horse, Flower, Bird* (both Coffee House Press) as well as three novels, and editor of the World Fantasy Award winning and bestselling collection *My Mother She Killed Me, My Father He Ate Me: Forty New Fairy Tales* and the World Fantasy Award nominee *xo Orpheus: 50 New Myths* (both Penguin Books). New fiction has recently appeared in *The Iowa Review* and *The Adroit Journal* and is forthcoming in *American Short Fiction*. Her books have been translated into Chinese, Korean, Russian, Spanish, Catalan, Italian, Greek, Hebrew, Turkish, and Japanese.

SHE ASKS YOU HOW you are and you notice how nicely her hair is made-up and her make-up is in all the right places and you try to remember how to answer that question, partly because it's been so long since you've had a conversation with an adult but also because you're having one of those days, you know, the ones where the baby won't nap, it starts to rain as soon as you finish hanging the washing out, the baby still won't nap, you burn lunch, spill your tea, run out of chocolate so you go to the corner shop and despite it having been dry since you got the washing in, as soon as you go outside it starts to rain again, but you figure it'll be ok because the walk will send the baby off to sleep and then you can have your chocolate with a cup of tea on the sofa and the baby can nap in the pram in the kitchen, but then you remember that the kettle is in the kitchen and after you've oh-so-carefully maneuvered the pram inside, you're not going to risk waking the baby by boiling the kettle, so you unplug it and boil it on the landing, rush downstairs for milk, hold your breath as the fridge hums and omits light, but it's okay, the baby stays asleep and you creep back upstairs and decide, actually, to take your tea and chocolate to bed, you get in and you've been horizontal for, maybe, 4.3 seconds when you hear the baby cry and you want to cry too, you want to scream and cry, and cry some more, but you don't because if you start, you'll never stop, so you check your watch and think: she's already in the pram, I'll go to playgroup, so you get out of bed, get your shoes and coat on and go, before you can change your mind, and you're slightly delirious when you get there because of all the almost-crying, the lack of sleep and the sugar-rush of two chocolate bars and initially no one talks to you and you nearly cry again, but finally someone asks you how you are and you do that open-mouth, closed-mouth thing a couple of times trying to weigh up how honest to be and then you say, fine, I'm fine.

Laura Besley writes short (and very short) fiction in the precious moments that her children are asleep. Her fiction has appeared online (*Fictive Dream, Spelk, EllipsisZine*) as well as in print (*Flash: The International Short Story Magazine*) and in various anthologies (*Adverbally Challenged, Another Hong Kong, Story Cities*). Her debut flash fiction collection, *The Almost Mothers,* was published in March 2020 by Dahlia Books. She tweets @laurabesley.

MAYBE THREE YEARS AFTER the divorce came through, I asked Gloria if she ever thought about getting back on the old horse, and she said she only had room in her life for two men. One of them was me. The other was this guy she went to high school with, this guy whose parents named him Buddy Hooley, and maybe it was destiny or it could have been desperation, but he ended up a small-town professional wrestler. Did these underground shows in Dubuque and Waterloo and Marshalltown where he'd take dumbbells to the skull. Get tossed on thumb tacks. He used his real name and entered the ring to Weezer on account of some promoter said "Oh Boy" didn't have enough bass, and he carried this cheap imitation Les Paul that always wound up smashed, and sometimes it was over his own head after the referee'd been knocked out or else otherwise kicked aside. Gloria said his signature move was called the "Big Bopper," and it involved climbing up to the top rope and doing this kind of whirling splash attack with his body all perpendicular, and one night she watched him at this show in Mason City, or maybe it was Clear Lake, and, anyway, it was right along I-35, and they had Buddy in the main event against some guy who wore sagging pants and called himself Prince Cheese. It was a back-and-forth match, she said. Both guys used the razor blades. There's blood on the canvas, popcorn, broken glass from a beer bottle Cheese stole from some asshole in the front row, and sometime toward the end Buddy starts climbing up to the top rope. Someone tosses him the guitar. Cheese is staggering around in the middle of the ring, and, come to think of it, Buddy's woozy and off-balance too, only he's perched up in the more precarious spot, and he kind of half-launches himself and half-slips and next thing you know he's falling in the wrong direction. Going headlong toward the concrete. Gloria sees him land dome first, and she says there's this sound like a ring toss, like a woodpecker, and he doesn't move for five, ten seconds, and the last thing anyone sees is two of the other performers, these guys some people say were dressed like

Ritchie Valens or maybe Elvis Presley, and they drag him out the back entrance while the referee raises Cheese's hand and declares him the winner, and the crowd is stunned silence. Is nobody knows what the fuck. And they don't see Hooley afterward either. Not for weeks. Not for forever, and he doesn't do any more shows, and he never answers his phone, but Gloria says his voicemail still works, and she swears the message changes just slightly, and it's not the words exactly but the sound, the cadence, the way it feels like he's talking to her, and as far as she can tell there's no death certificate, no county autopsy, and some people think the promoter buried the body out near the actual crash site, and some say it was all planned, all scripted and theatrics, and Gloria, she doesn't know what to believe. She knows her phone rings sometimes. Number unknown. There's nothing but static when she picks up. Heavy breathing. Rock n' roll all soft and haunted in the background, and she wonders if it's him on the other end, or maybe the promoter. She wonders what's real. She looks at me, and it's like the first night we met, and her eyes are green, and they look ten years younger, and she says, "Tex, I can't wake up." And "Everything feels like it's part of the show."

Brett Biebel teaches writing and literature at Augustana College in Rock Island, IL. His (mostly very) short fiction has appeared in *Hobart, SmokeLong Quarterly, The Masters Review, Emrys Journal,* and elsewhere. *48 Blitz,* his debut story collection, is available from Split/Lip Press..

NOTHING ABOUT IT IS fair. Little darling, baby bird. Smashed up crumpled on the side of the highway, one wing detached from iridescent body. Blood like the rust that collects on your grandfather's old boat, the one right now bobbing on a lake a hundred miles north of here. You promised as he lay dying of rotten tumors that you'd keep her going strong. But you've never taken that boat anywhere.

Little darling, baby bird.

Your mother used to pluck chickens in the backyard surrounded by puddles of shit, hummed Vivaldi as she wrung the scrawny necks. All that white fluff twirling in the air. You vomited on your boots, ill-fitting relics from a sister gone too soon, vanished from the farm one winter night when the stars were blue and the empty road was calling. Your father never spoke her name again.

Nothing about it is fair.

Alien images on a screen, a screen they turn away from you when they see the lives beneath the surface have stopped their ceaseless flutter.

Little darling, baby bird.

When he left, your husband took the books with glossy pages where you had circled your favorite names. *Sandpiper, starling, siskin.* You kept the other books, the ones filled with pages of his first choices. *Ava, Callum, Evelyn.*

Nothing about it is fair.

The hospital parking lot teems with seagulls fighting over half a drive-thru hamburger. Over and over, the smallest gull is shoved away. You can't stand the starving look in his black eyes; it reminds you of the hollow tube of the MRI machine before you were pushed inside, where for two hours you lay still and compliant, holding your breath and letting it out whenever the radiologist said so in her pretty sing-song voice.

Little darling, baby bird.

You watch a robin outside your kitchen window, her russet belly, the white circles around her eyes, so small and bright, alive. The doctor's on the phone. His voice is sad, serious. You make a follow-up appointment to let him feel better about delivering this news on such a sunny gorgeous afternoon. But it's an appointment you'll never keep. It's early summer, and your mother's expecting your visit; she's depended on you ever since your father took off on the same dark road your sister took so long ago.

Nothing about it is fair.

Your mother hasn't plucked chickens in years, but she still hums Vivaldi as she watches the metal cages in the corner of her living room, where two yellow cockatiels chatter all day. She used to have a conure, boasting vibrant feathers that brushed against her face when it perched on her shoulder. It died. Some sort of autoimmune disease. You spared your mother the grief of carrying its lifeless body out to the backyard. You dug a hole six inches deep. The plumage a rainbow underground. Little darling, baby bird. Nothing about it is fair.

Shannon L. Bowring's work has appeared or is scheduled to appear in numerous journals, and has been nominated for a Pushcart and a Best of the Net Award. She is in her MFA thesis semester at USM Stonecoast, where she is finishing out her time on the *Stonecoast Review* by serving as the journal's Editor-in-Chief. She lives in Maine and works for a public library. Placing a story in a publication such as *Best Small Fictions* has always been a dream of Shannon's, and she is thrilled and honored to be included in this anthology.

WHEN THE PREGNANT GIRLS first arrive at St. Eulalia's Home for the Lost and Wayward, the nuns take them to see the Frozen Child. The Frozen Child, her feet locked in ice, her mouth wide and dark as an open grave. The grave is never satisfied, say the nuns, neither is the barren womb, nor the eyes of man. The girls rub hands over swollen wombs, think of their lover's eager eyes. The eyes of the Frozen Child are like white marbles rolled back in her head. The girls hang their heads and contemplate their sins. Sin, say the nuns, is conceived by lust, and sin, when finished, brings forth death. But the Frozen Child is not dead, think the girls. They think that dead can also mean asleep, like in fairy tales, like Sleeping Beauty and Snow White waiting for True Love's Kiss. Snow falls in big, wet kisses, and the girls close their eyes, catch the flakes on reaching tongues. The tongue, say the nuns, is a spark that sets the entire body aflame.

When the pregnant girls first arrive at St. Eulalia's Home for the Lost and Wayward, the nuns take them to see the Frozen Child. The Frozen Child, her hands stitched into icy mittens and lifted toward the heavenlies. In heaven, the nuns say, there will be no crying, neither grieving, nor death. But the Frozen Child is not dead, think the girls. They think that inside her frigid tomb lies a bleary, slow-beating, glass-apple heart. The heart brims with betrayal and above all, say the nuns, the heart should not be trusted. The girls trust they will have a moment to hold their babies, time enough to note the color of their marbled eyes, to kiss their blood-apple cheeks. The Frozen Child's sunken cheeks are like half-eaten apples, and the nuns have nothing good to say about fruit.

When the pregnant girls first arrive at St. Eulalia's Home for the Lost and Wayward, the nuns take them to see the Frozen Child. The Frozen Child, a sheet of ice glistening atop her head like a crown. The crown of life, say the nuns, will be given to those who are faithful to the point of death. But the girls know the Frozen Child is not dead. They know she will emerge from her crystal cocoon one day, all wet and wobble-legged and hungry. Cold licks at the girls' cheeks like a hungry animal, bites their mittenless fingers. The girls lace their fingers and pray. They pray their babies will make room in their hearts to forgive, that the nuns know not what they do. But the nuns know there will be a sound when the babies are taken, a sound like shattering glass, the sound of hearts breaking. Rows of broken icicles cling to the Frozen Child's arms like jagged teeth. There will also be a great gnashing of teeth, the nuns know, followed by an even greater silence. A silence like the hush of snow falling as the girls clutch their hollowed wombs, wombs still and empty as robbed graves.

Audra Kerr Brown lives at the end of a dirt road in southeastern Iowa. Her fiction has appeared in *Wigleaf's* Top 50 (Very) Short Fictions list, *X-R-A-Y, People Holding, Outlook Springs, Flashback Fiction, Milk Candy Review,* and more.

TURKEYS SCREECH ON THE oil-stained concrete driveway. She watches them through the louvered glass windows of the living room, strutting back and forth over greasy rainbows as she sprawls on the couch, her right leg draped over the top, calf grooved with curved indentions of rattan. She hopes the neighborhood dogs won't scare them off or some asshole driving a truck too fast along the road. She likes the idea of wild turkeys wandering around the rainforest behind her house with their red wattles dangling on plump chests, pecking their way through the ferny undergrowth. She'd told other students on the mainland about them, but no one had known about the turkeys. They like to eat the fallen avocados from the tree next to the driveway. She doesn't blame them. They are delicious. Really, what kind of person would bring a turkey here and release it? She'd heard stories of pythons curled up near tiny streams, Jackson chameleons cruising tree branches, flocks of parrots buzzing people's houses. Turkeys? The idea of someone, or multiple someones, bringing in a turkey as a pet or as food and then thinking hey let's just let them go and see what happens makes her smile and cringe at the same time. She'd once found a polaroid she'd never seen before in her sister's photo album. She was small, sitting on the hood of a white sports car at night, holding a baby cougar, the dark sepia bleeding in from the white edges. If someone could bring in something that dangerous, then a turkey wouldn't even be a big deal.

She listens to their squabbling as the breeze raises tiny bumps along her exposed arms. She can smell the afternoon rain coming. Its green, wet scent nags her to take the clothes off the line. Instead, the sounds and smells drive her deeper into the hard, bird of paradise patterned cushions, the rattan creaking under her. She hates it. Hates its cheesy, mocking aloha print, reminding her of mu'umu'u worn for weddings, funerals, May Day celebrations, long, stiff material scratching her skin. The rattan furniture was for company, her parents insisted, but she likes the breeze that passes through the room. She stares at the palm leaf fan above her, dusty webs clinging to its wide bamboo fronds. The whole room makes her think of a hotel. Not a nice hotel like in Waikoloa, where the rich tourists stay, but an old hotel like Uncle Billy's in Kona with worn carpets, faded drapes, and chipped furniture, remembering better days when Kona was just a small fishing village and the hotel was a primo place to stay. They used to stay there for family reunions when rooms were cheaper. Now, they just have reunions at Old A's in one of the pavilions or camp down Napo'opo'o. Going to reunions always meant work, cooking, cleaning, babysitting. People she didn't like talking to her about things she didn't care about. When she was younger, she always felt like she had to please everyone. Now, she counts the days when she can just be away from them again.

She forces herself to roll off the couch onto the ceramic tiled floor. The rattan bites into her side while the grout between the beige tiles presses into the edge of her knee. They are almost too cold to touch. She pushes up, each of her hands spread wide, fingers soothed and repelled by the chill, and gets to her feet. They don't feel the cold as much as her hands. Years of walking barefoot on smooth lava rocks to jump into the ocean had hardened and widened them. She hates shoes with their heel bleeding blisters, toe cramping, make your feet look pretty in not quite Chinese foot binding ways. She walks through her mother's idea of a haole country kitchen, all white crockery and towels you can't use, and out the screen door. She puts on her slippahs and realizes she'd forgotten to grab a laundry basket. She hates laundry. She hates the sorting, hanging, folding. She hates that she can't use the dryer unless it rains all day. She kicks off her slippahs and slams open the screen door, hitting the side of the house with a loud bang. She hears a concert of squawks from the front of the house. She walks quickly through the kitchen and into the living room only to see that all the turkeys have vanished.

Melissa Llanes Brownlee is a Native Hawaiian writer. She received her MFA in Fiction from UNLV. Her work has appeared in *Booth: A Journal, The Notre Dame Review, Pleiades, The Citron Review, Waxwing, Milk Candy Review* and elsewhere. She was a finalist for the 2018 New American Fiction Prize and the 2019 Brighthorse Prize.

Rest Stops and Parking Lots

aaron burch

After Kristine Langley Mahler

BECAUSE I DIDN'T WANT to pay for a hotel.[1] Because I could afford to pay for a hotel, but it seemed like a waste.[2] Because, as much as I enjoy sleeping in and then being lazy and watching TV in bed[3], I wanted to get up and moving and on the road as soon as possible.[4] Because I'd paid for and slept in a hotel the night before, and I'd do so again the night after, and I thought a night in my car would both save me a little money and make me appreciate the nights when I did get a hotel.[5] Because, despite a near inability to make decisions regarding large amounts of

---

[1] Because I'd grown up with parents who always thought about money, always worried about it, fretted over and considered and reconsidered every financial decision, and that worry and fretting and considering and reconsidering is hard to shake.

[2] Because I didn't have a plan and so I just drove until I was tired, and sometimes that meant until it was pretty late, and I wanted to get up and back on the road in the morning, and so if it were just for a bed for a few hours, the cost-benefit ratio seemed off.

[3] Because I didn't have a TV at home, and so laying in bed and watching TV, even bad TV, maybe even especially bad TV, was a kind of treat specific to staying in hotels, even bad hotels, maybe even especially bad hotels.

[4] Because there's something exciting and energizing and life-affirming about waking up at sunrise; there's something hard-to-describe about squinting into the light of the morning sun coming through a windshield and locking into your eyes.

[5] Because sometimes, even when you can afford something, there is a specific kind of pride in finding an alternate option, in doing something another way, in moments of money saved.

money, I had just bought a new car.[6] Because I had in every other car I'd ever owned, and so now I wanted to in this one, too.[7] Because I had in my 20s and my 30s and I wanted to prove to myself I still could.[8] Because I'd left the passenger seat empty as well as the seat behind it so I could fold it down as far as it would go.[9] Because it made for a good story.[10]

---

[6] Because I had just gotten a raise and because, although I didn't yet explicitly know I was about to get divorced, I knew it implicitly enough, and because I knew I was about to drive across the country and because the savings in gas alone wouldn't do that much to offset the cost of a car but it was at least something, and because I wanted to treat myself.

[7] Because it felt like a kind of christening, a rite of passage, even if I wasn't sure if for my car or me.

[8] Because there can be something a little reassuring or comforting about these kinds of repeating or echoing or rhyming life moments, and because there is a kind of pride in doing something as you get older that may seem reserved, or at least better suited, for the young.

[9] Because I hadn't exactly planned to but I'd known I might.

[10] Because sometimes it feels good to do something that you know is going to prompt someone to ask you why you would do that. Because sometimes it feels good to do something just because.

Aaron Burch is the author of the memoir/literary analysis *Stephen King's The Body; the short story collection, Backswing*; and the novella, *How to Predict the Weather.* Recent short-shorts, fiction and non, have appeared on *Pidgeonholes, X-R-A-Y, Rejection Letters, Jellyfish Review,* and *Bending Genres.* He is the Founding Editor of *HOBART* and he lives in Ann Arbor, MI with his collection of almost every ticket stub from a movie and concert he went to in the 90s and early 00s.

ONE LONG NIGHT IN December, Orion—yes that Orion—was my lover.

We met at a diner. Orion waved away the cream that came with his coffee carafe. He took his coffee black, and said that milk was like a crude street lamp leaking artificial light into something pristine.

He was a bit mean, but I was drawn to him anyway. Like I was lost at sea and he was there, taking up the whole sky to help me navigate safely.

When we got back to my place, I tried to stay up all night. I ate caffeine pills when I ran out of coffee grounds, black tea, and chocolate-covered espresso beans. But on my last cup of budget-brand dark roast, he shook his head and laughed when I added in a few drops of half-and-half.

I didn't have a plan of seduction. In general, I am drawn to liquids and warmth, and so I thought he might be the same. Of the soups I could make on my single burner—condensed cream of mushroom, condensed chicken noodle, condensed beef stew—he didn't have a preference.

But we took our bowls out onto the balcony in the below-zero weather. Polar night of an Arctic winter. I could only handle about five minutes of the cold, even with my many layers and the hot soup burning its way down my throat. Orion stood out there for hours, looking for his place in the sky. The soup froze.

We had the rest of the night, and we took it. He told me to turn off the lights, close the blinds and the curtains. I found another blanket to cover the window. In the blackout, he was bright like alarm clock numbers at three in the morning.

Only he was bright that way everywhere. At the tips of his elbows. All across his freckled nose. Luminescent eyelashes. Fingernails. Happy trail. He tasted like good espresso and felt like a first wish—sincere and deep.

He told me, in our afterglow, that he was wandering because he was fading. There was too much light in and out of the city. When I woke up at polar twilight, pink horizon at the edge of a navy blue sky, he was gone. And he didn't return when true dark fell again.

Now I drive incessantly. City to prairie to mountain. Arctic to Antarctic. I avoid the midnight sun. Every time I stop, I look up and count the stars inside the four corners of that body; less than ten and he's not really there. I burn fuel to move and linger on the three pins of his belt.

Caroliena Cabada is a writer currently based in Ames, Iowa. Her writing has appeared in *As It Ought To Be Magazine, Barren Magazine, JMWW, perhappened, Whale Road Review,* and other online and print journals. Find her on Twitter and Instagram @cecaroliena.

THE GREATEST SHOW

Tara Campbell

WE CLIMBED DOWN FROM our platforms and out of the ring, inhaling deeply of sawdust and popcorn, sweat and dung. We turned out the lights and broke down the tents, ropes biting into our palms. We watered the elephants and fed the lions; we waved at stragglers and kissed our new lovers goodbye. One last campfire, one last harmonica bray, one last cloud of dust kicked up by our dancing feet. One last paycheck pressed into our hands. No train tomorrow. No makeup, no spangled costumes. We'll tip our heads back, way back, and spread our arms for the net.

Tara Campbell (www.taracampbell.com) is a writer, teacher, Kimbilio Fellow, and fiction co-editor at Barrelhouse. She received her MFA from American University. Previous publication credits include *SmokeLong Quarterly, Masters Review, Wigleaf, Jellyfish Review, Booth, Strange Horizons,* and *CRAFT Literary.* She's the author of a novel, *TreeVolution,* and four collections: *Circe's Bicycle, Midnight at the Organporium, Political AF: A Rage Collection,* and *Cabinet of Wrath: A Doll Collection.*

MICHELLE DONG LIVED WITH father and fourteen cousins in a butter-soft house at the end of the block, the only family in the neighborhood not directly related to us. In another country, Uncle Dong used to be some kind of teacher, but now he sold parts of his car. For years we watched him strip his car part by part, the tires rolled away and the headlamps gouged out, until there was only a hood the color of a cockroach, and even that was gnawed gone by fog. His own yard, the only one in the neighborhood, was a chorus of beheaded poppies, which my brother said was used to make opium. He said that's why Uncle Dong spent most of the week asleep, all his windows pasted with newspaper, his house balled up and hungover. Inside their garage, the Dongs raised finches, multiplying to six hundred. Every weekend the Dongs would open their garage door in an attempt to thin out their colony, releasing them by the hundreds, a stream of birds as thick as milk.

White birds are bad luck, and that's why Michelle painted their badness away: she brought the white finches to the driveway in shoeboxes and pinned them to the pavement with her left hand, painting their feathers with her right. She painted them with an assortment of nail polishes, shades I couldn't name except by making sounds that matched them: clap-yellow, whistle-silver, gut-punch gold.

Michelle invited me over one time to play a killing game. We went to different high schools—hers was the Catholic school where girls wore skirts like sails, and mine was the public school where police dogs sniffed our asses—but I saw her every day, carrying buckets of water in and out of the garage through the side door. I believed the water was for the birds to drink, but later when I looked into one of the buckets in her side-yard, I saw that she was drowning them, all the bird-bodies clotting the water. They floated on the surface, their bones borrowing more air. My mother always told me that when she was little and raised chicks and pigeons and ducks, she had to fill their water bowls with stones because the baby birds would drown themselves by falling asleep mid-drink. I thought they were stupid to do so, but my mother said I used to fall asleep with her nipple in my mouth all the time when I was a baby. *Be glad I dried up eventually,* she said, *or my milk would have drowned you, my beautiful little bird idiot.*

When I went to Michelle's garage, she told me to leave my net behind. Instead, she handed me her Chemistry Honors textbook, its cover stained with something dark-sweet and viscous. She held another textbook—Calculus—that was symmetrically stained. *This is how I kill them,* she said. We entered through the side-door and she turned on the lights, fluorescent glow that slid to the floor as slow as mucus. Birds sewed the air into a sky. Some of them were small as wasps, and their shadows speckled the concrete floor where bird-bodies decomposed, some that had already been pared to bone. Birdshit collaged the walls and floor, streaks like an oil painting, and I breathed only through my mouth. *Like this,* Michelle said, and arced her textbook through the air with both hands, swinging it like a baseball bat, slamming it against the wall. When she lifted the book, there were stains branding the cover and the wall, the finches broken like fruit. *Now you go,* she said, and I watched the necklace of sweat around her neck, the way it swung in the dark.

I swung the textbook, felt the finches flinch against it, slammed the book against the wall. Lifted it: a dead finch flattened into a comma-shaped shadow. *Not bad,* Michelle said and spat on the ground of the garage. It was the way men in our neighborhood spat on the sidewalk: the tongue flicking easy as a whip, the spit thick as bird-shit. Later, we sat outside on her driveway on two upside-down buckets and I tried to spit too, to exile the taste of blood in my mouth, but nothing came out of me but a sound, thinned-out.

Michelle wore her cousins' wifebeaters and kicked gravel back onto the street with her toe. Her hair was ironed to the back of her neck with sweat. Later, I would practice spitting into the bathroom sink, mimicking her mouth so that its shape would become familiar to me; so that when I looked into the mirror, my mouth was hers. There was beauty to her brutality, the way she angled her chin like the sun was perched on it, but I saw that her hands were fluttering like birds. I cupped her hands in my own, the way I imagined you would rescue a bird that had tipped out of its nest, but Michelle jerked her hands back.

Here's a story, she said, and sat on her hands so that I couldn't see them. *About my father. He had a pet pigeon he leashed to his wrist. Everyone tried to cut it off his wrist and eat it, but he wouldn't let anyone come near it. One night it happened, the bird was snipped loose and stewed, and my father was so upset he almost slit his own throat, except he couldn't find a blade because everyone in the village was holding theirs.* I asked Michelle if that was why he bred so many birds, if he was trying to pay off some kind of debt, and she looked at me. Her shadow on the asphalt was fading like a bruise. She laughed and I leaned closer to her mouth, wanting to smell her breath, its bait.

Later that summer, my mother woke me early one Sunday morning and told me to come look, come look. It was hailing birds. I looked out at the street and saw: finches freckling the street, their feathers like snow, non-native to this weather. There were so many dead I lost count. Some kind of disease, my mother said, it must be. I watched Michelle from my window, raking up the birds while her cousins got into their cars and drove over the bird-corpses, splaying them open, grinding their bones to light.

K-Ming Chang is a Kundiman fellow, a Lambda Literary Award finalist, and a National Book Foundation 5 Under 35 honoree. She is the author of the *New York Times* Book Review Editors' Choice novel *Bestiary* (One World/Random House, 2020), which was longlisted for the Center for Fiction First Novel Prize and the PEN/Faulkner Award. Her short story collection, *Gods of Want,* is forthcoming from One World. She is currently the micro editor at *The Offing*. More of her work can be found at kmingchang.com.

BEFORE THEY WERE MARRIED, they met in a photograph. They stood on opposite ends of it, and beached between them was a dead sea lion, breaded in sand. The way she tells it, they were the only two people at the sea that day, the shoreline like a sleeve, something to slip out of, and when the sea[1] lion corpse shouldered itself onto land, he was the one who called out to her and suggested they take a commemorative[2] photograph with it. She's the only one looking away from the camera, her eyes so dark they look cored out of the sockets. The skin of the sea lion, enameled with blood, is tugged thin around its face. The lantern of its ribcage lifts off the page.

---

[1] I liked visiting her when my brother wasn't there and we could speak alone. When I could pretend it was me she'd been waiting for, been calling to come home, hurry. I liked the way her shadow shrouded mine on the floor of her kitchen. She said, I've always liked water even though I can't swim. I thought it was a strange thing to say – how could someone like or dislike water? Do you like/dislike air, or like/dislike having a mouth? Can we love what we're made of? And she told me she didn't really like air because it was a vehicle for wildfires and farts. She also didn't like having a mouth: I did not choose to renew my thirst, she said. We laughed. After that, she always talked to me with her lips matted together, gargling her words, until my brother overheard her on the phone with me and said stop it, you sound like an infant. But I liked how she sounded: like paragraphs of falling rain, water writing us down.

[2] After she married my brother, I went to the salon where she worked and asked for a haircut. As soon as I sat down, she recognized me from the number of cowlicks on my scalp. The same as my brother. She said the number cowlicks on my head corresponded to how many lives I've lived. This is your fourth, she said. You've had twice as many lives as me. I told her I'd heard differently: that the number of cowlicks corresponded to how many debts you'd accrued in a previous life. How many people you owed. You're one of my four, I wanted to say to her, but her scissors trimmed my sentences to silences. She looked at my scalp the whole time, and when it was over, I tipped her two times more than I could afford, an advance apology. I paid for the nick she left in my neck. When her fingers had touched my chin by accident, I imagined them inside my mouth.

She says she loved him for smiling[3] in the photo, as if they were posing with a mascot or a president, and she wonders what happened to the sea lion after they left it, if someone came to incinerate it, if they slit it open and filled it with cinderblocks and sank it, if something nocturnal ate it. In the photo, she stands farthest from it and says, *isn't it supposed to have tusks*, and he says only the males, because they fight to the death[4] for mates, and this one must be a female, look how full it is, pregnant. *Maybe the babies survived*, he said. He parsed the sand for anything sharp, a broken beer bottle, green[5] as the veins in his neck. She could tell from the way he lifted it to the light that he was literate in loneliness. That his kidneys were stone-studded. When he crouched, she looked at the back of his neck, a name tattooed there that she couldn't read: it cursived around his collarbone like a necklace.

With the broken bottle, he steered open the sea lion's belly, navigating its skin with the intimacy of a bird dragging its feet through the sea. It was bloodless surgery, the fat cutting like a cake, the blue belly-sack writhing alive. She could see the belly contracting, beating like a fist. He slipped his hands through the slit, gloving his hands in brine, bridling what was inside. The

---

[3] One time, before our youngest sister was born, I told my brother I was afraid that our mother wouldn't love us anymore, that divvying a mother between three mouths was too many. My brother, who wore the same Air Force pajamas every day even after he outgrew them—we had to cut slits in the collar so that it could dilate around his head—said don't worry, we'll band together and bully our little sister into leaving. We invented all the ways we could get her evicted, like convincing her to shit in our hands so we could smear it in the kitchen, or showing her how to hold scissors and cut our mother's laundry line, all our clothes curdled like milk.

[4] She called me at night once and asked me what kind of girlfriends my brother had before her, if there was a reason why he wore a peach pit around his neck engraved with a woman's face. I told her not to worry, that was our mother's face preserved in that pit, that he learned how to carve faces from our grandmother in Mianyang, who peddled melon sculptures. He was sent to our grandmother's house for four years, I explained, when we were kids and my mother couldn't afford all of us. Those days, whenever he called, he asked if he'd been sent away because he ate the most out of all of us. He said, I promise I don't eat as much anymore. Can I come home? Waipo bought me a book on how to shrink your stomach, such as eating one stone fruit a day and only drinking one tadpole of water at a time so the belly stays the size of a balled sock. It's like how you can fold clothes flat when there's no body inside them. I leave myself. I eat three melon seeds per sitting. That's all I need, three melon seeds. He kept repeating that to us, three three three. Even after he came home, he only ate one mouthful of every meal, even when my mother cried or spanked him with a spoon. He held up his fist and said my belly is the size of this.

[5] I met her coming out of the grocery store with bananas hanging from her hands, a chandelier of bitter. They were all green and glowed. The trick is, she told me, you have to buy everything green and then wait a week. A week later it's almost rotting, it's so sweet. I looked at the bananas because she wanted me to. I did not look at her face. I did not guess from the ripeness of it how many days ago my brother made a fist.

photograph, she says, should have captured this instead: the sea edged like a broken bottle, stabbing the shore, and his hands cemented in darkness. *Inside that belly,* she says, *was me.* He lifted me out, dangling me by the hair. He beat my chest, blued me into breathing. I looked down at the hole[6] that once harbored my body. I promised to grow up and sew it shut, to guard its dark. And then I would boot the carcass out to sea, island me.

---

[6]According to my brother, she stole his car and drove all the way east to Reno where her cousins lived. The last time I talked to her was at church, where I hadn't been in years. I went there because I knew she was a Baptist—my brother told me the story of how she baptized herself by striding into the sea in a string bikini, except she didn't realize that the tide would wrap around her like a tourniquet and pull her under. By some miracle she was yanked onto a sandbar half a mile from shore, and when she stood up on it, she thought for a moment she was standing in the middle of the ocean, her legs long enough to reach the seafloor. She could walk anywhere, to any country. They should make stilts like that, she said, stilts for people who can't swim. I went to church even though I knew nothing about god or Jesus, except that one of them had walked on water and that was what she wanted most to do. In the parking lot, she told me to get a trim soon. I said I was worried that if I cut my hair, I would look like my brother. Exposed cowlicks. True, she said, but hair is dead. It doesn't matter what it resembles. I only care about living things, she said to me. Before she got into her car, which was my brother's, I tried to tell her a story. I tried to make her stay, even though that made me the same as him. I wanted to kiss the back of her neck. Where her scissors shipped silver across my skin. One time, I told her, when my brother was in Mianyang, he found a dog in an alleyway, a runaway. It must have been a bait dog, because its face was scrolled away and it was scared of people. Except my brother. It followed him around, even to the outhouse. He gave it a glass eye, a green marble he preserves in the back pocket of his jeans and shines, fogging it blind with his breath. When he flew back from Mianyang to be with us, he wanted to take the dog back with him, so he put it in a bamboo cage and carried it. The dog had to go in the cargo hold, and somehow it died during the flight. The air pressure or an aneurysm or something. He buried it in our yard, and we planted a lime tree there. Maybe I can show you sometime, the limes tender as eyes. She smiled then. She said, Don't tell me. I can live without knowing that. But what about you, she said, how have you lived. God knows, I said. God knows my brother. She laughed at me and reached out, her fingers strumming the cowlick at the base of my skull, reversing its current, and when I close my eyes, feeling only the friction of her fingers, her sweat tiding over my skin, I pretend it was me that day on the beach, it was me, the one she was going to meet.

K-Ming Chang is a Kundiman fellow, a Lambda Literary Award finalist, and a National Book Foundation 5 Under 35 honoree. She is the author of the *New York Times* Book Review Editors' Choice novel *Bestiary* (One World/Random House, 2020), which was longlisted for the Center for Fiction First Novel Prize and the PEN/Faulkner Award. Her short story collection, *Gods of Want,* is forthcoming from One World. She is currently the micro editor at *The Offing*. More of her work can be found at kmingchang.com.

NO ONE KNOWS HOW deep the pond goes. We've never been able to find the bottom. The ranch land is posted "No Trespassing," but where else are we supposed to go on a Sunday when it's this hot? Rotted wood creaks as Tammy steps onto the makeshift diving platform, reaches for the thick rope swing. She straddles the knot and steps back, launches out, soars over the water. The surface glitters like shattered glass, like the air-spun daydreams our parents once held for themselves, might still hold for us. My breath catches at the top of her arc; *Now*! I want to yell. *Let go now*! But she hesitates, misses her perfect moment—that flash of crystal impossibility floating a fingertip's graze away—and she slips, made clumsy by this time and this place, falls into the cattails on the murky edge. I swallow the last of my beer and toss the can. My turn now. The platform is weak, splintered and sagging. It won't last much longer. I reach for the rope. Its stiff bristles rake my skin; I accept the sting, grip it hard, fists and thighs, shimmy the knot into place. Hold my breath. Push off. Fly.

Myna Chang is the winner of the 2020 Lascaux Prize in Creative Nonfiction. Recent stories have been featured in *Fractured Lit*, *X-RAY Lit Mag*, *New World Writing*, and *Bending Genres*. She was a finalist for the New Millennium Writing Award for flash fiction. Her work has been nominated for *Best Microfiction*, *Best Small Fictions*, and included in *Best Indie Speculative Fiction* 2020. She lives in Maryland. Read more at MynaChang.com or @MynaChang.

Day 3.

THESE DAYS I FEEL out of touch with myself, like I pawned my soul for a bunch of medically-induced feelings. I like to think that people should be happy, or sad, on their own terms, and the idea of attaining true peace by gulping a few blue and yellow things still doesn't make sense to me. But they mean well, or at least that's what I'm led to believe.

I'm of the view that Joy in itself is a gift, and not a composition of certain chemicals; a thing that people spend their entire lives searching for cannot be reduced to an issue of hormonal deficiencies! My body has developed a weird sense of humour too, playing a silly prank on me throughout the previous day's latter hours, but I am still here.

Day 6.

I've never been so unsure about everything, every single thing that my hours revolve around. These walls should provide comfort, they should reek of solace, but the yellow paint snubs me tonight. The nightly winds saunter in through a raised curtain, but there is a deeper chill I find myself struggling with, like the night itself chose to wrap me in cold arms, the kind of cold which twenty duvets would not cancel out.

These things should make me "feel alright", but then again, the thought of being alright for indefinite periods is enough to make me forfeit the few hours of sleep handed by Nature; green vegetation never comes with as much depth as blue dark oceans, and if there has to be colour in the room, it should find its way there on my own terms, and not because I am spurred on by the voices in these little dual-coloured things. Wouldn't it be out of touch with my nature if I never get to see things from a greyscale perspective? Wouldn't it be fraudulent on my nights if there were no cloudy storms to row in anymore? Well for now there is an impasse, a deadlock in terms of what levels of Serotonin are permissible, a raging debate on whether Happiness should be subjected to a question of chemicals and hormones in the first place, but at least I feel something.

The debate keeps me going.

Day 9.
3.16am.
My mental landscape is a boulevard of wingless dreams, false starts and a pile of what-would-have-beens. It's not enough that on many nights the sailboat rows rudderless, the chilly waters are seeping in now, making it hard to move.

The jar of pills is empty, and I crave for a new fix, a new pastime, or better still, a new excuse to justify the fact that I'm not on the race course with the rest. At least on the dark days I could feel, and I had found a way to grope in the shadows, but I do not know what to make of this colourlessness. It's not grey, but there are no rainbow-like hues either, and for more moments than one tonight I feel colour-blind. These thoughts have executed an invasion and rendered my duvet useless, and their marching sounds won't be shut out even by five pillows to each ear.

What do you do with a tree whose leaves hold colours that cannot be defined? I miss the nights of plunging down the ocean, I could describe the situation then, but not this. I can't wrap the fingers of my mind around what I feel. No, the question should be, is there even anything to feel? Logic is taking a power nap, and all the ones who said they would be on hand to cancel out the unsure moments are fast asleep.

I guess I'll just keep floating, that is, if I can even call it that, because it's difficult to make out a concrete description of your movements in undefined space.

Day X.
Morning continues from where night left off, as there is nothing to pull me out of this stream of the unsure. I can't place a finger on how I feel, nay, I can't confidently say if what I am doing at the moment is actually "feeling". There is no motivation to sleep, but there is no reason to be up either, and I am left to half-heartedly stretch towards all the places that show no concrete signs of really wanting me.

Half the world is asleep, and the other half couldn't be bothered, but I have never particularly embarked on a quest for sympathy. Words come with limited potential, and no amount of Affection has ever, or will ever be enough. Maybe I love groping my way in the dark, or to put it in context, rolling in the mire, unwilling to embrace light and fresh air. . .or maybe I am not just keen on believing in ideas and situations that seem so alien now.

If there were no bad moods, I probably wouldn't have any moods at all, and I have seen enough to know that when things go so well, I only have to wait on the sky to see how the rainbow clears out, and watch the clouds return to their gloomy schedule. There's no happiness, only rare flashes of light, and there's no peace, only dementors that go on recess.

Jerry Chiemeke is a columnist, culture critic and lawyer. His works have appeared in *The Inlandia Journal, The Johannesburg Review of Books, The Guardian, Honey & Lime, Bone and Ink Press* and *Agbowo,* among others.

I GREW UP IN South Korea during the US-backed military dictatorship. I was born a year after General Park Chung Hee led a military coup and came into power. My father filmed the day of martial-law declaration in front of Seoul City Hall. Back then, he worked as a freelance photojournalist for UPI. The saluting lieutenant general is one of Park's collaborators. The man in the background below the window, holding a small camera in front of his face, is most likely a police or intelligence officer. My father is at the bottom left, holding his film camera. After the parade, my father was briefly taken into the building where he stood face-to-face with Park. My father said that he was not afraid. He said he wasn't afraid of Syngman Rhee, the previous dictatorial president, either. He wasn't afraid of anything then, he said; instead, he complained to Park about the censorship of the news. That day his film made it out of Kimpo Airport to Tokyo, and his news footage appeared worldwide. Because I was an infant, I have no memory of this infamous day except through my father's memory. Memory's memory. Memory's child. My memory lives inside my father's camera, the site where my memory was born, where my retina and my father's overlap. When I was old enough, I always accompanied my mother to the airport to greet my father, who returned home every three to five months from Vietnam. Overlapping memory always longs for return, the return of memory.

What I remember about my childhood are the children, no older than I, who used to come around late afternoons begging for leftovers, even food that had gone sour. The drills at school in preparation for attacks by North Korea kept me anxious at night. I feared separation from my family due to the ever-pending war. I feared what my mother feared—my brother being swept up in protests and getting arrested and tortured. Our radio was turned off at night in case we were suspected of being North Korean sympathizers. At school, former North Korean spies came to give talks on the evil leader of North Korea. I stood at bus stops to see if I could spot any North Korean spies, but all I could spot were American GIs. My friends and I waved to them and called them Hellos. In our little courtyard, I skipped rope and played house with my paper dolls among big, glazed jars of fermented veggies and spicy, pungent pastes. I feared the shadows they cast along the path to the outhouse. Stories of abandoned infant girls always piqued my interest, so I imagined that the abandoned babies might be inside the jars. Whenever I obeyed the shadows, I saw tiny, floating arms covered in mold. And whenever it snowed, I made tiny snowmen on the lids of the jars. Like rats, children can be happy in darkness. But the biggest darkness of all was the midnight curfew. I didn't know the curfew was a curfew till my family escaped from it in 1972 and landed in Hong Kong. That's how big the darkness was.

In 1980, my father filmed the rising waves of student protests against the dictatorship in Seoul. He also witnessed the brutal military crackdown on the pro-democratic uprising in Gwangju. He believed then that the dictatorship would never end and that it would be too dangerous for us to return home. He sold one of his cameras to pay for surgery when my older brother was injured during his mandatory military service. He gave the South Korean government news footage of a student protest in down- town Seoul he had filmed—from far away, from a rooftop—in exchange for the release of my injured brother from the military and a permit to leave South Korea. He believed that he was saving us from a life of perpetual darkness. In 1983, my family scattered all over, as my mother said. My parents and my younger brother headed to West Ger- many. My sister remained in Hong Kong, my older brother left for Australia, and I went to the US as a foreign student to complete my degrees in art. In light, we all were ailing from separation and homesickness. In light, we had to find a way to settle down, as my mother said. In light, we lived like birds.

In December 2016, I returned to South Korea. I returned in the guise of a translator, which is to say, I returned as a foreigner. And as a foreigner, I was invisible to most. I flittered about in downtown Seoul searching for my child self that had been left behind long ago. As a foreigner, I understood only the language of wings—the wings on totem animals on old palaces where I used to run around and play. The traditional tiled roofs I grew up beneath had grown wings, as had the mountain peaks behind Gwanghwamun Square. They no longer recognized me in a crowd of other foreigners—tourists, rather. Nevertheless, I went on searching for more wings, my lan- guage of return.

Born in Seoul, South Korea, Don Mee Choi is the author of *DMZ Colony*, which won the 2020 National Book Award for poetry (Wave Books, 2020), *Hardly War* (Wave Books, 2016), *The*

Morning News Is Exciting (Action Books, 2010), and several chapbooks and pamphlets of poems and essays. She has received a Whiting Award, Lannan Literary Fellowship, Lucien Stryk Translation Prize, and DAAD Artists-in-Berlin Fellowship. She has translated several collections of Kim Hyesoon's poetry, including *Autobiography of Death* (New Directions, 2018), which received the 2019 International Griffin Poetry Prize.

I WAS AFRAID OF cockroaches until I looked at one underneath my microscope. Dialing the lens, my sight spun in and out of focus over a rough, brown landscape. Strange, unidentifiable details came into clarity—a dark canyon, a curving river. What was a cockroach, really, but unknown terrain, a world of cells and exoskeleton?

I began to use my microscope to look at everything that frightened me. Of course, I had bigger, better ones in my laboratory, but there was comfort in having one at home. When my W2 came in the mail, I slid the paper under the lens, pressed my eye into the dark tunnel of the eyepiece, and, as if I were skydiving, fell through unfocused haze into a view of rough, fibrous grassland. A woven nest to huddle in. I could be a young bird, flying high for the first time, heading home. I saw no more words, no more confusing fields to fill or money I didn't have. I was in the sky of another world and it wasn't scary anymore.

When I called to tell my ma that no, I wouldn't go on a date with our family friend's son, Jason Wang, and I would not go on any dates with any boys, ever, I slipped my phone onto the plate, put my cheek up against the cool hardness of the eyepiece, and saw a neon field of red, blue, and green arranged neatly like tombstones, a plain of ordered light. After the call, I collected my tears onto a slide and watched fracturing crystals form an unknown cityscape. I wanted to slip through the eyepiece, run through those mysterious streets. I wondered what it would be like to look at my ma's frown. What landscape would be revealed—fertile riverbeds, a striped red dawn, rows of fuchsia flowers? Some place safe and pretty, where I could lie down a while?

I went to a lesbian bar, my first. I'd passed it before on the sidewalk at least twenty times, faltering at the last moment. I was a shadow in a dark corner, cast against the wall. I didn't move until a woman paused beside me. She rested a hand on my shoulder. Then she was gone.

At home, I threw my shirt onto the microscope plate, crawled along its soft, looping chains, a net that had always held me, searching for an invasion, searching for what she had left behind. I found nothing.

I had a photograph of my mother from when she was young, my age. Wearing a scarf with her head tipped up, as if hopeful to see something just over the horizon. I slid it under my lens. I couldn't tell where I'd landed. It could have been her hair, her scarf, her sweater. I saw dark wavering lines. I walked along them for a while like roads. But as long as I walked, I never found what I looked for: the things her own mother had said to her, the things that had made her cry. The things she hadn't known how to explain.

When the first woman asked if she could come home with me, slipping her hand into mine, I wanted to soar over the ancient desert canyons in her palms. What if I traversed the volcanic ridges of her dark hair, instead of bringing her upstairs, panting from the slight effort, our clasped hands slippery? What cities did her sweat contain? What if, as she laughed on my couch, I slid down the glaciers of her teeth, rather than looked at her, her dangerous terrain I couldn't blur with a turn of my hand? What if I first looked at a swab of her cheek—just to know. Instead of this kiss that fell towards me. There was too much to examine. A whole world to run through and survey. Mountains. Rivers. Deserts. Ruins. Everything that hid within, that could make me afraid. Then her lips were on mine, a soft landing. And I saw what was there.

Samantha Xiao Cody is a queer, half-Chinese writer pursuing her MFA at the Iowa Writers' Workshop. She recently won the *Masters Review* 2019 Winter Short Story Award and was a runner-up in the *Missouri Review's* 2020 Jeffrey E. Smith Editors' Prize, and has had work published in *Split Lip Magazine, Jellyfish Review,* and elsewhere. She has been awarded a Best of the Net and nominated for the Pushcart Prize. She has a degree in Physics from Princeton University and previously lived in Phnom Penh, Cambodia, where she taught Math and Physics at a project-based-learning high school.

THE GIRLS ON THE beach say that Katya killed her twin sister in the womb. They say that Katya has a whole floor of her house to herself, that Katya eats whipped cream from the canister, that Katya never has to go anywhere if she doesn't want to. It is Katya's fourteenth birthday, and the girls are convinced that she is wearing a bikini under her shirt. Anne and I sit side by side on a yellow towel and listen to them gossip. We used to know Katya. Now all we know is what the girls whisper. We watch as Katya dances in the water, her back to us. None of us join her. We're too scared to unfold from our sitting positions and bare bathing suits none of us want to admit to, not if there is a bikini-wearer among us.

Katya emerges from the waves and walks towards Anne and I. Her blue shirt sticks to her stomach and goes down to her thighs. I can't tell what she has underneath. We make room for her on the towel and she sits and pulls her knees up to her chest. The other girls watch us. Katya keeps her eyes fixed on the waves as if she's looking for something. I wonder if she really is wearing a bikini underneath, and what's stopping her from revealing it to us. She should know we're waiting for her to make us jealous. She should know that we aren't here because of the cake or even because of our mothers, but because we're eager for miracles, and she's the only one who can give them to us.

Katya runs her hand through her blonde hair. When we were younger, the three of us used to tell each other ghost stories in the yard. Katya hadn't been Katya then, just the girl next door. We used to sit around a lit candle and say *what if, what if, what if,* trying to summon other worlds. We stopped after Katya moved to the house where she had her own floor and became the girl that devoured her twin in the womb, the girl that might have a bikini under her shirt.

Katya's parents bring her the birthday cake when the sun begins to set. Katya looks away from the water and back at us, waiting for her to reveal something spectacular. She takes off her shirt. Her bikini is everything we imagined, and we are hers once again. Katya looks at the cake with its delicate frosting, and we can see the hunger in her eyes. It is hers to devour, as is everything.

Katya leans over the candles and blows them out. As they flicker, I catch a glimpse of a blonde girl in the water, her arms reaching towards us. I can't tell if it's Katya-from-next-door, or Katya's devoured twin sister, or just a doorway to another world, closing in the light of the setting sun.

Noa Covo's work has appeared in or is forthcoming from *Passages North, Jellyfish Review,* and *Waxwing*. Her chapbook, *Common Ancestors,* was published by Thirty West Publishing House. She can be found on Twitter @covo_noa.

HEAT-RAVAGED RIVETS EXPLODE off the corrugated iron roof of our milking shed like corks from shaken champagne bottles.

A long drought wind scalds in from the north and the thermometer leaves 50 behind as pitiless gusts scour every nook of the farm. No easy pickings to be found; all that could be taken is long gone.

Dad wasn't a man you made a promise to lightly, his plea for me to stay burdened with the heft of eight generations. I crane my neck, spot his cross, remember the soil being so unyielding we used up all our dynamite. Not enough time or faith left over for funerals, so his pension cheque still ghosts in.

I lost Annie to the highway a week back. No goodbyes, only the midnight creak of our front door, the bloom of liberated fuel as her car engine fired.

Well rid of her two-faced grace, the lies that fell from those blue eyes as acid rain, but I can't seem to shake that afternoon before she left. The brutal whisper of, "Pete, we're in this together", as my tired, fractured head folded into her shoulder.

Joe at the Co-Op rings. The water tankers aren't coming. He chews my ear about it being the start of Australia's climate change but sure feels to me like we're already at the end of everything.

Three hundred cattle are all that remain and I've enough feed to get half through next week. The cull is almost a familiar dance now. I never remember grabbing my gun; never forget to keep a bullet in the chamber after it's done.

I'm not a brave man, and if soft bovine eyes ever boiled over in accusation it would unbind me. Turns out, their gratitude is what keeps me awake.

Simon lives as part of a dog dominated family in the Yarra Valley near Melbourne, Australia. You can find his award-winning Flash Fiction in various online and print publications. Two of his recent stories (one—runner up, one—shortlisted) appear in Volume Five of the *Bath Flash Fiction Anthology*, published in December 2020. In 2019 he joined @VirtualZine as editor/reader. Simon tweets away at @lockedinatardis, and more of his work appears on his author website: www.simoncowdroy.com. His first crime novel, *Cut of a Knife*, was a Pitch Perfect finalist at Bloody Scotland in 2018. Now renamed *Sleep Bringer*, this novel is currently out in the world looking for a home. His hobbies include writing, reading, the art of Caravaggio, lifting heavy objects and awful puns.

Cook time: 60 minutes | Easy | Serves: 30-100

IMPRESS YOUR GUEST WITH this bittersweet chocolate cherry gateau, a revamped version of a retro classic. Bound to delight, considering you have no retirement funds.

Ingredients:

- The top three award-winning butter sculptures from Iowa State Fair
- Every block of chocolate that Whittaker's can produce on a night shift
- Your bodyweight in the morning, measured in flour
- One bathtub of caster sugar, marinated by dusk
- A full head of hair's worth of cocoa
- As many eggs as you can steal from a free-range farm
- One shaken pump bottle filled with bicarbonate of soda
- More buttercream than can be weighed on a bathroom scale
- A bag of refrigerated O+ donated blood
- One Himalayan salt lamp with working batteries, left to thaw

To assemble:

- All the cherries you can cram in your mouth, stolen from a South Island fruit farm
- A jar of strawberry jam, untouched in purgatory
- The topmost layer of a nebulous cloud

- Four pack of Smirnoff Ice from the kitchen bench of a teen house party
- A retirement village's rose garden, dipped in sugar
- Countdown's supply of Chewy Caramel Tim Tams
- One pack freeze dried raspberry powder
- One pack Nestlé choc bits
- Store-bought fondant

Method:

1.Rent crematorium the morning of or day prior to the funeral. Heat cremator to 180°C. Grease and line casket (180 x 55 cm). Boil the kettle. Melt butter sculptures and chocolate in transfer pan. Gently heat until melted.

2.Crush Himalayan salt lamp in an industrial food processor. Place with other dry ingredients in an XL-sized urn loader. Add pinch of soil. Sift.

3.Scrape wet mixtures into urn loader, add boiling water and whizz by throwing on an electric fence until the batter is lump free.

4.Call your mother while stirring gently.

5.Pour mixture in caskets and bake for 25 minutes in cremator.

6.Prick with the anxiety of whether you're getting into heaven. Allow thoughts to cool to room temperature. Carefully cut body-sized trench into middle layer of cake using large dessert spoon. Place the pillowy body of a loved one in the middle of the batter. Keep body cryogenically frozen until time of baking.

7.Mix together Smirnoff Ice, juiced cherries and bag of donated blood. Drizzle over the cake, letting the earthy flavours mingle with the cocoa into a complex mélange of grief and stunning beauty.

8.Tip half of a nebulous cloud into a separate transfer pan and heat until just below evaporation. Chop chocolate, pour until the texture resembles clotted cream.

9.Stack cakes, with body placed firmly in the middle layer and pinned in place with clothes pegs. Dollop jam and sky between layers. Decorate surface with buttercream, sugared roses, freeze-dried raspberry powder and Nestlé choc bits. Place wafer-thin white chocolate with *Sorry for your loss* message in centre (this sign can be purchased in advance from a local baker). Pipe small rows of fondant across the periphery like dewy morning grass. Layer a row of Tim Tams along the bottom like gravestones. Pile remaining fresh cherries in and around the cake. Serve immediately.

10. Bon Appétit!

Comments, Questions and Tips:

MirandaJuly

Delicious! I made a smaller version of this for the death of my cat. Just third the mixture.

KayFee

Wow, this is a gorgeous recipe. Made this for my uncle's funeral and got high praise for it. Lovely and moist. Like a cordon bleu except as a dessert. One tip I picked up. . .I put in extra party poppers and popcorn with the body. The children got such a fright when Brian's hungry, ghostly resurrected corpse turned up and had enough spiritual laissez-faire to burst out of the cake during the mourning procession. It was a delightful stripper-cake-cum-casket but make sure the younger ones have napkins and diapers ready!

mykitchendrools

Got served this "pièce de résistance" at my grandmother's funeral. Thank God there was yoghurt served with it because it was so dry I almost bit into her arm just to get a bit of moisture. Make sure to bake for less time than the recipe suggests.

Vanessa Crofskey (born in 1996) is a writer and artist of Hokkien Chinese and Pākehā descent. She graduated from Auckland University of Technology with a degree in Sculpture in 2017. Vanessa currently works for *The Pantograph Punch* as a staff writer, and as a curator at Window Gallery (University of Auckland).

A BITTEN MOON LOOKED over him as he licked acorns in search of his sister. There was dew and the palate of dirt with each lick brought a memory, each lick so painful, so wonderful, so magical, every acorn that touched his tongue became of pebbles as if planted in a riverbed before history existed. Earth settled against the inner walls of his mouth, a cave full of grit, and his sister, in flashes, would simmer throughout his body. There they were—standing between two bronze bales of hay in a field full of dandelions, holding yellow and orange balloons, as if to mirror the set sun—a celebration of their birth. There they were—creating currents in the pond, moss drooped over, splashing each other and teaching one another how to multiply in their heads using the number of times each of them had been stung by wasps. 8. 6. 48. And there they were, in their shared room, wooden floor, cold air, she in her bed—a soaked washcloth on her forehead as he held her frozen hand and sang a lullaby about shovels and watermelons. Sing to me about the way the blisters mounded on our palms. He put three more acorns in his mouth and juggled them around like the marbles in their hands when he and his sister played stars of the universe out on the porch drizzled by mosquitoes under a flickering lantern. Eyes closed tight—the humid air pressed heavy on the back of his neck, he closed his eyes tighter, hurting his own skull—a jawbone of no release. There they were—on their backs, fingers pointing toward a tilted sky as they counted sparrows and clouds. 3. 4. 5. 12. 13. His mouth now, cheeks puffed and pierced with acorns, he swiveled his cut tongue around, in search for more of her—throwing pecans in a rusted bucket placed on top of a wheel-less tractor, speckled with feathers and ants. And he opened his eyes and there she was—in land, amidst the soil—her new world under the stars of the universe. Let us play. Let us play. Let us play. He spat out the acorns and called out her name and cried, crying so loud the roots of the oak looked sad and soft. And so he lay on his back and looked at the night glittered through branches and there came a smile. He reached for another acorn and licked it and let the moon fall on his eyes.

Shome Dasgupta lives in Lafayette, LA. He is the author of *i am here And You Are Gone* (Winner Of The 2010 OW Press Contest), *The Seagull And The Urn* (HarperCollins India), *Anklet And Other Stories* (Golden Antelope Press), *Pretend I Am Someone You Like* (Livingston Press), *Mute* (Tolsun Books), and the forthcoming books, *Spectacles* (Word West), and *Iron Oxide* (Assure Press) which is a poetry collection. His stories and poems have appeared in *McSweeney's Internet Tendency, New Orleans Review, New Delta Review, Necessary Fiction, Parentheses Journal, Magma Poetry,* and elsewhere. He can be found at www.shomedome.com and @laughingyeti.

CURL YOUR NAILBEDS INTO the meat of your palm, thumb on top. This is the letter *S* in American Sign Language. This is *S* as in stomach, where Uncle Sean's hand now goes instead of his chest when he signs *me* and *mine*. *S* as in scars marking where his colon should be. As in *sorry* when he draws that hand, his thumb, in circles on his chest.

This shape is for resting your chin while the geneticist speaks. His diagnosis is nothing new. You'd seen pictures of your uncle's infested colon already. This was only about identifying his polyposis, spread now to his lungs.

This is for pulling your jacket tighter, for seeking comfort, alone. You're standing in the chill of the Central Sierras three hundred miles away from all of it, in a meadow Uncle Sean loves but hasn't seen in years, waiting for the Perseids. The meteors crest over trees and draw blue trails between them. They hurtle down the creek toward the sliver of moon. You want to catch their light and bring it back to him.

It's also for marshmallow-roasting sticks made from Oregon grape shrubs growing along the creek, just like he taught you. Pick the greenest one you can find. Cut it long, just above a knot so it grows wild again.

And for hanging the lantern on the nail his grandmother hammered into the ponderosa pine, ninety years of butterscotch sap clinging to it. For dipping towels in the creek to lay over the ice chests, keeping them cooler longer.

Fists are for opening a hospital door and holding a surprise. You give your uncle something he missed: a pressed alpine shooting star from the meadow, *Dodecatheon alpinum*, bright purple against his pale palm.

This hand is for hanging on.

If you touch your fingertips to your chest and make a fist as you pull both hands away, you've signed *bold, courageous, whole,* like your uncle. You've also signed *heal, recover, feeling well.* He knows you've never handled grief well. He sets the flower on his bedside table and nests your fist in his hand. Inhale deep, your uncle signs, and imagine it floating up from your toes, through your stomach, across your collar bones--imagine it glowing in your fist. You imagine the Perseids streaking down your arm, pooling in your hands. When you're ready, exhale, uncurl your fingers, and let it go.

Leah Dawdy is an elementary school teacher living in Spokane, Washington. She was born and raised in Southern California and taught in the Inland Empire for several years. She is a recipient of the William Henry Willis Memorial Poetry Prize. Her work placed second in *The Masters Review*'s 2020 Flash Fiction Contest.

MY DAD HAD STUDENTS. He taught social work. They'd call to discuss the reading. They must've been insomniacs or late-night readers—or maybe vampires. They'd call at all hours of the night. I'd pick up. I'd hold the receiver in my hand. Then my dad picked up in the other room. Hang up, he said. OK, I said. I fake-clicked. I may have done this a couple times.

The girl talked, for the most part. Neither of them said anything really interesting. She said "like" or "really." My dad nodded. But she couldn't hear him. I could hear her mentally self-correcting. She'd try to "like" less but this only made it worse. It was like—

"Like, like, like" (dad's breathing/nodding) "LIKE"

(Really.)

I felt bad for her (maybe). I wanted her to see my dad. He sat there in his underwear. His camel coat was off. It was as if he'd hatched, it had given birth to a smaller man. He slumped and his belly dipped. He had a bald spot. It was in inverse proportion to his charisma. It was like he'd been cursed/blessed. Some evil witch said: you have this bald spot, yes, but women will still love you.

It was important to hang up first. The woman knew this. My dad knew this. I knew this. She knew this and still couldn't pull the trigger. I tried sending her psychic signals (now, now, NOW)—but if she heard me she didn't let on.

Our apartment filled with smoke. Mom smoked in her room. She watched Lifetime. She loved Lifetime. It featured her favorite kind of person: Women Worse Off Than She. Men treated women badly and then they murdered them and this made my mom glad. She said, run, run, but what she really meant was: die. Die already.

She ashed her cigarettes into the milk. The cones dimmed and mixed in with her cereal—Lucky Charms and Apple Jacks. These were Bronx staples. The rest of the house was

Father but my mother's bedroom was the Bronx. It was like a film set, her props included: a wooden bedroom set from the 70s, circa Son of Sam; a defunct A/C unit (we had central); and our dead dog. Her name is Carrie. She is invisible and deceased. I miss you, my mom would say. You couldn't tell who she was speaking to, but I knew. Her legs stretched, accommodating Carrie's shape.

The woman sat there on the line. She held her breath. Finally, my dad hung up. You could always feel it before it happened. He sounded annoyed. Or not annoyed—checked out. It was like he had a "do not disturb" button. The iPhone people got the idea from him—all notifications will be silenced.

I covered the phone. I waited with her. She knew this was happening, she still couldn't move. She couldn't get herself to pull the plug, to be first. I knew exactly how she felt. I remembered my dad walking me to school, watching him. I'd do this from my class. My dad stood outside, talking to someone on a payphone. He'd smile and twist the cord, and I imagined that person on the line. She'd light up. The sun would come from my father's smile. It wasn't a particularly nice sun. It was kind of gray and there was dirt in it. There were sunspots and wayward pigeons that migrated the wrong way. Still, she was blinded.

Finally something clicked. My dad was getting tired. Not on the street, but in his study. The woman wanted to hang up. She couldn't. Some kind of force of nature was preventing her. She began to speak and then my dad said: it's getting late. It was already late—this was beside the point. He clicked and she waited there, holding the phone. We breathed, together. Finally something kicked in—survival instinct—or maybe she had to pee.

She hung up. I *69ed and wrote the number down. I had pages of these. They were marked: "Top Secret." It was reverse psychology or maybe direct psychology for dummies—Dad would find it and think: What's this? What is my daughter up to? Or Mom would find it and be pissed. She'd divorce him. I wanted this until I didn't.

I'd be the one to find them. I was 15 or 17. I walked out in the rain. Or I imagined rain. Rain to me = something romantic and clandestine. I held an umbrella. I stood there. I fed some quarters in the phone. I felt the ringing connecting me to a person. Or a voicemail. Or a voicemail that said: this is a wrong number.

Then I hung up. Or I stood there with the phone. I heard breathing—an annoyed voice saying: hello, hello. It was a woman's voice, slightly older. I waited for acknowledgment—like oh, oh! you must be that professor's kid. Somehow they would know. And I would *feel* them know.

They breathed and this time their breathing was more confident, less *like-y*—and I hated it. I wanted to ask if they could give me lessons. To be my mentor. To cut my "likes" with some toenail clippers. But I didn't. I hung up. Or I stood there for a while. Someone was waiting to use the phone, or it really began to rain. Or maybe it was my period.

I waited. I wanted one—one "like." Or even a "really." I'd settle for a "really."

Leonora Desar's writing has appeared in places such as *New South, No Tokens, The Cincinnati Review, Black Warrior Review,* and *Columbia Journal,* where she was chosen as a finalist by Ottessa Moshfegh. Her work was included in the *Best Small Fictions* 2019, the *Wigleaf* Top 50 (2019 and 2020), and *Best Microfiction* 2019, 2020, and 2021. She won third place in *SmokeLong Quarterly*'s 2020 Award for Flash Fiction and *River Styx*'s 2018 microfiction contest, and was a runner-up/finalist in *Quarter After Eight*'s Robert J. DeMott Short Prose Contest, judged by Stuart Dybek, and *Crazyhorse*'s Crazyshorts! contest. She is fiction editor of *Pidgeonholes.*

#After Emily Johnson

HAVE I TOLD YOU of the oak / that grew where we are now / that you can find in aerial shots of the city / going back sixty years / before it was slashed down for this conference centre / which would fit within it / so wide was its trunk / I was thinking how flimsy my limbs would seem held against its slimmest branch / I looked up to check its wondrous penumbra of leaves and saw instead the cast-iron beams of the ceiling / and not the sky I had seen earlier this morning / outside / when I noticed again how impossible it is to fully grasp / such clear and present borderlessness / in which a sparrow hawk swooped / and above it flew an airplane / and though I knew the plane was thousands of feet further up / I stood there / just in case the hawk needed me to catch / my fingers laced into a fleshy ready nest / my breath trapped / my chest clenched / my shuddering shuddering heart / and I was that sky / our bird / this tree / these leaves / the building / you / and me

---

Born in Nigeria in 1984, Inua Ellams is an internationally touring poet, playwright, performer, graphic artist & designer. He is an ambassador for the Ministry of Stories and his published books of poetry include *Candy Coated Unicorns and Converse All Stars*, *Thirteen Fairy Negro Tales*, *The Wire-Headed Heathen*, *#Afterhours* and *The Half-God of Rainfall*—an epic story in verse. His first play *The 14th Tale* was awarded a Fringe First at the Edinburgh International Theatre Festival and his fourth *Barber Shop Chronicles* sold out two runs at England's National

Theatre. He is currently touring *An Evening With An Immigrant* and completing his first full poetry collection *The Actual.* In graphic art & design, online and in print, he tries to mix the old with the new, juxtaposing texture and pigment with flat shades of colour and vector images. He lives and works from London, where he founded the Midnight Run, a nocturnal urban excursion. He is a Fellow of the Royal Society of Literature.

RED ZONE, GREEN ZONE, blue zone, street zone, food zone, bed zone, dead zone, as if looking round cloud nine, seventh heaven, some resort island, or some slum, where the poor live, and dream of owning something larger than themselves. The suntanned rough sleeper sits cross-legged on his traffic island, complete with coconut palm. The bearded rough sleeper in a blanket lies flat along the bench at a bus stop. The manic pram-pusher, whose baby buggy contains only a loaded boom-box blasting rap music, hurries, skittering along, but stops to dole out a couple of dollar bills to each rough sleeper, fishing in a clutter of bags, and the day is as dry as hot sand grains blown in from the beach two blocks away.

The man paralysed from the neck down steers his electric wheelchair onto the bus-door ramp, and down the street. He trundles a block or so to his busker's pitch on the boulevard next to Waikiki Beach. He stops first at a bike shop, where the friendly manager helps him drape the set of small bells around his neck and over one arm that he then jiggles to make delicate music. His Stetson hat that travels on top of the canopy over his wheelchair is now on the pavement in front of him, and here is where this wheelchair-bound performer will remain all morning, his jingle of bells competing with the roar of refrigerated ice-cream trucks, the clatter of open-sided tourist trolley buses and the clamour from Sheraton Hotel workers on strike further along the road, using megaphones and steadily banging on drums.

David Eggleton lives in Dunedin, New Zealand, and is a former editor of *Landfall* and *Landfall Review Online* as well as the *Phantom Billstickers Magazine Cafe Reader*. He has published a number of poetry collections, and one collection of short fiction. His stories have appeared in various anthologies of *Best New Zealand Fiction* and elsewhere. He is the New Zealand Poet Laureate 2019-2022. His poetry collection *The Wilder Years: Selected Poems* is out in April 2021 from Otago University Press.

I DON'T TELL MY mother what I'm thinking as I look around her dark, musty room. *Throw things away, Mom.* What she's keeping is torn, faded, crumpled, dirty. Another metropolis of Styrofoam cups has gone up beside her kitchen sink. Again, she's stuffing empty cups into the love seat. Does she think they're hidden? The second sister bought her a pack of Styrofoam cups from Walmart, thinking kindness might outsmart our mother, but the fresh ones are in the cupboard, out of sight, and maybe this is the problem? So I toss what I can while my mother pleads for me to leave things alone, and I feel like a raider. My Polish grandmother hoarded. Her basement was a treasure hunt for kids who don't separate what's finished from what's worth saving. My first sister and I would dress in moth eaten hats and scarves, tarnished costume jewelry, set a table for ourselves with chipped dishes, a tureen with a petunia pattern, a mismatched gravy bowl missing its handle. We'd dine on imaginary buttered toast points and sip fresh squeezed orange juice from cracked tea cups like the Queen and Princess of England. My mother used to have an eagle eye. Colorful pillows dotting the sofa, tchotchkes clustered on the coffee table, stacks of art catalogues, their spines color-matched; her violin bow placed on her music stand, just so, and waiting for her to come back and play. She smelled like flowers, and dressed for dinner. A silky blouse, her hair pulled back, slim black pants. Did she ever wear jeans? Out in the yard, Nina and I would practice gymnastics: back bridges, cartwheels, handstands, tricking gravity until our mother called us in to wash up. On our dinner plates would be an edible garnish, usually parsley. Now we worry our mother never gets clean because she needs help in the tub, and to allow someone in risks what she savors being taken for trash.

Pia Z. Ehrhardt is the author of *Famous Fathers & Other Stories* and *Now We Are Sixty,* an illustrated book with Nina Z. Temple. Pia's fiction and essays have appeared in *McSweeney's Quarterly Concern*, *Oxford American*, *Narrative Magazine*, *Virginia Quarterly Review*, *New World Writing*, *Matter Press*, and *Guernica*. She is the recipient of a Bread Loaf Fellowship and the Narrative Prize. Her work has been performed at Symphony Space, Word Theater, and on WKQR. She lives in New Orleans, LA and Queens, NY.

THE OPENING CEREMONY

THE COMMON

bushra elfadil

translated by elisabeth jaquette

EVERY FRIDAY MORNING, ALL the residents in the neighborhood of Wilat in this drab African city wait for the General to appear, to officially open the narrow street that passes between their houses. They had paid for the street's construction themselves. And they could have used the road without any fuss, but neighborhood authorities had informed them, six months earlier, that His Eminence would be arriving to open the street himself. These authorities, and several other authorities, had ordered the residents to line up in the early morning on the first Friday of the month, but the General did not arrive, and so they repeated this scene on Fridays for months, in hopes of greeting him. Then an order was issued that forbade residents from driving their cars on the new street before it was officially opened. The residents kept lining up as usual for this tiresome wait, whispering and murmuring, but the opening did not happen. Many cursed the day on which the idea arose to build this now-postponed street, and after a long wait, they eventually dispersed in time for prayers, without having been cheered by the sight of His Eminence cutting the ribbon. That act was expected to last only seconds, and which point the neglected street would become well-known, and the media would add the street to a list of the government's accomplishments. Really, any local official could do the job.

It was a marvelous, fine-looking street, the planners had made it as stunning as could be, and it cut through the middle of the neighborhood with a dark metallic sheen, between dusty dirt houses the color of uncooked camel liver. A street built thanks to the forearms and savings of its own residents, both those residing there, and those who had moved away. A sparkling new road that ran through the poor, dirty neighbourhood like a modern electric fitting inside a car as old as internal combustion itself. The road began at patch of dirt and led to an inevitable fate among the potholes.

Meanwhile, the General was too busy with his annual hunting trips to open the street;

he was off staying at hunting camps with leaders of neighboring counties and other important figures. The General was rotund, and the more successful the hunting, the shorter he appeared, since he and his companions ate the good meat from the hunt, and he grew ever fatter and heavier. And so he kept hunting, and eating, and growing fatter, and thus shorter. He increasingly became attached to the nation's soil. And so he set off on his triumphant journey from west to east, penetrating the patient, ancient, virgin continent, until he and his companions fell into the Great Rift Valley. The convoy of bulldozers and other heavy equipment were summoned to save these important figures. And the bulldozers, which could have been filling potholes in every city street if they hadn't been transported overland to the valley, dug all day on a Friday the street was meant to be opened, in an attempt to open a passage out of the valley for the procession of cars carrying the General and his friends.

The neighborhood residents had grown bored with this mendacious delay, so they decided to search for someone to take the General's place. In the end, the opening ceremony happened in an unusual way: people lined up all day Friday as usual, waiting for an alternate to the General, who did not arrive either. The drudgery of waiting had lasted into the afternoon, when a slender little boy tossed a brightly colored glass marble into the air. The child's eyes gleamed like the rising glass, and beams of afternoon sun glinted off the marble. It seemed massive to the onlookers, mesmerizing to thousands of eyes as it rolled down the street alone, confirming how beautiful the marble, and how well-constructed the road truly was. As the neighborhood residents watched in collective astonishment and expectation, the marble proceeded along, thousands of eyes watching in amazed delight as it made its way across the asphalt like a skilled spaceship. The road's engineering was exemplary. The glass ball rolled further with impressive speed, still watched by rapt eyes, until it dropped into a hole at the end of the street like a golf ball. The hole swallowed it up. And so the neighborhood residents observed the glorious opening of their illustrious street. But when they turned towards the boy, he was gone without a trace.

Bushra Elfadil is a writer, translator and columnist. He is the author of five short story collections, three novels, and a book of poetry. In 2012 he won the El-Tayeb Salih International Prize for Creative Writing in Arabic, and in 2017 he was awarded the Caine Prize for African Writing for his short story entitled "The Story of the Girl Whose Birds Flew Away," translated by Max Shmookler, which appeared in *The Book of Khartoum* (Comma Press, 2016).

Elisabeth Jaquette's translations from Arabic include *Minor Detail* by Adania Shibli, *The Queue* by Basma Abdel Aziz, and *Thirteen Months of Sunrise* by Rania Mamoun, among others. She was a finalist for the 2020 National Book Award for Translated Literature, and her work has been nominated for the Best Translated Book Award, Warwick Prize for Women in Translation, and TA First Translation Prize. She is also Executive Director of the American Literary Translators Association (ALTA).

SANITIZE YOUR HANDS, SANITIZE your daughter's hands, sanitize the kitchen countertops, sanitize the kitchen table, sanitize your daughter's Nalgene water bottle, sanitize her iPod touch, sanitize her pill box, sanitize *The Giver*, sanitize the fluffy purple pen, sanitize your daughter's diary, sanitize her toothbrush body, sanitize the knob to the bathroom door, sanitize your daughter's bedside table, lay your daughter on the flowery bedspread and sanitize the site of her central line, sanitize the blue spout and attach the tubing to the plastic ball filled with vancomycin, sanitize the vancomycin ball and wait five hours for it to drain into your daughter, sanitize the phone and watch American Idol season eight together, sanitize the remote control, sanitize the kitchen countertops, sanitize the kitchen table, sanitize the bottom of your daughter's plate, sanitize the handle to the salad tongs, sanitize the handle of the spaghetti casserole spoon, sanitize the handle of your daughter's fork, sanitize your daughter's beads and lanyard string, sanitize your daughter's instruction book, sanitize the scissors, sanitize her bedside table, sanitize your daughter's pillbox, sanitize the Nalgene water bottle, sanitize your daughter's diary, sanitize the fluffy purple pen. Cover your daughter's central line in plastic wrap and tape so it doesn't get wet with water. Sanitize the bathtub and fill it. Sanitize your daughter.

Maia Paras Evrigenis is a writer from Sacramento, CA. She received her MFA from CalArts and BS from NYU Steinhardt. Her work has been featured in *Necessary Fiction, The Black Fork Review, Entropy, Arkana Literary Journal, The Sacramento News and Review,* and the *Sacramento Bee*. Her piece "Just Another Day at School" was selected as a Stories on Stage winner for the 2020 writing contest in Northern California.

ITHACA, NY: C, SIX MILE CREEK

MINOLA REVIEW

katherine fallon

AT FIRST, I WORRIED ABOUT the rented Victorian, supported by a wooden pole made of nailed-together scraps above Six Mile Creek, which acted like a river, rushing so loudly we couldn't hear each other a room away. We watched the railing lean bit by bit throughout summer and into fall; each time the house breathed in, it breathed out, and the motion began.

C did not live with me but she might as well have; she came at me over my sweatpants and made it work, which no one expected. Should have, though, with her callused fingers, viola strawberry like a hickey on her neck. We had always heard strength in numbers, so became too much too soon.

Over time, the creek, gone flat as glass—snow compacting into denser ice as it continued and continued to fall—became foundation and we did forget to fear it. Instead, every day was filtered through the bald lens of winter: not a season but oppression, discomfort, leg warmers stained black from salted sidewalks, cups of tea gone cold in the immediate wake of the kettle's whistling. Icicles formed on the roof's edge, thick in the middle like a corn-fed cow, but there was ice inside, too: each morning, we ripped the curtains from the panes like Velcro. Impossible to forget the cold, even sleeping, even fucking, though I often thought of *Taxi*, Latka in his dead cab, having sex with a stranger to avoid hypothermia, which worked but had consequences.

Late in the freeze, I met some other woman and straddled her on the porch with a jug of Carlo Rossi within reach. It didn't go any further but it didn't matter. My chattering teeth had been elsewhere, my core was molten anew. She was like a tire track in snow: something was where nothing was.

When the ice finally began to melt, we compensated, dragging the heavy sofa onto the street side of the porch with its flaking balusters. We moved the grill, the recliner, the bed, and jumped the middle railings. Even that proved too extreme a change in weight, so we quit leaving altogether, languished on the dew-wet mattress, collected more strangers. C wanted them gone, but we needed them. We beat the house's murder/suicide by anchoring it with stagnation. Then the lease was up. We examined our bedsores, leapt into the street and watched it all go down, taking the trees, my bed, our winter coats with it. The creek ate it all, back now to roaring. C tried over and over to forgive me. I did not want her to. Winter wasn't ours anymore.

Katherine Fallon is the author of *Demoted Planet* (Headmistress Press, 2021) and *The Toothmaker's Daughters* (Finishing Line Press, 2018). She is Lead Poetry Editor at *MAYDAY Magazine* and reads for *[PANK]*. Her poems have appeared in *AGNI, Colorado Review, Juked, Meridian, Foundry,* and *Best New Poets 2019* among others. She shares domestic space with two cats and her favorite human, who helps her zip her dresses.

THE SAUDERS ARE ALMOST prepared for winter. Silo shuttered, woodpile tarped, perennial bed snipped of spent blooms. Mrs. Sauder is canning in the kitchen, she leaves the radio loud to listen for bad weather. The girl is upstairs stitching. Mr. Sauder kills a pig in the barn.

Mr. Sauder slaughters to celebrate winter's first snow. He's past the hard part, bolt gun and leg binds, the thing is now meat and exsanguinates above a bucket in the barn. He walks the barnyard as it drips; he likes empty acres in the cold. Behind, the home looms. His daughter wilts in her room. His wife is an opaque haunt within the windows. Dead corn rattles. Lucky sows snuffle wet muck in their pen. Mr. Sauder's father taught him young to need such things more than anything else in the world.

The girl can barely stitch straight; she's crying her eyes gummy above a rip in her sweetheart's jacket. The shoulder and the sleeve have parted ways, sleeve cap gaping wide, fraying lips. His last name sweeps across the yoke like a long groan. Some lonely tune echoes up from the kitchen, her mother's whine adds to all this sad. She kicks up the pace of the pedal, shouts foul words when the thread gets caught.

Mrs. Sauder hears the sharp cut of a Singer going slack and sighs as her daughter spits. Her daughter never used language like that until her father spit it all right into her mouth. Just last week she'd seen a pale blue stain on the jugular of her daughter's throat and felt the ache that accompanies the loss of something loved. Out the kitchen window, Mr. Sauder paces the barnyard and she tries to remember the first time she thought she loved him. Green eyes smile up at her from the neck of a glass jar. Hulling soy is hard work. Behind her, the pressure canner whistles and she is comforted by bottles of beans kept still in water and salt. *I fall* the radio hums *to pieces*. Mrs. Sauder joins the verse.

The hard part of slaughtering a grower pig is knowing where to place the bolt gun.

Despite his father's teachings, he cannot bring himself to use a blunt-bolt gun for fear the pig might wake as he is ripping through its jugular. The pointed-bolt feels good, the tinny click of a spring release and the crack of the skull are final sounds. Never mind the maybe of brain matter leaking to the ribs, the tongue, the feet—he'll put the meat in a trough. He puts a hand to his ribs. He'll rinse until it's all clean.

Mrs. Sauder plunges her hands into un-hulled soybeans. Her daughter weeps in tune with the whistle of the pressure canner and she sighs. Some sweet-talking thing has eaten into her daughter's heart. She remembers everything and nothing from days spent just like that—the taste of lust memory only to her mouth. Never mind that now, she runs her fingers along the lids of canned beans and relishes the eternality of a tinny pop! New beans in the canner. Immortal ones on shelves. The whir of a Singer needle resumes. She feels the sudden urge to drown in salt water.

Mr. Sauder slaughters a pig to celebrate winter's first snow because his father taught him this. As the grower pig exsanguinates above a bucket in the barn Mr. Sauder tends to lucky sows. He fills their trough and filters swill from their water. He cannot meet their eyes. As they nose their way through potato clippings and soy shells, metal rings in his mind. He wonders if they understand the sound of a pointed-bolt splitting up the skull.

The girl is crying so hard her stitches skew uneven through the sleeve cap. The shoulder yawns away in a loosening of thread, downstairs her mother is popping the lids of canned beans and singing along wrong to some sad tune. She wasn't supposed to be wearing it but he liked the look of his name stitched down her back. Slam of a door like the blow of a bolt gun—this is not the first hurt she has known. A bit of blood would make the seam stick, she pushes her finger and the Singer eats.

It's starting to snow and Mr. Sauder is eviscerating a pig. He's ticked the list, penetrating bolt-gun, bucket for blood, corpse bath, bristle shave, inedible organs on the floor. His father taught him how to skin a pig quick but this ordeal drags in an unusual way. Mrs. Sauder pickles grower pig feet and nibbles them down in the spring. His daughter chokes against the taste. Quick swipe of a folding knife and the pig is missing his chest. Mr. Sauder has it in his hand. He feels sick and slides the bones back into the pig. Mr. Sauder considers swallowing the bolt gun. The pig is whole again.

In the kitchen Mrs. Sauder cranks the radio to drown her daughter's upstairs ache. *I fall to pieces* she sings and realizes the song has changed. Same tune, sadder story, it's not her favorite but it will do against the silence of the house. It's snowing outside. Cold glass goes for a soak in hot water; she is appreciating the way the bottle prepares itself to entomb green eyes when one shatters in the sink. Someone is singing *pieces each time* and she guts her thumb on a sneaky shard lost within suds. Pressure canner whistles, the girl upstairs screams, the barnyard sounds like cracked bone. The sink is full of blood. She can't bear it. The lids won't pop.

From the barn a bolt-gun blows, blood drips tinny in a bucket. The sleeve gapes as the girl cries, cradling all her hurt. The radio sings and Mrs. Sauder hums the wrong tune. Pressure canner steams. Something breaks—glass, bone, baby. The prairie is swallowed by snow.

Abby Feden is a fiction writer from Nebraska. She is the winner of The 2020 *Smokelong Quarterly* Award for Flash Fiction. Her work has been nominated for a Pushcart Prize and the Best of the Net, and appears in *Smokelong Quarterly.* She received her MFA from Western Washington University and is in her first year of Oklahoma State University's PhD in Creative Writing.

THE DOCTOR TOLD HER it wasn't exoskeleton. "Melanoma can hide in surprising places," she said.

"But," Cassie said, "our bodies acquire trillions of new mutations every day. Why couldn't it be exoskeleton?"

Dr. Orr patted Cassie's melanomed claw. "Always look on the bright side, we caught it early."

There would be a scar. Right in the middle of her lifeline. She had spots of melanoma in her right ear, inside the shell of her ear, too. She could hear houseflies humming from across the room. In the key of F. She hummed with them, harmonizing.

Her daughter treated her like the enemy. "You never let me have a childhood!" she said. Of course there'd been a childhood. Cassie had documented it meticulously.

"See, it's here, it's right here, your childhood, it's in my phone, on the Cloud too, see, here's where we went to the botanical garden and here we are at Johnny Cash's childhood home!" she said, brandishing the device at her daughter.

"Mom, that's Instagram. That woman has hands, not claws. That child is happy. It's not even us."

Cassie sat under the umbrella on the back porch. She'd always thought she'd become something beautiful, that the death and regeneration of cells would at last produce a work of art or, failing that, at least someone who knew how to be a good mother.

Cassie watched her daughter, her young cells regenerating every day, and she tried to stop it, to hold her daughter in place with filters and funny captions. There were so many pictures. Band concerts and plays, softball games and science fairs. She used her elbow to slide the screen. Her mutated scorpion hands could no longer do it.

"Even a small amount of alcohol will make a scorpion go crazy and sting itself to death," she said, reaching with pincers into the bottle for the worm.

Epiphany Ferrell lives perilously close to the Shawnee Hills Wine Trail in Southern Illinois. Her stories appear in *Best Microfiction 2020, New Flash Fiction Review, Ghost Parachute, Dream Noir,* and other places. She is a two-time Pushcart nominee, and won the 2020 *Prime Number Magazine* Flash Fiction Prize.

CAN YOU PUT ME on tilt? my leaning son asks. He can't help this leaning, even though he's seat-belted and secure in this wheelchair he's been sitting in living in declining in the past dozen years. He can't grip the chair's controls he can't control his grip he doesn't have a grip not anymore. His muscles are wasting away, he's losing strength, he needs someone to put the chair-back back. He needs someone to put him on tilt. Tilting relieves the pressure on his neck his spine his back his butt he's got no padding there no padding anywhere not on this young man my son who's wasting away. *Tilt makes me dizzy but it's better sometimes,* he says. So I put him on tilt and he's ok for a moment—suspended, he's at peace or looks like he is, like the dream is over, like the worst has passed, like a decision's been made. I make a joke like I do, it's a joke he usually laughs at, it's a thing we do, the two of us, a thing we have, the two of us, but he doesn't laugh at this joke he doesn't smile he doesn't respond. Not while he's on tilt. And I feel this flash this bolt it's more like a shiver—the dream that ended, the worst that's over, the decision made: *He's giving up,* I think, and I have no reason to think this no reason not really not now not yet where's this coming from so I bite my tongue or my lip or my left arm or is it shame I chomp down on—I chomp down on it hard as in hard without holstering. But it is here in this moment, with trapdoors and trapezes, among horsemen and hangmen, that I know what I know, that I'm not what I thought that I'm not what I believed that I'm not what I hoped. This kid who doesn't complain never about pain not once not ever this young man of a kid who never feels sorry for himself not once not ever this darling young one the strongest one I know—the one I lean on, I lean on his strength—he takes a moment for himself he takes a moment to regroup he goes on tilt and he found him some peace yet here I shiver and I simper and I dizzily posit if-thens: *If he's giving up, how am I going to lean on him, lean on his strength? If I can't lean on his strength, how am I going to be strong, strong enough to be there for him? I mean he's tilting. I mean*

how can you lean on a guy who's tilting? I mean he'll fall. I don't understand what I'm positing I don't understand what I'm saying to myself but I fear the worst a worst that's not over a weak moment that isn't a moment but a river of them a river that says *Uncle* a river that says *Quittin' time* a mirror of a river that says *Look hard look hard look real hard whose face do you see?* I look at my tilting son's face that darling young face he looks so peaceful I mean peace like a real river and I remember something he'd say after I'd tell a joke he didn't get *Why do I have to understand what you're saying all the time*? he'd say and I hear that river the peaceful one the river that turns tables on unsuspecting levees the one that turns cartwheels at crunch time. *Can you put me on tilt*? I say to my son *Are you just kidding*? he asks *I don't know* I say and I picture a pinball heart riding shotgun on the peaceful river the one that's leaning the one that's lurching the one that's letting go *I'll try* I say in words neither one of us understands.

Pat Foran is a writer in Milwaukee, Wisconsin. His work has appeared in *Wigleaf, Tahoma Literary Review, Best Microfiction 2021* and other places.

AUNTY TAKES ME OUT to gather kai moana, climbing over the rocks with our skirts tucked into our knickers. Aunty's legs are fat and sturdy as she finds the safe places to stand among the seaweed and the rocks that tilt underfoot. I follow her step by step.

There any rats out here, Aunty? I hate rats.

Āe, says Aunty over her shoulder.

The tide's left mussels clinging to a big rock that looks like a beached whale. Tap, tap. Aunty uses a rock and knocks them loose. We pile them into bags, dripping down our sides as we walk home up the beach.

We sit on the back step with our bare feet on the ground and clean the mussels. We scrub away the grit and pull off their beards, the shells hard and cold in our palms. There's no other noise except the beach and the bush.

We build a fire to cook over, and when it's ready Aunty ladles broth and clattering mussel shells into my bowl, the salt and garlic steam puffing up into the dark evening. *You don't want that one, kōtiro.* She picks a mussel out with her fingertips. Doesn't matter they're hot, fresh from the pot. *It's not open. Means it's no good.* She throws it away. The gulls will get it, or maybe the rats. *Shame you can't tell that easy with people, eh girlie?*

Next day we crush up the shells for the garden. They smell like yesterday's tears.

Mary lives and works in Wellington, capital city of Aotearoa New Zealand. She writes flash fiction and short stories, performs spontaneous theatre and stand up comedy, and earns money as a faceless government drone. "The gulls, or maybe the rats" won second place in the 2020

New Zealand National Flash Fiction Day competition, in which Mary also won the regional award for Wellington. To hear the story read aloud by Mary in her Kiwi accent, visit youtube.com/watch?v=jG7L9GTNo8E.

ONCE A FISHERMAN

carol jean gavin

PITHEAD CHAPEL

ABOVE EVERYTHING ELSE, THE fisherman was kind. We didn't know why he gave us names like Angelfish, Surfperch, Bluespine, Wobbegong, Salmon, Stingray, and Orca. We assumed it was because he had found us washed ashore with our namesakes. We assumed it was because he lived on the beach. We assumed he was a fisherman of old, even though he was younger than the fathers we had been carried away from when the big one shook us silly, broke the land we stood on, and the waves came and washed us away. We saw his hooks, how he polished them. He fed us. We didn't know what was in the bottles he shook into our meals. If we asked, the fisherman told us they were vitamins. He bathed us in saltwater warmed in a large pot over his fire and poured into a tub he dug with his own hands. The fisherman scrubbed us with sea stars and braided kelp into our hair. "Seasoning" he called it, for the coastal life was a harsh one. When Tang grew a tail, we thought maybe it was an anomaly. Then it started happening to more of us Lionfish, Wrasse, Grouper. And the rest. Every single one of us, dragging ourselves across the sand by our hands. We assumed he was building a mermaid menagerie of us. We were fine with it to be honest, living so close to the sea. Most of us had inhaled so much water out there. What was a little bit more salt in our mouths? Most of us couldn't remember our names from before anyway. Most of us liked the idea of seashell bras and not having to worry about drowning if the earth bucked us back into the deep. Most of us didn't give a shit about high heels anymore. Or makeup. Or loud music, and baked goods, and books. What good had those things ever done for us? They never made us less willful, wild, irresponsible. We were just being turned in to what we had already essentially become. Mermaids were beautiful. Majestic. Mythical. Clearly the fisherman would take one of us for his wife. That's what we assumed. The scales that had tailed our legs together, spread up our bellies, finned our arms, parted just slightly to gill our necks. Our lips had fattened. Our ears disappeared. Our eyes went silent. We could no longer pull ourselves along the sand. We could no longer breathe where we had breathed effortlessly before. As we flopped, panicking for life, the fisherman smiled. The fisherman told us we were beautiful. All the while untangling his rods. All the while building a new boat. The fisherman said our tragedies had not ruined us. The fisherman was the one who saved us. The fisherman was the one who pulled us from the sand, brought us back our lives, took good care of us. The fisherman could have left us there where we washed up in the first place. The fisherman was the one who picked us up when we could no longer walk. The fisherman was the one who gave us our true forms. We were so grateful to the fisherman. The fisherman was the one who loved us when everything else had gone wrong. The fisherman was the one who took care of us when we wouldn't even take care of ourselves. The fisherman was the one who wanted us when the rest of the world threw us away. The fisherman was the one who would never give up on us no matter how far we tried to swim.

Caroljean Gavin's work has appeared in places such as Barrelhouse, *Bending Genres, X-R-A-Y Literary Magazine,* and *The Forge.* She's the editor of *What I Thought of Ain't Funny,* an anthology of short fiction based on the jokes of Mitch Hedberg. She can be found on Twitter @caroljeangavin.

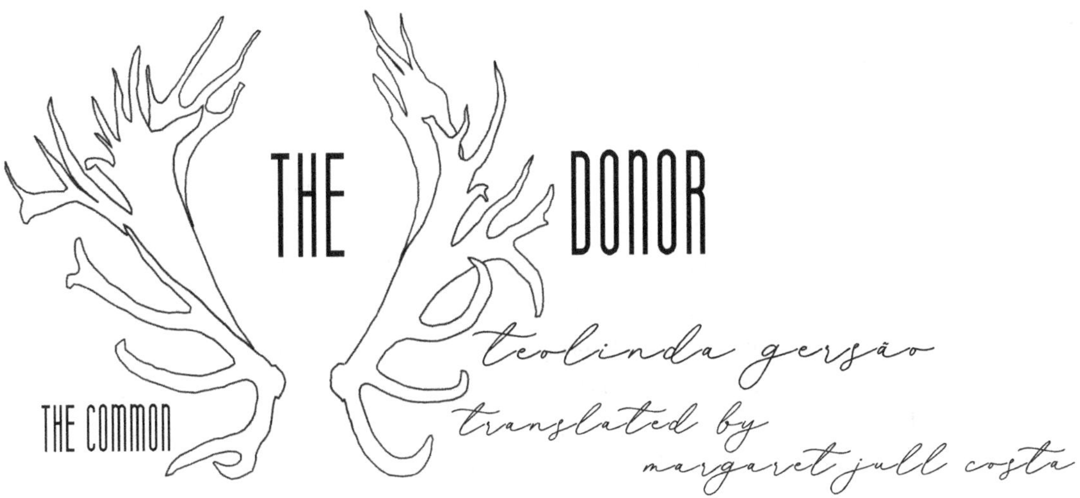

THE DONOR

teolinda gersão
translated by
margaret jull costa

WHEN I WAS A YOUNG man, I became a sperm donor. An act as simple and banal, I thought, as donating blood or bone marrow or some transplantable organ. Donating sperm just received less publicity, that's all; at least it did at the time. The only advertisements I remember were for blood donors.

There was no public call for donors of sperm, but we played a no less important or useful role, which is why we were paid, not much, it's true, maybe forty dollars or so, no more.

I also noticed that more restrictions were placed on who could give sperm, or so it seemed to me: apart from the health checks they did, physical and mental, you could donate sperm far less frequently than you could donate blood.

Why, I wondered. I guessed it was because it wouldn't be a good idea to have too many children from the same man; unfortunate, incestuous situations might arise if two siblings fell in love. And I found this argument convincing.

At the time, though, because I liked the idea, I would often consider how it would, in theory, be possible for a man to have hundreds or even thousands of children. Such cases occurred in the Bible and in ancient civilizations. Having hundreds of children had been the privilege of kings and other great men of the world.

Such a privilege no longer existed in our modern, technological civilization. I wouldn't make thousands, hundreds or even dozens of women pregnant. Rather disappointingly, the process was rigorously controlled.

At the time I'm talking about, I was nearly six foot three and mad about skateboarding; on my favourite route, around a park, I would race along beneath the trees at dizzying speed, kicking up clouds of dust and crunching over thousands of dry leaves.

I genuinely felt that I did reach dizzying speeds, leaving a trail of thousands of leaves sparkling in the sun.

On a skateboard I was bigger than my actual self, not just because it added an inch or so to my already considerable height, but because speed gave me attributes I didn't have, as if it propelled me into another dimension.

I would look up at the highest branches of the trees, at the birds, the clouds, the sky, and be filled by an intoxicating feeling, almost like orgasm.

And yet the reason I first donated sperm wasn't in order to fill the world with children, but to buy a new skateboard and go to the movies more often.

In fact, the idea of that mind-blowing number of children only occurred to me one day when I was skateboarding in a park, and I sped past a gardener who, hosepipe in hand, was watering a huge bed of marguerites. The water was like sperm, I thought, a seamless flow, glinting in the sunlight, watering the whole bed from one end to the other, quenching the plants' thirst with a kind of primitive generosity.

The inexhaustible potency of a young man. I felt almost superhuman, jumping off and picking up my skateboard in one smooth move, going up and down steps, plunging down slopes and performing acrobatic leaps. I was inexhaustible, invulnerable. This was a truly dizzying feeling: being immortal, almost like a god.

I would look at women with a feeling of superiority that would probably have struck me as absurd before I became a donor. At the time, though, I felt immensely powerful: I had impregnated one woman, possibly several. My children would be somewhere walking the earth.

As I swooped past groups of girls, I would think:

'I could give all of you children.'

With a glance, and without slowing down, I would choose the prettiest girl and think:

'I could give you a child. And you. And you. And you.'

I was a young male, potent and fertile, and that, I felt, was all I needed to conquer the world.

But life didn't turn out quite as I expected. Perhaps I wasn't as clever as I imagined. Perhaps my mind was not to be trusted.

I lost jobs and friends, I lost two marriages and a few lovers who, having walked into my life, walked out again.

This happened before and after a few unfortunate encounters, which led to years of alcohol and drugs, from which I have more or less recovered. The cure was, let's say, a relative success, and allows me to earn a little money sometimes, mowing people's lawns. Apart from that, I'm homeless.

When I'm feeling really low, I try to conjure up something to hold on to, for example, a few good memories; I try, but each time I fail.

I often find myself thinking about my children: who they are, what they're doing, where they'll be, what kind of job they'll have, what kind of life.

Obviously, should one of them attempt to get in touch, I would never agree to meet. I wouldn't want them to see me in this state, for them to find out what I've become.

I would like to see them, though, but without them seeing me, to know more about them, to see a few photos perhaps. A trace of me left in the world.

Needless to say, I'd want them to be the person I was in my skateboarding-beneath-the-trees days, I'd want them to be strong and beautiful, and hope that, like me, their ambition would be to conquer the world. I wish them every possible success and happiness.

Yet I never think about their mothers. In my imagination, the women are irrelevant, just as I was to them when I impregnated them from a distance, thanks to those technological advances; they, after all, only wanted my sperm and deemed me, the individual, to be entirely dispensable. Non-existent in a way.

Those imagined children are also now mine alone.

I think about them almost every day. They grow and shrink in age and size, depending on my fancy. One moment, they're still very small and sleeping in a cot, then suddenly they're waving goodbye on their way to school, they're running on the grass, playing with the dog, playing rugby, finding a girlfriend, going to university and getting a degree, marrying and leading their own lives.

But I'm never entirely alone, because I know they're out there somewhere. Thinking about them gives me a certain imaginary satisfaction, a sense of pride almost.

Even if they haven't found happiness or success, I still feel love for them, or perhaps compassion. Because things might not have turned out as they expected either.

Some might never even have been born.

There was one in particular, I sometimes think, who was never born and who has long since been forgotten by everyone, starting with the mother. For me, though, he's always existed, and I'd even go so far as to say that he's my favourite. I bought him a tiny music box, the size of a matchbox, and often, at night, I set the music playing, turning and turning the little handle, until he falls asleep.

Teolinda Gersão is the author of nineteen books, and has translations (novels and short-stories) in 20 countries. Some of them have been adapted to theatre and cinema. She received some of the most important Portuguese literary awards and she was also the writer-in-residence in Berkeley university. She is published in English by Dedalus Books, UK, and by *Dalkey Archive, Two Lines, The Common, The Threepenny Review* and many other American reviews. In 2019 she received the Albert Marquis Lifetime Achievement Award.

Margaret Jull Costa has translated the works of many Spanish and Portuguese writers, among them novelists: Javier Marías, Benito Pérez Galdós, José Saramago, and Eça de Queiroz, and poets: Sophia de Mello Breyner Andresen, Mário de Sá-Carneiro, Fernando Pessoa and Ana Luísa Amaral. She has won many prizes for her work, among them the Portuguese Translation Prize for *The Word Tree* by Teolinda Gersão in 2012. In 2014, she was awarded an OBE for services to literature; and in 2015; in 2018, she was awarded the Ordem Infante D. Henrique by the Portuguese government, and a Lifetime Award for Excellence in Translation by the Queen Sofia Spanish Institute, New York.

LET'S SAY WE GREW up with parents who loved each other. Let's say that we don't both know that Mom should've packed you up and made her escape long before I was born. Let's say you don't resent me for that. You don't resent me for coming onto the scene in the most untimely of ways, the ultimate pain in your rear that you'd never be able to slide away from. A baby sister. The trap that held us all there.

Let's say we played checkers and sometimes you let me win. Let's say the board never got flipped in a huff. Hard to say which one of us that wasn't. Let's say that we did the dishes together after dinner and there were no such things as girl chores and boy chores, that my hands could push the lawnmower as easily as yours could dry the dishes. Let's say the punishments were divvied up equally, and you were never whipped with the certainty that you weren't as loved as me. The swish of the fishing pole whipping through the air as it found your bare flesh never happened. Let's just say that. Let's pretend you don't blame me. Let's pretend I don't either.

Let's say we both remember the blue skies more than the midnight black. Let's say we're sitting on our lawn right now. It's Labor Day. The sun is barely up. Our shoulders and noses are peeling from a summer spent racing down waterslides headfirst, and school doesn't start until tomorrow, and we are in denial that summer will ever end. Let's say there are hot air balloons peppering the sky and this is one of those magical years when the wind is just right, and they will drift over our house scaring the shit out of the dog and delighting us like nothing else ever could. Let's say there are enough strawberry toaster pastries for both of us but we share one bottle of orange juice, and you don't mind my cooties for once. Let's say we lick our lips and everything is sweet.

Diane D. Gillette's work has appeared in many literary venues including the *Saturday Evening*

Post, Blackbird, and *Middle House Review.* Her work placed 3rd overall in *Reflex Fiction's* Autumn 2020 Flash Fiction contest. She lives in Chicago and is a founding member of the Chicago Literary Writers. You can find more of her work at www.digillette.com.

A POEM WITH TWO MEMORIES OF VENEZUELA

monica gomery

THE FIRST TIME HER hair was sunlight and it moved in loud wet rivulets and it warmed me and it darkened my eyebrows to be so close to her. She passed small beads of fruit into my mouth and my teeth became seeds and my blood became guava. My own hair became highways, knotted and tangled, and she patted my exhaust-fuming head to tell me I was beautiful. I was a child, squinting into how huge and how warm and how mine and not mine her body. The plane ride home was always about something unhitching and floating away. Always a sterilizing, dream-bleary goodbye. Arriving home with one less limb or finger, buttons wiggled loose on their threads, tongue resting slack on jangling teeth.

Later, when I became too busy for her, lines of age scored both our cheeks and skin spattered from the cloud-lust of storms. From great distances I spoke her name aloud, then less, then more, her gales up-throating a continent, scaling a continent like a stairwell to sweep a voice through the wind chime of my memory. She carved me out of distance, condensation, certain objects stowed in the closet in the room my grandmother would stay in when she'd come to visit. She carved me out of oil-slick waters, salt-encrusted rains, mud cascading over city hills becoming clay, carrying dust of human origins. She carved me out of pixelated images of street protests, socialist revolutions, grocery stores with barren shelves. She slid a tongue into my mouth, so I've made do with two. She taught me supple light, and forests lacing between coasts, and pregnant mammals braying on their haunches in the always-summer wind.

It's hard to say what an immigrant is. A cluster of ants held in the palm. See how they circulate urgent on skin, see how they spiral, how their legs never stop moving. Certain children are prone to tip over the rock and upturn a whole city of ants, then track their escape routes.

It's hard to say what an immigrant is. There is a place in you, fertile as soil but changeling as weather. There's a place in you. It raised you and gave you the letters of too many languages, it gave you your tenderness, your distance, your rage.

What a child of an immigrant is. Thrice born, three sets of eyes. Belonging to no one. Carrying documents written with invisible ink. Speaking languages scavenged from cousins and radio hosts. Or else speaking the silence, that primary language of people who have been exactly everywhere and nowhere, excavated and learned by the gaps in between.

Mónica Gomery is a poet and rabbi, raised by her Venezuelan Jewish family in Boston and Caracas, and now living on Lenni Lenape land in Philadelphia. Her current work explores queerness, diaspora, ancestry, theology, and cultivating courageous hearts. Mónica is the author of *Here is the Night and the Night on the Road* (Cooper Dillon Books, 2018), and the chapbook *Of Darkness and Tumbling* (YesYes Books, 2017). She is the winner of the 2020 *Minola Review* Poetry Contest, and has been a nominee for Pushcart Prizes and Best of the Net, and a finalist in the Newfound Gloria Anzaldúa Poetry Prize. Her poetry can be found most recently in *Foglifter, Frontier, Black Warrior Review, The Journal,* and as a Poetry Foundation Poem of The Day. Read more at www.monicagomerywriting.com.

IT WAS THE LAST day of the decade and, for insurance purposes, Mama had to pass her stone. This was not her first stone. Like Sisyphus, she'd been up the hill and back more times than you or I care to count.

It happened like this. Mama was dozing in her recliner when she snorted awake. "My back," she whined. I looked at my brother. He smiled. He knew I hated when she whined—her labored breath, the scrape of pain shoveling up her throat.

I returned to my reading: essays on erosional landscapes in Southern Utah. The essays were, at times, too Earthy in spirit, too precious in word, though I agreed with her politics.

"I might have a stone," Mama said. Where do stones even come from? Dehydration. This far Inland, we mined for water. The Ogallala aquifer, look it up.

Brother and I speculated what the stone might be. Obsidian, he said. Pumice, I said. We were prejudiced toward volcanoes. You see, we both knew the new decade would bring us away from our prairie home so far Inland. I hoped for an island of mud. He hoped for a canyon of wind. I raised my shovel, "Pumice." He smashed his bottle, "Obsidian."

I drove Mama to the mine. The radio was off. The windows were up. It was winter and we saw the last light of the decade. It was every color I ever knew. The color of opal. I'd take a sunset here over anywhere: all the pollution makes the sky burn so pretty. Like a gas-slick puddle.

We entered the shaft and boarded a rail cart and see-sawed into the mine. A thousand feet deep, a dozen parties waited. Mouths masked in cotton to filter dust and disease and desire.

We waited for an opening. A balloon of a woman next to me, a death rattle in her lungs, croaked to her mama, "We've been here three years."

Thankfully, time behaved differently down here. It trickled, pooled, flowed. It was a gamble and we had no choice.

"Feel this," said Mama and leaned forward. I rubbed the largesse of her back until I felt it. A calcified knot, worried to the surface by sugar, poor finances, and tears. Tears, I learned from my reading, are chemically distinct depending on the emotion they emit.

A room surfaced, meaning a body had been buried. A canary called our name. We boarded the rail cart and I squeak-sawed us deeper into darkness.

The miner put the wishbone in his ears and rubbed the stethoscope over the knot in Mama's back. "This isn't a stone," he said and raised it to his headlamp. "This is a gem."

That's when I realized we got it all wrong. There was no mine, no stone. There was only a lighthouse, half-buried, beckoning a great white moth.

Connor Goodwin can't stop. His writing has appeared in *The Atlantic, Wall Street Journal Magazine, Inside Hook, American Prospect,* and elsewhere. His fiction has appeared in *Hobart, X-R-A-Y,* and *Back Patio Press.* He is working on his first novel. Find him on Twitter @condorgoodwing..

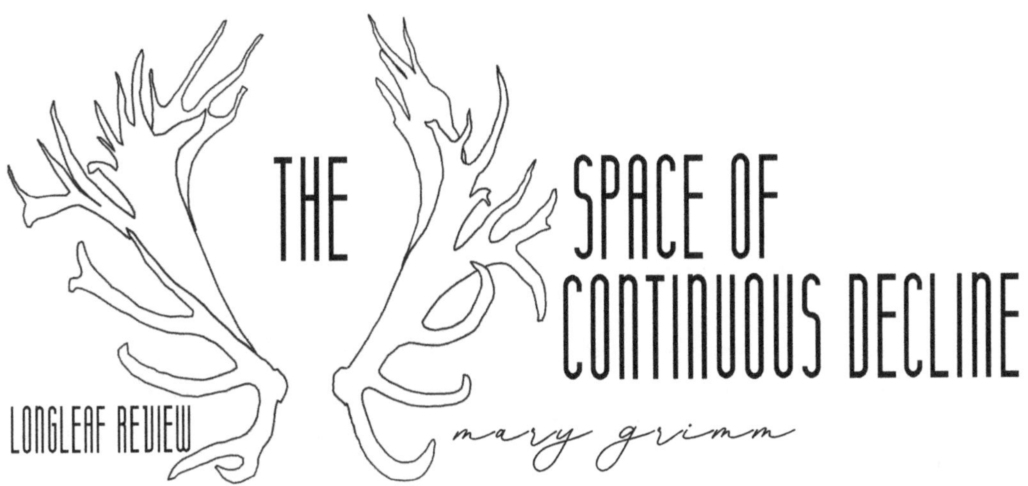

I'LL GIVE YOU UNTIL midnight, she said, and I could tell she meant it. She opened her eyes wide so that her mascarared lashes stood out like the rays of small black suns. What she wanted me to do was leave, but I had decided I wouldn't even though it made good sense, for what good was sense to me now? The windows were crisp with frost and it was cold enough in the house that the floorboards creaked and snapped with it.

I tried to project a kind of genius patience and forbearance, a stick-to-it-iveness, but she had turned away. She had a jar of sand with which she was making a circle on the cold floor. The sand was from the beach where she'd gone swimming when she was a teenager and where she claimed she'd lost her virginity. The jar had once held maraschino cherries. The circle was an aid to meditation which she claimed had been taught to her by a holistic doctor who'd once been a nun. When she finished she stubbed out the cigarette she'd been smoking in a can which had once held peaches. She sat in the middle of the circle with her back to me.

Once she'd let me hold her when she felt like she did today, but I had done a bad job of it. I was a parasite, she'd said, a crumpled newspaper, a smear of jam on the kitchen table. From where I was lying (on her bed, as soft as bread dough, but cold without her in it), I could see the back of her head, her hair swinging when she moved, her shoulders sharp and tense. She was sitting criss-cross applesauce and I could see the sole of one foot, small and a little dirty. She had on a green sweater, buttoned backwards and a pair of cotton underpants.

You'll never know how much you love me, I told her. You won't let yourself know. My voice was low and I hoped soothing. I had been taught or had taught myself that the important thing was to stay in the game, to keep pitching, even when you had done the worst things, even when you had gone beyond what anyone would stand. Even when the winds of everywhere howled and bellowed, when the floor fell away to the pit that was underneath, that was always there except you could forget about it for a while, for a month or a year.

She was humming something which I couldn't catch. The frost on the windows was growing, lace upon lace, web upon web. I thought that when morning came I'd be as hard as stone. Useless, but impossible to move.

Mary Grimm has had two books published, *Left to Themselves* (novel) and *Stealing Time* (story collection)—both by Random House, and a number of flash pieces in places like *Helen, The Citron Review, Longleaf Review,* and *Tiferet.* Currently, she is working on a YA thriller. She teaches fiction writing at Case Western Reserve University.

GRINDING STRAW BETWEEN CROOKED teeth, he spat in a can he was angling to have replaced, tipped discreetly at volunteers scurrying past. He muttered, hobbling to the cooler next to trays of food he'd been instructed not to touch—hadn't had an assistant in years, and didn't need one, but could recall decades he'd never asked for a drink. It'd allowed him to do what he did best: strum, blow, and holler timeless rebel-songs about railroads and voyageurs. Some called him the pillar of his generation: a fifty-year career spanning coffeehouses to halls on most continents, periods ranging from a dabble with the blues to an ill-fated foray into punk rock, and more women than he'd known existed during his youth on the farm. Never married, miraculously childless, he'd been a loyal servant to the road but escaped after an obscure festival appearance—done as a favour to a prospective business partner—went something his old assistant had called *viral*. He called it cracking the Wild Turkey a little early, but quiet years followed till bad investments in two breweries, a minor league hockey team, and an unscrupulous money guy forced him back on a circuit where he was now Grandpa's music—playing a Canada Day picnic, and the cooler was empty. He kicked it, hard enough to feel vindicated without causing a fuss.

Ready, Mr. Coffinberry?

A teenager stood behind him, peering through thick glasses. Tapping her clipboard.

Call me Jay.

Ready?

I'd like another drink.

No time, she said. People are waiting.

He peeked around the stage. From where he stood, folks nibbling salad and hotdogs seemed pleased continuing their days without ballads about caribou migration. She cleared her throat, and he lifted his guitar, slung his rack around his neck, pocketed his harps; she led to the wing, held up a hand for him to stop, then pointed at the emcee in the opposite wing, who burst onstage.

Heya folks. Tom Edwards here, from your KCLA Morning Medicine. Really honoured to be your host this evening. Nothing going on, anyways. No, I mean it. Wouldn't be here if I had a single excuse.

He laughed, mugging for the unresponsive crowd.

I kid, folks. Come on. Hmm, lemme see here. The festivities are brought to you by Banana Split Bonanza, Hank's Collision, and Lucy's Café. What's wrong, couldn't nail down Horton's?

He chortled, scanning his card.

So, he said, the reason we're all here. You know, besides the grill skills of the Optimist Club. Am I right? Give those guys and gals a round of applause.

A few clapped half-heartedly.

Tough crowd, Jay said. The girl shushed him.

Put your hands together for the Titan of Trad, the one, the only…who, I must admit, I thought had died twenty years ago. Glad to see you're okay, man. Ladies and gents, Jay Coffinberry.

The girl whispered, You got till sundown, then shoved him onstage.

Uh, hey, he said, adjusting the mic. Name's Jay Coffinberry, from Davidson, Saskatchewan. Don't worry, won't be Coffinberry much. Mostly singing.

Crickets chirped. People gnashed egg salad.

Alright, then.

He launched a tribute to the beavers' sacrifice in the fur trade, fingerpicking the elegiac intro, through pounding verses, a rousing chorus, soaring bridge. Hammering the final chords, he blew a tailing screech, ending sharply, expecting a mild rumble from the mesmerized crowd, at least. He heard his own breath, an offstage yawn.

This next song's about another true Canadian beast, he drawled, tuning his guitar. Got the idea driving cross-country in sixty-two, when I stopped in Wawa for fuel and seeds. All I could afford back then.

He smiled sadly, strumming the opening chords to the highest-charting song he ever recorded. Halfway through the second verse a child squealed, inciting three others, then two dogs. He finished but skipped the banter; they stared at phones or chatted, anyways. Eyeing the darkening sky, he had a choice. Soon they'd kill his mic, cut his piddly cheque, and kick his ass down the road. He could squeeze in two or three hits—a reasonable choice by a wily vet who knew how to work an audience—but this wasn't the sixties, and these weren't flower-haired folkies. He had an ace, so experimental he'd never recorded it—but if there was ever a time, this was it. Choosing to claim what the road usually took, he tuned up, switched his G for a C, blew a few notes till he heard it, then leaned to the mic.

Gonna finish with a special one. Inspired by a big prairie presence. He paused, breathing cool evening air, breeze tumbling off the waterfront. Embracing silence.

This is Diefenbaker.

It began: an opus, epic, ten-minute rollercoaster of rifle-fire harp, blowing till his gums bled. Knobby fingers stretched to unreachable chords, cramping, fearful he'd be forced to stop but pushed, fought, desperate to finish. He couldn't hear chatting, laughing, crying, barking—he was young, wowing Innsbruck and Wellington, putting Canada on the map like a lifetime ago. He slammed the strings, fingers dancing, harp wailing—eyes closed, but when they opened the sun had set.

Fireworks burst, crackled. The silent crowd shuffled to face the waterfront, away from him. He played on, so close to the end, but his mic was cut. The stage lights died. He finished, muted, in the dark, then slunk offstage. A sharp, sparkly pop, and the crowd oohed.

A graduate of York University's Theatre and Community Arts Practice programs, Stephen Ground spent the years after school shifting west, east, west, and back—landing pizzas, writing grants, and selling a wide variety of disposable things. His fiction, nonfiction, poetry, and photography have been featured in print and online journals around the globe, and his collaboratively-produced and self-written short films have been named Official Selections at indie festivals in Canada and abroad.

I PHOTOGRAPH THEM IN black and white. Never color. Color alters context, I tell their grieving families, friends, lovers. Like illusion, a sleight of hand, a figment of my artist's imagination. I want to make them real, candid, hidden truths exposed, my lens wide open.

Mine is an anachronistic art, photographing the dead, the Victorian age, when such a somber practice was in vogue, itself long dead. I have no business cards or social media presence, no brick and mortar studio with anodyne décor and anemic backdrops, funereal blackout curtains adding insult to injury and illness. My services are advertised by word of mouth in my hometown, a bible-choked Southern hamlet from which I never escaped, like most of my subjects. I come to them when I am called, racing rigor mortis for pliable limbs and tractable faces, to capture them, frame by frame, through monochrome viewing filters, hues and tints excised like tumors, essence, if not existence, restored.

I have perched ashen infants, swaddled in christening blankets, in the arms of wailing mothers with eyes deep as the grave; arranged beloved dolls at the feet of an emaciated young woman strapped in a bentwood rocker, Kaposi's sarcoma lesion on her neck marking her like a scarlet letter; propped a scowling teenager against his saturnine sister, whose middle finger covered the bullet hole in his temple; nabbed a young widower sprawled beside his seraphic wife on their marriage bed, her face veiled in white lace and lilacs, his hand covering her missing breast as if it were a placeholder. I have documented my own mother, the photograph like a painting—a Cezanne peasant woman enveloped in darkness, clutching her prayer beads as if they were an antidote for despair, head bowed, eyes open, downcast, submissive, the barren white walls as desolate as she. Hers were the secrets I most wanted to reveal—her crippling Catholic guilt, as grotesque as a Flannery O'Connor tale, for the black baby her white womb had expelled, silent and breathless, and the lover she'd sacrificed to a posse's noose to assuage her family's white rage in the days of separate but equal.

Her father, or perhaps her brother, had photographed the broken body, dangling from an oak tree like a piece of Billie Holiday's strange fruit, a verse from Hebrews written on the back of the sepia snapshot in her father's imperious hand: *Vengeance belongeth to me, and I will repay.* She'd kept it, even after she'd fled the house of the father and son, buried it in a box in a closet beneath years of aftermath and artifice, this holy image, forsaken and alone. Her death was the will of the pandemic spring, another breathless black body—like her lover, named George—captured on film stoking her guilt, her sacred photograph, exhumed, cradled in her supplicating hands, both past and prologue.

I wish I could peel back the layers of resin and polyethylene, strip his image bare of pain and paradox, set him free.

Christy Alexander Hallberg teaches literature and writing at East Carolina University and serves as Senior Associate Editor of North Carolina Literary Review. She is the author of the novel Searching For Jimmy Page, forthcoming fall 2021 from Livingston Press. Her short fiction, creative nonfiction, book reviews, and interviews have appeared in such journals as *North Carolina Literary Review, Main Street Rag, Fiction Southeast, Riggwelter, Deep South Magazine, Eclectica, Litro, STORGY Magazine, Entropy,* and *Concho River Review.* Her creative nonfiction essay "The Ballad of Evermore" was a finalist for the *Sequestrum* 2020 Editor's Reprint Award. Her flash story "Aperture" was chosen Story of the Month by *Fiction Southeast* for October 2020.

I DREAM ABOUT YOU and the train all the time.

This is how it ends:

There is the train and there is you and then there is only the train.

1.

Sometimes we're on board the train, together. (This is my favourite dream because I'm next to you.) You have the window seat and you're sleeping—your face bereft of all defenses, eyelids shivering with secret visions, hidden nightmares. Outside the dirty glass, the darkness unfolds itself while the train rocks us, softly, like I would rock you when you were still small enough to be held. Our reflections are superimposed on the world outside, afloat, like sky and clouds in water. We are uncertain apparitions, and, for a moment, I fear we are nothing *but* reflections. Maybe there is no me, no you, no us, only these images floating across the world without being part of it. And if I were to try to touch you in that moment of dread, my hand would dip into cold water, marring what I thought was us.

Then you wake up and look at me and you smile and I know who I am again, that I am real, that you are real, that this is the world as it is supposed to be.

2.

Sometimes, I'm driving the train. I'm the engineer. It's night and I'm coming down the tracks at high speed, traveling through that narrow section where the vines and bushes hang over the concrete edge from above (where the sparrows nest; you know the place). I'm used to the smell of diesel and metal, the thunk of wheels on rails, holding on to my insulated coffee mug, humming some old tune to myself. And there you are: just a kid, shoulders too slight to carry the carcass of the world, stumbling along the tracks. It's as if you don't hear the train bearing down on you with all its steel and rust and rain-streaked dirt. As if you don't feel the thrum of its approach through the soles of your shoes, the rumble of it in the chill night air, rattling the spikes and sleepers, shuddering through the sharp gravel and rocks beneath you. Maybe you've got your headphones on. Maybe you're drunk or sick. Or maybe you chose to walk here, knowing the train would come.

When I see you, I do whatever an engineer does. I make that whistle blare. I pull the brakes, but the train is too heavy, too long, one hundred cars (give or take), boxcars and hoppers, centerbeams and tank cars, carrying coal, ore, lumber. Or maybe it's a passenger train, full of people, containing all their love and their loneliness. Or maybe the cars are empty, the contents already unloaded, the spray-painted graffiti on the sides of the boxcars vaguely luminous in the starlit dark.

It doesn't matter. You are in front of the train and I can't stop it.

3.

Sometimes, you call me in the middle of the night.

"Hey," you say, and the sound of your voice is a silvery thorn of suffering, like those tiny spines on a cactus that hurt even though you cannot see them, much less pull them out of your skin. Although I'm muddled with sleep, I get out of bed.

"Where are you?" I ask, and you are silent for so long I fear you've hung up on me.

I put on my clothes, fumbling for my purse and keys. My glasses fog up in the cold when I get into the car. I drive through the dark, past the 7-Eleven and across the train tracks. My car is a mess and so am I, but there you are, waiting on the sidewalk. You don't smile when you see me, but you get in the car and that is all that matters.

When we drive away, I hear the bells clanging at the railroad crossing.

4.

Sometimes, I go through all the trouble of building a time machine and I travel back to stop trains from ever being invented. But it's hard work to stop an idea when it is determined to become real.

5.

Sometimes, we are train robbers you and I, characters from an old pulpy western. We wear snakeskin boots, faded denim, and bandanas. We rob the train. We ride away. My horse is a steady old bay. Yours is a showy blue roan. You ride so fast across the golden grass of the prairie it makes my heart shudder to see it. Leaning low over the neck of your horse, urging it on, your long hair streaming like a banner behind you, and I know you're smiling even though I cannot see your face because you've left me so far behind.

I don't mind being left behind. You were always moving through this world with the quick grace of a sparrow's wing, or soaring high, like a spear point piercing starlight.

6.

I don't like the sixth dream.

In the sixth dream, I sleep through it all, safe and warm in my own bed, unaware that you are walking the tracks. In the sixth dream, I don't see you, I don't hear you, I can't help you. Maybe you called and I didn't answer. Or maybe you never called, because you thought I didn't care or love you enough to come for you when you needed me.

This is how the sixth dream goes:

There is the train and there is you and then there is only the train.

When I open my eyes, I can't hear the train. I still feel the thrum of it beneath my feet, but I don't know if it's approaching or receding. Standing outside your bedroom door, I listen for the sound of your voice, the shiver of your breath, the flutter of sparrow wings. Hoping you're here, hoping you'll stay, hoping we're both awake.

Maria Haskins is a Swedish-Canadian writer and translator. She writes speculative fiction and currently lives just outside Vancouver with a husband, two kids, a snake, several noisy birds, and a very large black dog. Her work has appeared in *Black Static, Fireside, Beneath Ceaseless Skies, Flash Fiction Online, Mythic Delirium, Shimmer, Cast of Wonders,* and elsewhere. Find out more on her website, mariahaskins.com, or follow her on Twitter, @mariahaskins.

I MET HER ON the Japan Tour, late in '66, a diminutive smiling girl called Ali. I couldn't pronounce her last name, so she wrote it across the back of my briefs, laughing like a child crazed with her own inventions. On plum wine, we were limitless. She said she had aspirations to be a pop singer but she hated her own demos. She gave me some copies. Mostly songs of love and loss in Japanese, she said. Well, what songs weren't about love and loss, I thought. One night in her apartment over a crowded Meiji Street, where our shadows against walls were larger than us, she handed me what she called John Lennon's left shoe. She said he and I have similar shoe sizes—an intuition on her part or perhaps a put-down. I asked her what if he returns and wants it back? She said he would never come back, a gut feeling in her core. I didn't know what she meant.

When I told her my band would soon be leaving for the States, she said we must not say goodbye abruptly. It's better if we part by expanding distances. It's how she was able to cope with her grandfather's death, until he became completely inarticulate. The way the essence of wind becomes something other than music. We stood and gazed at each other across a wood bridge, from opposite sides of a stream, or with her hidden in a tree and I gazing up, so many deceptive branches. With each distance, she grew progressively smaller. I imagined fitting her in my palm, protecting her from the rain, from people who pretended to be John Lennon. Until I shouted goodbye over the ocean and into a void. But I had her voice on tape and I hired a translator. While playing the recordings in a country-house converted studio, I would open my mouth during the chorus of her first song. I stumbled over the pronunciation of the Japanese syllables. Could I make the sounds my own? The translator kept saying, *You are so far away.*

Kyle Hemmings has short prose and visual art in such zines as *Peacock Journal, Large Hearted Boy, Sonic Boom, Kyso Flash,* and elsewhere. His most recent chapbooks are *House of Three Corners* and *Amnesiacs of Summer* published by Yavanika Press. Kyle's favorite 60s rock bands are Love and Spirit.

I CALL A NUMBER that gets me a person on the line whose voice will ask me questions and quiet the house around me. *I'll have product 29485*, I say, looking at the raindrops midair, smile wrapped around a girl's face held up to a sun only she can see. She is hugging something, a prop to this happiness, and the woman on the line tells me I've made a great choice and I think *I'm a person making a great choice* and I keep her on the line with: *How durable is it? How do I take care of it? Does it come with a warranty?* She is patient and kind, says, *those are great questions*, and I think, *I'm a person asking great questions.* The empty house moans, tries to remind me of what I am not, but I'm only hearing my great questions. I pull out my credit card and read the number over the phone, misreading two digits, asking if she can hold on, and I think *someone is waiting for me, I am a person worth waiting for.* That minute stretches and I hear frustration in her breath so I apologize because I've let it get too far, I'm losing that feeling I'm paying for and I wonder if I should hang up, but I can't because she might turn to someone next to her and say quietly she was speaking with a real weirdo, someone who wasn't worth her time. I start to forget what I'm buying until I see the raindrops midair and the smile on that beautiful little girl's face and I think, oh yes, and I get the numbers correct this time. I read them aloud and when she repeats them back to me I say *yes, yes, very good* because maybe she needs something positive too. Maybe she's having a terrible day and this makes her think she's done something very good by reading the numbers back to me correctly. Sometimes all we can ask for is this small miracle of a well-received performance. And I give her my address and the house moans so I put my hand over the receiver and say, *Hush up you!* and she asks if I have kids and then says, *Of course you do,* because of product 29485, which is generous of her when I know she wanted to say grandkids but then thought better of it, which means she's very polite and I want to tell her she was raised well, not by parents who have no time to parent, the kind found on planes, in the aisles of stores, ones who can't bother with phone calls or visits. So, I say, *I do.* I say, *They're beautiful just loud. The kind of beauty that doesn't last though or forgive,* and I allow myself a look at the framed photos of people I remember from long ago who mail me packages twice a year, Christmas and June 3, adding to the unopened boxes in the garage, piling higher and higher, suffocating the space where my car used to be, spilling into each spare room until they are claimed. She says she understands but I hear something shift in her voice the way I do every evening with Peter, the delivery man, who used to be Mike and before him a large woman named Jeannie who smelled like peppermint and Dial soap, so I tell her she has a lovey voice because she does. It slips into each syllable like silk, like maybe she is somewhere South and before I can ask where she is from because I want to imagine I'm with her on a front porch sipping lemonade, smelling jasmine, gossiping about neighbors, she ends with it was so nice to talk to me and my order should be 5-7 business days and I should have a wonderful evening. And I have. I've had a wonderful evening tasting those raindrops.

Sabrina Hicks lives in Arizona with her family. She has work in *Atlas + Alice, Cheap Pop, Split Lip Magazine, Milk Candy Review, Barren Magazine,* and numerous other publications. Her work has earned a spot on *Wigleaf's* Top 50 (2020), Honorable Mention for *Best Microfiction* (2019), Grand Prize Winner of Writer's Digest Competition (2016), and has received numerous other nominations. A comprehensive list of her publications can be found at sabrinahicks.com.

MAVIS COULDN'T HELP THAT her boy ate dirt.

Alex, she told Roy, does not have a problem. He's eccentric, she said, over the rotting fence. He lives in his own little world! she laughed, to hide the wrenching in her throat. She watched her son kneel by the azaleas and scoop a handful of soil. She watched him bend his lips to his hands, the way he might one day mouth a lover's body.

Alex Donald, you quit that right now, Mavis yelled across the yard.

Maybe it would've been easier if she weren't alone. Two years ago, Clive was struck by a feral bolt of static when Alex was barely three. He worked for Sprint, up on the poles. He hung in his harness for fifteen minutes, blood pooling like pale lichen in his face and shoulders.

There was a crash-pad, Mavis said. What the crap does that do, if he's already dead?

I'm sorry for your loss, she expected Roy to say. That's a real shame, or, you're in my thoughts and prayers. Mavis was used to these platitudes.

Sinkholes, Roy said. Those are a real problem.

Here? Mavis peered into her fallow, dandelion-strewn lot. She bought this place with the insurance money. Kids need a yard.

Everywhere there's groundwater and erosion. Pavement ain't like your trees and vines. Your kid's eating dirt again.

Mavis didn't look at her son. Let's go inside, she said.

In her bedroom, she took off her blouse.

I have tendonitis, Roy said.

That won't stop us.

As she kissed his navel, she asked him to talk about water tables and inundation. She wanted to hear about houses sucked under the earth, roads trafficked by subsumed asphalt. Roy couldn't think about much with her tongue between his thighs. He stood shivering like an aspen as she took him her mouth.

Between the azaleas, Alex lifted a palm of garden soil to his lips. He smelled the inner life there, a dusty and comforting smell, like a favorite sweater. Between his teeth the dirt was cold and bitter and his saliva turned it to a wet paste so when he swallowed, it almost choked him, the drowning what he most desired.

Jules Hogan is a writer from the blue ridge mountains. They are the 2021-2022 Fiction Meets Science fellow at the Hanse-Wissenschaftskolleg in Delmenhorst, Germany, where they're witing a novel about whales. Jules is a fiction editor and reader for *Split Lip Magazine.*

I AM TRYING TO keep myself busy while the world is on hold. And so I do what I have always done: I chop. I cannot go to the store, I cannot go to the beach, I must stay inside, but I can chop. Keep the muscles active, keep them steady, keep them taut, keep them firm. They cannot stop me from chopping. I cannot sleep at night. In my dreams, I am chopping. Carrots, beets, onions, tomatoes, squash. I behead shrimp with glee, tugging at their spines with extra brio. In my dreams, I chop vegetables that do not exist in the daytime. Maybe they are somewhere under the earth, undiscovered. Maybe they are vegetables grown in the underworld. She does the shopping, I do the chopping. She comes home with misfits. A misfit can be anything from a cucumber that looks like it has a tumor to a tomato that's gushing its guts. I chop without judgment. Since we have been getting the misfits, I have stopped remembering what perfect fruits and vegetables look like. Sometimes I'll go online to remember. It's like looking at a fake world, though. A turnip cannot possibly look like that. The dreams grow more intense, sprawl out. In them, I am no longer confined to vegetables and fruits, to organic things. I chop buildings, which makes me sound like some kind of monster out of a Japanese disaster film, someone who would do battle with Godzilla one day and team up with him the next, but in fact that is not me. I chop at the seams, where the apartments and hallways meet one another. There is an elderly woman somewhere on the fourth floor, and not only do I chop carefully around her, I delicately remove a mole she has borne for the entirety of her eighty-something years. As she gazes in the mirror, searching for it, at first she thinks her sight is going, then her mind. She might never set foot outside again, not the way things are looking, but every time she steps in front of that mirror, it's as though she's dancing again as she did sixty-two years before, before she'd been self-conscious about the mole, when it was a soft little gemstone. Before she'd thought she was a misfit. We'd passed each other a hundred times and nodded hellos. Then once

in the lobby, rain shearing, me in chef's garb and no umbrella, she with dinged gray radio in hand, antenna fully out and bent toward that mole, barely pulling in the station, she spoke about a night in Gdansk. I told her I made a mean pierogi. When the storm eased I made a dash for the train, and our hellos were different from then on. She might never go into a restaurant again, and thus I will not be in the kitchen, but I like to be behind the scenes anyway, chopping fierce, like I can outchop time itself, make the slices so thin you can see through them, so if I put my finger up to one you'd see the whorls of my prints and what might be a scar, who can be sure?

I wash the food before I chop it. I will let you in on a secret: if you spend a full twenty seconds washing an apple by hand, by the end you will know that apple intimately, will feel like you made that apple from scratch. You'll be a charter member of the Apple Maker's Guild. With that apple you could tempt Eve, you could tempt Adam, you could tempt God. God chopped first—split the light from the darkness with the very first sweep of the hand. I'm not sure if I believe anymore, not in these times. What I believe in is the next chop. I know that eventually all the knives will go blunt, go dim. I'll have to go and get them sharpened. There's a guy who's started coming around the neighborhood again in his truck. He comes in a mask, and I almost think of him as an executioner, except he's going to breathe new life into these knives, and, in so doing, into me. I can't wait to see him. But right now we can't afford anything extra. We're buying misfits and saving our coins. I dream I pay him with a coin I've chopped so thin it is many coins, some of them dull, at least one of them gleaming.

Tim Horvath (www.timhorvath.com) is the author of *Understories* (Bellevue Literary Press), which won the New Hampshire Literary Award, and *Circulation* (sunnyoutside). His stories appear in *Conjunctions, AGNI, Hayden's Ferry Review, Big Other,* and elsewhere. He teaches for various places, including *Catapult, GrubStreet, StoryStudio,* and the Maine Writers and Publishers Alliance, and currently is at work on both a novel and a second collection. "Chop" was written in response to music composed and performed by Rafaele Andrade on Knurl, an electroacoustic reprogrammable cello that she designed and built. You can learn more about Un-bow and Andrade's other projects at www.rafaeleandrade.com.

HE WAKES IN THE landscape of his childhood, the karst. The house is surrounded by stone that dissolves in water, limestone that becomes fissured and hazardous because of its own weakness. The clints are the parts left standing. Grykes are the absences between. It is in the grykes you find life: hart's tongue fern, butterfly orchid, primrose. Sheltering in the sinkholes.

This is a place of constant change. Changing stone. Changing light. As a child, he would go out at morning and all around him the light would be shifting, glowing, shaking, darkening. In the hedgerows, he'd find blackberries that he ate green and sour in case someone else got them before they ripened. Ma would be home in the kitchen, peeling potatoes. No need to ask where's Ma.

After her stroke, he and his sisters had decided to keep her in familiar surroundings, this house overlooking a turlough that fills with rain in winter. They would do that for her, after all she had done for them, after all she did for their father while he was on his way out. Sacrifices easily accepted because willingly made. Each of her children takes four days a month: that makes twenty days. They hire a nurse for the rest. So he is here, blinking in the morning sun, listening to the bright call of the curlews, in the Burren, County Clare, among the endless gray hills of weather-scored limestone.

He has woken because she has woken. They are sharing a bed. His mother, who was never one for kisses and cuddles, often asks him to get under the covers with her now. A body against the cold. It has been a year, coming home, four days at a time, reading to her from books she half remembers, cleaning loose water from her eyes with a handkerchief, feeling her papery skin in his hand as they walk from room to room. And then, when his time is up, passing his sisters at the door. They are glad to share this trial together. And it is a trial. They smile at each other wearily.

Evidently, Ma has been watching the ceiling for some time, and he feels a lurch of guilt as he helps her out of bed and into her dressing gown. They pause at the window and look out at the rounded hilltops and ragged incisions of the limestone pavement, carved by mere rainwater. He can't help feeling proud that they have kept her at home, this space that meant so much to her: its acanthus leaf wallpaper and musty brown carpet, her enormous bed—far too large for the room—and the sliding doors that had been purposely jammed shut since he caught his finger in them as a child. He glances at his mother, who is still staring at the hills. Her voice is fickle these days, often betraying her, but now she speaks clearly.

"What a desolate place," she says.

The words take him aback. He stands for a moment, wanting to ask what she meant, then he pulls her arm, guiding her to the dining room table. He sits her down with a view of the kitchen. While he makes breakfast, she averts her eyes, muttering sharply. He can tell that she is having a violent argument with herself in a language she can't express. He watches from a distance.

By the time he sits down, she has forgotten that he was there. She is glad to see him. She is tranquil, back to herself.

Later, when she is gone, those words come back to him. "What a desolate place." He had thought, in some imprecise way, that after she died she would remain a physical thing: firm, substantial, knowable. He had thought he would be able to hold her so close that the heart would burst out of his chest. But while he lies in bed at his house in Dublin, ruminating, those words spread over his memories like floodwater, pouring into gaps he had not known existed, and his head will become heavy, and he will hardly be able to bear how little he had known her.

Ben Jackson's work has appeared in the *London Review of Books, American Short Fiction, West Branch* and the *Guardian,* among others. He received an MFA in fiction from Boston University. Find him online at www.bhjackson.com.

EVERY THURSDAY NIGHT GRANDMA'S house coat comes off and her body expands like a gas to fill every part of the bathtub. I set a bucket of soapy water to my side and dip into it a cloth coated in eucalyptus oil. She says it helps with the stinging feeling she feels in her bones. Kak khorosho! Rub that spot, right there, yes, just for a little longer. Just like that. I run the cloth across her body and trace the constellations of liver spots, new and old.

When I was a kid all the Ukrainians used to get together every week, that's back when it was just a bunch of first-generation, fresh-off-the-tarmac types, and they would throw extravagant parties, crazy shindigs in my step-uncle's unfinished basement with booze and sliced meats by the steam shovelful. There was no such thing as the kid's table back then; we sat with the adults, conveying shot glasses back and forth. I remember still, between the slap fights and awkward whirling dances with the older girls, the way all the men looked at grandma with their sailors' faces. And at the breasts she wore like a piece of heirloom jewelry.

She has disavowed her body now. It is no longer hers, but some formless thing she has been saddled with. Everything except her breasts. She still takes a special pride in them, their size and slope, their largesse, as if they are two children who had grown up to be doctors or lawyers. She still boasts about how they had helped her win over grandpa from another woman, still lets her bras ride the clothesline in the backyard longer than the rest of her wardrobe.

I turn on the water and she lets it fall through her hair.

You need a woman, she says.

A good woman, she says.

With a good head on her shoulders and a large family.

I let the faucet run until the tide starts pooling up around her. Her belly floats on the water like a far-flung island.

Once the adults started singing war ballads, we knew it was time to scram upstairs. We bounced and scattered like loose particles across the house, some on the first floor, the second, some in the backyard. For me and Vicki, it was the room lined with dubbed over VHSes of every movie you could imagine. Labeled: name, date, running time. This was how my step-uncle made a little extra green on the side. I never asked how they all came to be. I just assumed they had always been around.

Inside was a single rolling office chair on a plastic mat, and we sat there doubled up on it like a couple of horned-up tetris blocks. She hardly even looked back to see if I hadn't melted into the leather or if I was staring at her with some serious weirdo vibes. Just watched the static edges of a little TV with its built-in VCR. When words fade, you remember the sounds: the chair exhaling every time Vicki adjusted her hips, the whine of Europop filtered through the vents. You feel the bass and what must have been love in the hearts she'd bedazzled on the backside of her jeans. Then the sickly sweet bouquet of days-old deodorant. Eventually you remember things more by what didn't happen than what did.

Look at your grandpa, he can't cook a damn thing.

But he's got me.

Have you been eating? she says.

I scrub grandma's neck and behind her ears. I tell her to reach for the moon and the stars, the way she used to tell me, and I scrub under her arms. Back then I was just bone broth soup floating around in the tub, no matter how much food she put on my plate.

One night grandma came barging in the room with a guy I didn't recognize, probably new enough to the country that he was still spending down his resettlement money, attached to her hip. Vicki loped right off of me and pretended to peruse the collection. The guy, he must've gotten a kick out of it because he had beer dribbling down his chin from trying not to spit it out laughing. She didn't say a word, grandma. Didn't do anything except politely closed the door back up. We never talked about it, just drove the usual route home with grandpa sloshed in the backseat. I knew it then, that I was never going to see any of those tapes again.

I scrub her chest and across her collarbones, and move down to the breasts that slalom off to her sides. I lift their loaves and scrub underneath and around, and that is when I feel it. She is still reaching when I push harder, deeper, trying to describe the outline of a space rock that she has pulled down, that has fallen and landed inside her right breast, just under her nipple.

57 years.

Your grandpa and I are married 57 years.

Uh-huh, I say.

I push from different directions, angling for a simple explanation, hoping I am not feeling what I am feeling. She complains that I come here too often. She insists that they'll be just fine, that I need to spend more time being young.

I put the cloth back in the bucket. She looks at me, her face red as spilt borscht from the heat.

You need someone to take care of, too.

Life is easier that way.

After all, she says, I will not be around forever.

Alexsandr Kanevskiy's work has appeared in *The Wayne Literary Review, Pithead Chapel,* and *Atticus Review.* Born in Kiev, Ukraine, he calls Detroit, Michigan home, and currently lives and writes near Los Angeles, California. When he's not writing, he's either watching basketball or trying to wrangle his two cats.

THERE IS MUD AND rocks on the ground and tire tracks from trucks carrying cement and bricks. I see footprints, small ones- four holes drilled in, sometimes eight. There's the smell of fish, stagnant in the air, coming from the stands by the gravel road. Silvery scales glitter under the sun as men pour water to keep them fresh; fat ones, long ones, thin ones laying next to each other, some overlapping. A trail of blood and water drips from the wooden tables. At times a tail flaps, seizure running through the body.

"They're alive!" I scream. I'm scared of the open mouths of the fish, their round yellow eyes. They stare at me and I run away.

My father is bargaining with a man, who has almond eyes with fish scales stuck to the sweat on his shirt.

"That's my final price!"

My father tries to be firm. His shoes are stained with mud and he hovers over the fish to protect his light jacket from getting dirty. He's wrinkling his nose at the smell. So am I.

The Fisherman shakes his head. My father is terrible at bargaining, my mother says.

"But these poor people," my father says. He somehow never wins- sometimes paying even higher the original price.

"How did you manage that?" my mother sulks. "A man like you..."

She touches the fish with both hands, caressing their bellies, flipping them back and forth quick, the way she would when frying them in the pan with oil and breadcrumbs. I cringe and turn away from her.

There is a mountain with cabins built on large rocks, now on the verge of falling. There are sheep on the grass around them, like woolly clouds hiding in the bush, sharp green in the aftermath of rain. I breathe in the green, the dew, the soft wool, the pillow of my dreams- of wooden cabins flying above mountains, where I go with my parents and our friends during the spring break. There a fluffy golden retriever is my friend and I don't wash my hands to keep the smell of sheep, making my mother upset.

"Don't lay in the hay," she yells.

I roll and roll on the grass. I eat all the seeds of a sunflower in concentric circles on a tree. I put my cheek on the soft wool and chase the mini tornados sweeping across the grass on dry days. My mother shoves me into the shower. The cold water condenses the air in my lungs for a moment and I swirl in a refreshing mix of suffocation and laughter. She waits for me with a towel. I'm shaking, dripping my way inside our cabin.

There are three boys- ten, maybe nine, approaching our car. They speak a language I don't speak. They're wearing plastic boots. They have grey wool sweaters with navy stripes across the chest and muddy pants. Their heads are shaved. Their hands and faces are unwashed. They press their foreheads to the glass and cup their hands to see us cramped in the backseat eating baked sweets we got from the last village. They see me and my friends putting our hands into the large white box, licking our fingers one by one. We look at them. They look at us.

"Daddy, look!" I say pointing to them.

My father rolls down his window to face them. My mother gasps and covers her mouth. He takes the box from us. I never know if it's the noise of the automatic window rolling down or my father's bushy moustache, but they run away, never looking back.

My father holds the box out the window, shouting after them to come back, come have some sweets. But the louder he shouts, the faster they run.

"Don't ever do that again!" My mother says, locking the doors.

Maybe somewhere in their memory remains a moustached Russian that shouted "Fire!" to the squad that executed the men, while the women and children watched from behind the dusty glass with dew running down on it, later shattered and burnt with the sheep, leaving only the grass.

This my father says, looking at us from the rearview mirror, which I carry with me with a mixture of awe and terror until I am old enough to understand. We hold each other's hands on the backseat as he drives in between the fields of tulip, yellow, pink, red and white, stretched to the horizons of *Turkmen Sahra* in Northern Iran. There I see clouds forming and condensing to rain.

Mehr-Afarin Kohan is a Toronto-based writer, psychiatrist and psychoanalyst. Her fiction appears in *The Missouri Review, The Citron Review,* and *Belletrist Magazine,* and she has one upcoming in *The Antigonish Review.* Her stories have been long-listed for *The Fiddlehead's* Short Fiction contest and the Thomas Morton Memorial Prize. She lives with her husband and three-year-old daughter. You can find her at mehrafarinkohan.com.

I DON'T KNOW WHAT drew Mama to the bay window that morning, but it was her almost inaudible *what the hell?* in her Ozark accent while she looked towards the street that drew me there.

There was just enough room between the gray-on-gray checkered curtains for me to fit next to her, and I leaned in to see what Mama saw: our 80-something year old neighbor wobble into the driver's seat of his rusted Cutlass. The car door creaked like an angry bird as he swung it closed. And then slowly, slowly he backed it out his driveway. The car moved like it weighed a ton, like it weighed more than it should, like I could have pushed it faster, at least with Mama helping. And I couldn't see why he was taking his time, but he was, and maybe it was just because he had the time to take being so old and all. But even when he pulled onto the street between our house and his, he inched the car slowly backwards, like he needed to position it just right.

It was that precision, the way he was painstakingly lining his car up in the center of the street that made me look at more than just my neighbor but at the whole street. And that's when I saw there was something in the street. Something across the street. A whole lot of somethings; somethings of every color glinting in the sunlight and looking like the Legos my brother leaves lying on the carpet sometimes. I squinted through the window and pressed my arm into Mama's to get a closer look.

It was the neighbor's collection of salt-and-pepper-shakers – not the man who was in the car but his wife, the one who died last winter. There were dozens of shakers: a pair of watchful owls, bright pink pigs wearing bathing suits, red foxes with their noses curled into their tails, old train engines, palm trees, Santa and Mrs. Clause, a squat pumpkin and a lean squash. They were all lined up like they could have been holding hands, like they could be playing a recess game of *Red-Rover-Red-Rover.*

My neighbor stopped his car and sat there for a long time, staring at his wife's collection. The salt-and-pepper-shakers stared back, at least those with eyes did, and I thought of my Mama and the way I'd catch her sometimes staring at the picture on the mantel of her mama; how Mama sometimes didn't hear me come home from school because she was staring at the picture so hard, like she was willing it to speak to her, or daring it to. I could never be sure with Mama.

And then, without hesitation, my neighbor laid on the gas. His old Cutlass jerked forward and a gulp of air caught in Mama's throat and my eyes grew so big they hurt but I still couldn't look away. It wasn't but a few seconds before that Cutlass, going full-tilt, plowed into the row of salt-and-pepper-shakers. There were two loud bursts like balloons popping as first the front tires and then the back rolled right over his wife's collection. One house down, he stomped the brakes, put the car in reverse and rolled over them again. Broken shards of colors flew up like dust around his tires and speckled both our lawn and his. And I can't say I ever knew which set of salt-and-pepper-shakers his wife liked the most or which the least. Which ones were gifts and which she'd selected herself. But all of them were smashed in the end.

When he finished, my neighbor steered the Cutlass back into his driveway, parked it, and shuffled into his house. Mama abandoned the window a few minutes later when it was clear that he wasn't coming back out, muttering *damn fool* before she strode into the kitchen and filled the sink with suds. But I snuck out the front door and into the street, examining the remains. The smell of pepper clouded the air. Our street was a mosaic, but a mosaic of what I wasn't sure. Grief maybe. Or loneliness. Or something else between husbands and wives that I didn't understand yet and maybe never would. But Mama, I was sure, understood it just fine. At my foot was the mostly intact head of one of the owls. It stared up at the sky and from where I stood it didn't look wise at all. It just looked empty.

Kristin Kozlowski lives and works in the Midwest, US. Some of her work is available online at *Lost Balloon, matchbook, Longleaf Review, Pidgeonholes, Cease Cows,* and others. In 2019, she was awarded Editor's Choice from Arkana for her CNF piece, "A POCKET OF AIR". She was also named a finalist in Forge Literary Magazine's Forge Flash Competition 2019 for her CNF piece, "RELATIONSTASIS". If you tweet: @kriskozlowski.

IF I COULD LEARN to habituate, it would be easier to cross the street. I would have a layer over my flesh that says, this is outside, this is inside. When I looked at the sign on the subway car, it would seem perfectly insignificant. The eyes on the faces of strangers would not pop out at me. And everything would be equally devoid of meaning. I would sit there on my little red seat, music in my ears, and the world would not bang along with its giant drum. And when I headed home, I would be protected from the salience of a cardboard box on a front yard. I would not particularly care that the box was filled with toys that had been chewed by a toddler and grasped by a five-year-old. And when I was mindful, as I would try to be, each breath would plummet into oblivion, sliding away from me into the already gone place I rarely think of. And I would not notice the banter from the other world, with fingers in my ears. And the invisible hands upon my shoulders would be forgotten in the midst of the next project. It would be good to be alive, because it would be quiet. And I would carry on with my life, doing the things I am expected to do. Meeting people at parties and writing my name next to my profession. I would be considered healthy and well-adjusted, because I would not feel the cries of the world deep within my flesh. My doctor would say, you are doing well. I would score low on every deviance test, and the Schizo behind my name would be crossed out in yellow ink. This seems like something to strive towards.

I practice separating inside, outside by sitting beside a stranger on the streetcar. Teach me your ways, I say. But he does not notice, as he digs his fingers inside his pocket, trying to find something that he lost. It is small and red and has four holes poked in the middle. A button, perhaps? I tap his shoulder, and smile. Is this what you are looking for? His eyes open into wonder, as they fill with button. I can feel him tremble wide open on his little red seat. And I don't ask what it is about this small circular object that seems to fit the whole world inside. It's rather big, isn't it? The button. He nods, his eyes fill with tears, and we agree it is best to exhale slowly and say nothing at all.

Ten months later, I exit the subway with a mask. There are no more parties, at least not the inside, inside kind. The salience of strangers' footsteps sounds a global alarm. The danger of an outstretched hand now sanctioned by the state. There are so many of us now. The maladjusted. And the cries of the world, well, they are harder to erase. She could be anyone, but she is not. She is unprotected, like me. Her exposed heart a safety hazard the world needs. We brush eyes on the stairway, and she feels me blush. I search for something to stand on, but fall deep into her gaze. The sound of her footsteps echoing against sound and shadow. I carry the memory of our silent collision inside me, as sunlight hits my eyes. She walks away, almost turning back. Her heartbeat quickening the space around her. Yes, it is. I mutter. Yes, it is very big.

Carol Krause is a poet who prefers caves to concrete. While she struggles to navigate the ordinary, her naturally psychoactive mind comes in handy when writing poetry. Carol's poetry has recently appeared in *carte blanche, CAROUSEL, PRISM international, The Fiddlehead, Minola Review* and *Into the Void.* You can find her inside a cavern at carolkrause.ca.

MY UNCLE WAS DRIVING us north, where the enemy planes hadn't yet attacked. He took turns drinking from a bottle with the man sitting up front.

My parents and I were squeezed in the back. My mother closed her eyes and held me close. My father kept biting his lips.

"Drink up," my uncle said, passing the bottle to my father. My father returned the bottle untouched.

Everybody else we knew had already left the city. My uncle was the only person still in town with a car. I didn't know why we hadn't seen my uncle for so long. He wasn't wearing his cologne, the one he had let me use before. He looked different from how I remembered him, with the moustache he had grown and his big beard with white strands showing through. His forehead had more wrinkles. He hadn't brought me a bag of chocolate as he used to.

The man beside my uncle had a sharp jaw. A tattoo on his neck was half hidden under his black hoodie. The car smelled of cigarettes.

"You know he robbed the biggest bank in the city," my uncle said. "But that wasn't why he was arrested."

The man smirked. I'd never seen my father so quiet.

"All of my brothers and sisters. None of them were there for me," my uncle said. "He was there for me." His eyes pointed at the man.

My uncle sped past all the other cars. The narrow road twisted as we rose through the fog up to the mountains. The cypress trees in the valleys became denser the further north we went.

When my uncle tried to pass the car in front of us, an eighteen-wheeler coming from the other side honked its horn.

"For God's sake," my father said, "there's a child in the car." He pressed his hand against the window as if his hand could save him, save us.

"What? You don't like my driving?" my uncle said.

The man up front closed his eyes, covered his head with his hoodie. Tears rolled down my mother's cheeks, falling warmly on my neck.

"Don't cry," I said to my mother.

At a gas station, my father and uncle shouted at each other in the wind. We could hear little of what was being said.

Across the road, a boy was selling honey. "Mountain honey," he shouted. I heard him well.

I wanted to taste the honey from the mountains, to see if it tasted any different from the honey I was used to.

The man with the hoodie smoked a cigarette, looking at my father and uncle from the corner of his eyes. He fidgeted in his seat.

After they got back in the car, we passed through rice fields and tea farms. Farmers were walking toward their houses as the sun set.

We turned onto a dirt road, drove up the hills through the vineyards and wild berry shrubs to a fenced garden. My uncle and the man didn't leave the car while we unloaded our luggage. They stared at us quietly until everything was out of the trunk.

Behind the car, the dust rose up in the air as they drove away.

What I remember from the garden: An old, deserted mansion. Ivy crawling on the walls and pillars. Two small wooden huts with spring beds inside them.

We slept in one of the huts. When the cat pissed on the roof, the piss dribbled through the wooden planks.

Later on, we filled the hut with tin buckets to collect rainwater.

There was a greenhouse with kiwi and banana trees. Blood oranges.

Wild horses roamed in the hills around the garden.

We grilled lamb chops and eggplants on a charcoal barbecue. We made a fire on the wood stove. My mother read to me from the few books we had brought with us.

My uncle returned to the garden several weeks later. The man from the car was no longer with him.

He brought two skinned ducks, eggs, a bag of rice.

"I've brought some food," he said, "and a radio." He put them on the floor. He gave the car keys to my father.

"All yours," he said.

My uncle took the other hut and didn't leave it. My father visited my uncle's hut several times a day, sometimes taking his food with him, sometimes staying there for hours.

"Don't go there, your uncle is resting," they told me.

I heard my uncle screaming and cursing from the other hut as my mother read to me.

During the day, my father drove us to the village. We bought eggs, bread, chicken meat, and fish from a small farmer's market. Sometimes we hiked in the hills.

Once, I tried to enter the other hut when my parents were taking a nap, but the door was locked.

I looked through the gaps between the wooden planks and saw my uncle naked, his hands and legs tied to the bed. His head was hanging from the mattress into a bucket, his long beard crusted with vomit. He was shivering and twisting in the bed when his eyes met mine.

The next time I saw my uncle, the war was over. He'd moved back with my grandmother and gained a lot of weight. He sat silently in the corner of the room and didn't talk to anybody. When we asked him questions, he just nodded.

Over the years, he gained more weight. He didn't leave the house and barely talked. He watched movies or listened to music in his room all day.

But somehow, whenever I think of him, I don't think of the ruins. Of shrapnel or shattered glass. I remember the north, the boy selling honey by the roadside, the sound of the rain falling into the tin buckets. The horses roaming in the hills.

Babak Lakghomi is the author of *Floating Notes* (Tyrant Books, 2018). His work has appeared in *American Short Fiction*, *NOON*, *Ninth Letter*, *Green Mountains Review*, and *New York Tyrant Magazine* and has been translated into Italian and Farsi. Babak was born in Tehran, Iran, and currently lives in Ontario, Canada.

I WAKE UP EVERY night unable to open my mouth. I'm grinding my teeth in my sleep. My dentist tells me it's either fear or stress. *Figure out which one, or both, and you'll figure out where the pain is coming from.*

Pain can be a symptom of something hidden, waiting. A phantom group of cells. If you're in pain, try not to think about the baby kidnaped from your neighbor's trailer when you were twelve. You saw it on the news. Everyone did. The family dog shot and left to die. You were scared and tried to sleep in your mother's bed but she pushed you away. You slept on the floor next to her bed, staring at her closet door. Your mother hid secret cardboard men in her, inside her, and in her closet. It scared you. Sometimes the hidden men turned out to be real.

The mandible is the only part of the skull consisting of bone able to move. Clenching your jaw while you sleep can cause overuse of muscles. Sensitivity to pain. It's a type of "hurt syndrome." Where the pain begins is unknown. Every pain has its root. Every pain must have an outlet, an ending. Everything is connected.

I've been feeling you in my bones. You're a low hum. You're the frozen field across from my house when I was seven. Seven was when I first realized I would die one day. Seven is the last time I was clean, untouched. In the field, no animal tracks scarred the snow. A perfect pasture.

The "Hum Phenomenon" stretched from New Mexico to the UK. Vibrations between 32 hertz and 80 hertz were reported. Once you hear it, you can never unhear it. The first time you were inside of me, I could never unfeel it, the static. I could never unfeel this feeling of static. This feeling is a frozen field. I want it to rest there, remain stationary, safe from itself.

When I was sixteen, our neighbor blew his brains out in his bathtub. The morning he died, I was touching myself under my fake satin sheets. The feel of the fabric against my legs was your skin, the feeling of your skin. More static. I heard the shot the second I climaxed, my knees buzzing. Later, the police said the suicide had been planned. Our neighbor woke up that morning and made himself breakfast. Eggs. Bacon. Hash browns. He climbed into his bathtub with his 9mm after writing a letter to his mother. His head exploded, his teeth scattering like pills on the blue bathroom tile. It took two days to find all of the pieces of his skull.

Suicide euphoria occurs after someone has fully committed to killing themselves. Happiness. Peace. Acceptance. These are all signs. Robin Williams was found hanging by a belt in his closet by his assistant. When going through his belongings, his wife discovered his watches were missing, and later found them in a sock, tucked away at a friend's house. When she asked the friend about the sock full of watches, they had no idea why Williams had hidden them there.

There are vibrations of our past that can never be buried. They said Williams looked like a cardboard cutout of a man when he was found dead inside his closet.

If we take away someone's euphoria, we'll never know where they hide their watches.

It took two days for the throbbing to stop in my jaw. It took two days for the hazmat cleaners to find the forgotten pieces of my neighbor's skull. It took two days for the family dog to drag itself from the abandoned field after it was shot, only to die alone on the doorstep, waiting for someone to return home. They never found the baby stolen from your neighbor's trailer.

I've been feeling static in my bones. Gun crack. Watches ticking. Frozen field cracks. You. Where pain begins is unknown. You're finding my forgotten pieces. They are hiding behind blood and bone. Untouched. Clean. Vibrating.

Hillary Leftwich is the author of *Ghosts Are Just Strangers Who Know How to Knock* (CCM Press/The Accomplices 2019), which is one of The Accomplices Best Sellers, a finalist for Big Other's Best Fiction Book of 2019, and voted as one of Entropy's Best Fiction Books of 2019. Her hybrid memoir, Aura, is forthcoming from Future Tense Books in 2022. Her writing can be found in *The Rumpus, Entropy, Denver Quarterly, The Missouri Review,* and numerous other print and online journals. She runs Al-che-my Author Services & Workshop, reads/selects/judges for The Colorado Book Awards, and teaches creative writing at Lighthouse Writers. Find her: hillaryleftwich.com and alchemyauthorservices.com.

YOU BUMP INTO WHITE Boy on a parched, irreverent Wednesday morning, power-walking your way to line up for the three hour commute at 6 AM, and too loud he announces, *I am in love with your country.* Falling in step with you, he adjusts the strap of his traveler's backpack, and he's bleeding joy, smiling the kind of smile that makes you feel like a jerk if you don't return it, so you do. *I love everything about it,* he says; your people, your beaches, your Jollibee. White Boy doesn't flinch from crowds, doesn't fear the Houdini flicker of a snatcher's wrist, and you wonder how that feels like. To be so at home in your own body you are unfazed by the oceans you've crossed to arrive here; the kind of ease where you can make a mess. Euphoric spittle flies, lands on your black polished shoes. He says, *Today, I woke up early to catch the sunrise,* and you think, how romantic.

White Boy is a buoyant force, a glass-half-full that runneth over. Squint, and it's him—your detergent model messiah, encased in rosebush essence and forgiveness. Around you commuters part for him,ski-boat cutting through the waves; giddy, you realize they are parting for you, too. Wet market stench scatters like oil on water. He stops by a fruit stall, and the vendor hunkered over her calculator perks up when she sees the glint of his camera phone and poses; all your brown people are performers.

White Boy asks, *You know where I can find any Boba around here*? She pauses, then repeats: *Boh-BAH*? He nods. She titters nervously. The world's largest fruit fly descends on your shoulder, but you are too busy battling this insidiously potent dose of embarrassment. *Boh-BAH? Boba. Bow-buh? Yeah, you know—Boba.* The hellish cycle doesn't end until her eyes catch yours, and you know—this is it. You've watched the soaps. Bagged the medals in English Lit, all those years hammering the fight from your tongue into taffy for this one prophesied moment: to spirit a handsome tourist away from this bleary-eyed mob and lead him to Bubble Tea Valhalla, because what sensible person calls it *Milk Tea*? Not you. Properly, it's *Boba. Bow*-buh.

Notice the slight inflection? The subtle nuance, a soft pillowed puff? *Boh-buh.* As in the tea, not *stupid girl,* a name reserved for contextless clowns who tangle their sentences.

Poor fruit vendor says, *Sorry, I do not know.* White Boy is forgiving, yet radiant. He turns to you with a question, but this time the words are too fast. Parsing error. Nothing slots. Fruit flies conspire in your ear. He repeats his question. *Whoosh.* There it goes—too quick for hands. Say it slowly, you want to say. *Say it slowly*!

Instead, you watch him leave—farewell, easy, pliant Philippines, taking the offered bag of sweet, discounted ripe mangos, and *pop*! The bubble breaks: you see, now, the sun-pinked line of his pale shoulders, the drenched pits, and in seeps the congealing sewer stench, swirling around your ankles, uncoiling its many mouths.

Andy Lopez is a writer and advocacy communications director from the Philippines. Her work has been published in *Longleaf Review, CHEAP POP, Non-Plus Lit,* and other magazines and anthologies. Find her on Twitter at @andylopezwrites.

What Not To Do, How Not To Live

DON'T GET BORN, DON'T be a person, don't get born as a person to a family of people. Don't be black or white or brown and don't be short or fat or skinny. Don't be a brother or sister or cousin or uncle or mother or father. Don't go to school or get a job or consult with colleagues or attend meetings. Never sit at a table where other people are already seated.

A Church By Daylight

The sky is not up in the sky and the moon is no longer the moon and there are no trees or dogs or electric fans or kitchenware and there is no daylight savings time because there is no daylight to save.

What's Not On The Radio

The song isn't on the radio because there is no song, the same as there is no radio. If there were a song it would be a slow blues or shuffle, probably in E major, probably called Milk-Cow Blues. There would be no person in the song as subject or object, no milk or cow mentioned in the lyrics, just as there would be no one playing the song and no one singing the song. Perhaps there would be the memory of a song, something like a faint echo barely audible, but there will be no one to remember or hear it.

Some Other Metal Than Earth

There might still be dirt and air and mountains but it doesn't seem possible if there's no sky up in the sky or no moon hanging in the middle of it. Just as carrots don't seem possible though they grow in the same dirt. But the dirt carrots grow in is called soil and there's likely no soil.

There's no way to differentiate dirt from soil, if there is a difference. There's no optimal time to grow carrots in either dirt or soil because there are no seasons. There's no fall and no spring, which is what's best for carrots, but carrots need fertilizer and there's probably no fertilizer.

The World Must Be Peopled

Go to a place called Road and try to make a life there. Learn a trade. Be a plumber like the guy in that movie or an electrician like the guy in that other movie or be a carpenter like Jesus even though people say that Jesus couldn't have been a carpenter because there was a paucity of trees in Galilee so he must've been a mason.

The Gun Is Where Any Could Find It

You live in America so there are guns. Always have your guns with you, take them with you to school and to work and to the movies and to the mall and to the barber or beauty shop. Have a gun for your right hand and a gun for your left hand and keep one tucked inside a boot or shoe. Only a certain kind of person looks at a lower-case r and sees a gun. Always be that kind of person.

Robert Lopez is the author of three novels, *Part of the World, Kamby Bolongo Mean River* —named one of 25 important books of the decade by HTML Giant, *All Back Full,* and two story collections, *Asunder* and *Good People.* A new book, *A Better Class Of People,* will be published by Dzanc Books in 2022. His fiction, nonfiction, and poetry has appeared in dozens of publications, including *Bomb, The Threepenny Review, Vice Magazine, New England Review, The Sun,* and the *Norton Anthology of Sudden Fiction–Latino.* He teaches at Pratt Institute and Stony Brook University. He was a fellow in fiction for the New York Foundation for the Arts in 2010 and Visiting Writer at Syracuse University for fall, 2018. He lives in Brooklyn, New York.

Scene I. Cabin. Farm and Woods. Late October.

BEYOND MY PORCH, A violent gust scatters leaves toward the afternoon light. The last train of butterflies flees south. A lone hawk rides a thermal, spiraling upwards. The sky spreads over us, as if yanked from infinity, still bleeding from its blue umbilicus. Straggling bands of cirrus cinch the wound.

The shot came from four hundred yards away, past the stream, up in the trees. I hear the dull thud of a bullet punching through flesh. The hawk dips slowly into the wind. From that height, it would see who took the shot: bolt action, hollow point, 33 grain, fifteen pounds of recoil energy. I've been around enough guns most of my eighty years to know.

The shooter was going for the heart but misjudged the spin drift. I wonder, *Why'd he do it from so far away*? Fucking amateur. I stumble down the porch steps, cursing. I can't be doing this. My hip is busted. I stagger through a grove of spruces. Spider webs sway from their clefted gibbets. Some stick to my face. Husks of blowflies sprinkle the ground, strewn like pistachio shells from idle spectators watching a hanging. A maple tree ahead beckons, a blazing loom, spinning gold leaves. Each step I take to it is some new land in an uncharted world of agony. At last, I gasp against the tree, shaking. My daughter is buried below. I mouth a broken prayer to her. I'm not sure why. I talk to her all the time.

A bear claw has left a two-inch gash in the trunk. I smooth the bark around, trying to mend the deformity. I lick my fingers. They taste like quinine, medicinal. It doesn't help my pain. Beneath the bear gash, though, swims a sweet sap, as sweet as the inside of a hummingbird's throat. Like hope buried beneath a thick rind of despair. I dig my nails into it, trying to scratch my way to that sugar. I've been trying to do that my whole life. But there's no time now. Forty yards away, more like forty miles, I wobble over to the woodshed. My body is going numb. On the floor, a cratered bee hive conceals the rusted spoke of a wheelbarrow. A shovel and a twelve-inch serrated blade sit in its cracked tub. I reach down for them. Time to bury mistakes.

Scene II. Fields. Hilltop Clearing. Late October.

Outside again, another wave builds up far away. I feel it in my knees. The ebbing away of air, the sudden drop of pressure, exposes a jagged shore of beetled carapaces choking up ruts in my fields. I am crawling over them. I have no strength to stand and walk. In my chest, hoofbeats gallop over crooked ribs, down a warped plank of spine. The pain is so bad I roll on my back to scream. I am drenched in sweat. The hawk is still up there, absorbing everything. Space suspends into stillness, as it does during an eclipse. I sense the air, like an invisible sleeve, getting turned inside out, summer's dead skin slipping away. I am passing through one season into another, getting turned inside out too, belly sliding now up a hill, dragging the spade behind me with one hand, clawing the earth in front with the other, the sharp metallic taste of steel clenched in my teeth.

The summit has a clearing where they always come to die. With a final push, I sliver through the undergrowth to the open ground. There it lies. Just as I thought: the hole four centimeters away from the heart. Not clean. Large black eyes plead with me. They are confounded by existence. I sense we are approaching each other from different universes, but will converge on the same thought. I sit up and cradle its head in my lap. I stroke its neck. Its eyes are like my daughter's beneath the blazing tree.

I sing it a lullaby, the same I sang to her every night. Its wheezing slows down, as if it's going to sleep. Maybe the song earns my trust. Maybe it understands my pain too. Maybe it's too tired to care. For a moment the three of us are together. My mouth tastes like salt. My eyes burn. The creature goes still. The knife won't be needed.

The wave breaks and showers us in leaves. The ground here is brittle and crusted like old scabs. The shovel will help me to stand up. I know it will break when I dig the grave.

Scene III. Woods. Hilltop Clearing. Late October.

There is a crack, like close thunder. There is pain with no previous memory. There is panic. There is a place I must get to. There is a dark cloud of flies who smell my blood. There is sunlight going cold on my back. There is a hawk watching from above. There is a hill and the baked scent of earth. There is a clearing where I can now go to sleep. A shadow crawls over me, panting and groaning. It smells sickly. It grips my head and howls as my children do when they are lost. It weeps into my mouth. The tears carry something sweet, something I have sought my whole life but never tasted. The water that flows deep inside the tree whose leaves turn to fire when the days grow short.

David Luntz's work has appeared in *Euphony Journal, Orca, A Literary Journal, The Journal of Compressed Creative Arts, Underground Voices, Word Riot* and other print and online journals.

IN THE DARK, FROM my twin bed, I listen to Romy and her latest visitor in the sheets. The wet stir of spatula in batter. Voices caught between skin. Like always, Romy asked me before the visitor arrived, "Are you good with it?"

We share a dorm room at Northern Arizona University where snow fell hours ago and it's April, where woodland creatures, as kinky furred as private parts, run the pine boughs and horde poppy seeds under their gums like greedy little pricks.

A pithy moan. I imagine mouths scoring stomachs, hips rocking like chef's knives. Romy is a beauty but not patently beautiful and this is why I lay here and listen as if she's a radio playing "Piece of My Heart," when I should go sit by the fire in the community room with girls who talk about where their families fucked up. I'm afraid I'd out-fact them.

The shower curtain hanging between our beds billows. Maybe it's Romy reaching for me. She tacked it to the ceiling after my comment last semester about light from the quad illuminating the "happymist" on her stomach. She didn't seem embarrassed, but fascinated by the word I'd let slip. "And, we'll call this curtain your *innocence shield*," she whispered.

I tolerate the visitors because she forgets their names by sunrise and writes sabotaging haiku about their shades of pink. She says haiku is a 5-7-5 syllabic poem, a shape like an imperfect woman's bodily ratio, and that haiku doesn't rhyme because rhyme ruins the emotion. My favorite:

Dick of Pepto pink
Mouth like rubber, no asphalt
Take next exit, please.

One night after a visitor, she said she fears losing body parts. She'd seen a documentary about a married Pakistani woman whose tongue and hands were hacked off because she waved at her male neighbor after dark. "She found a lover again. Had to get his dick up with her feet." I watched Romy clasp her wrists and tap her tongue like a tuning fork against her teeth. "No thank you. I'd rather be dead," she said.

Fact: I fear my body parts will multiply and I'll be like the soundboard in my brother's woodsy room. Those hundreds of touchable dials and buttons reminded me of a 747 cockpit. But he was hardly going anywhere those nights, just making shitty praise music. Until he came into my room and drove his body all over mine. He said I was his one-hit wonder.

Romy and her visitor's voices now are cakey and fast-rising to a dinner party din. I only catch, "For you?" The beginning of the question I assume was, "How was it?"

Thing is, Romy is all fearless whim. If the Australian swimmer built like a warhead turns her on, Romy doesn't pretend to love water, she walks her to the top of Lowell Observatory to spread their legs under the Virgo Supercluster. If the Peruvian in Calculus with the lips talks too much about derivatives, she shuts him up with a BJ at the Horseshow Mesa petroglyphs. And so on and so forth, until occasionally she decides the job of a serial lover is too much give and not enough get, and she sleeps alone. On those nights, she makes us green teas and recalls her lovers' tricks in blazing detail. I fall asleep thinking how lucky she is to know how to let her body have what it wants.

Fact: I wouldn't care how it was for someone else. I wouldn't speak a word, but only wonder how a body as used up as mine could induce raw, indelicate noise in another pure being. If it can. If mine is a body worth thinking about.

I burrow deep under my sheets and imagine I'm waiting on Romy to finish and call for me. There, I said it, don't ask for more.

Fact: I'm afraid of finding fingerprints. I have them everywhere, like Romy has her horseback riding scars. One story goes she landed ass-first on a spur. But a brother's fingerprints—they roil and crush like a Biblical flood.

Sister fact: Pink can tint toward brown. Brown is sugar, and he always dumped it on the pancakes he'd make the mornings-after. "Can't we get maple syrup?" I finally asked, one morning after he'd done worse that night than touching. "I don't know, can we?" he said, striking his air guitar like it was okay to be him and still be allowed music.

Sugar kisses. The lyrics from the song playing that afternoon I told Romy I was a virgin. A brother doesn't count. I didn't say that part; she'd balked enough at *virgin.* I told her I was waiting for "the one." She asked if I was religious. I said I prayed. That's what I think I did when he was inside me. But she said praying was dry-humping, not the real thing unless you fortify it with confession crap. "We'll change that," she said. Did she mean the praying or the virginity? Both probably; she didn't believe in God or deprivation.

Fact: Was I more "one-hit" or more "wonder?" And why was he inconsistent—why did he sometimes call it "happymist" and sometimes, laughing, "Jesus, why you doing this to me?" This is where you come in, Romy, and tell me when a big brother makes you feel both safe and dead, it's best to write rhyming poems and pray the rhyme wrecks the emotion.

The curtain rustles. I look up. Light splinters off the platter of Romy's back, down and over the pearled spur-scar, as she walks naked to let out the tall visitor. I scramble for a 5-7-5 in my head to recite when she starts letting me in and out like a visitor. I think she'll notice me. I think I'm ready to be the visitor and not the visited. I need to be. But tonight, all I hear is what he always whispered, "Be quiet, Kiva." So I am.

Tori received a journalism degree from Arizona State University and an MFA from Bennington College. Her stories have appeared in: *Glimmer Train, Cincinnati Review, American Literary Review, Chattahoochee review, Mississippi Review, Tampa Review, Cream City Review, ZYZZYVA, River Styx, AGNI online, Passages North, Jabberwock Review,* and more. Finalist for the 2021 Spokane Prize for Fiction, winner of the William Van Dyke Fiction Prize, the *American Literary Review* Fiction Prize, the Waasmode Fiction Prize, the *Cincinnati Review* Fiction Prize, and the *Lascaux Review* Short Fiction Prize. She lives in San Diego and is at work on a novel.

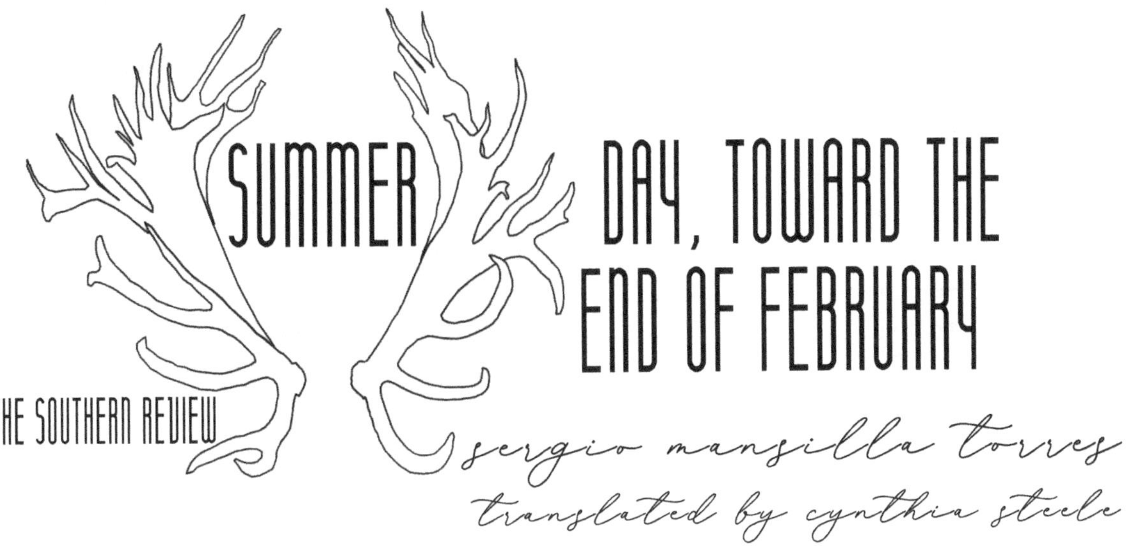

SUMMER DAY, TOWARD THE END OF FEBRUARY

sergio mansilla torres
translated by cynthia steele

SUMMER DAY, TOWARD THE end of February. Wheat harvest on a stubble field along the beach in Changüitad. Across the sea, coming from Dalcahue, the northern edge of existence, is a row boat with one sole occupant. He's rowing on foot, gazing toward the bow of the vessel. Who could that be coming? asks my cousin—who has been a woman for a while now—and she stands there staring, with her eyes turned inward, at the wide sea calling to her with its paddle of salt and foam. (Shortly afterward, she would lose her way forever along the highways and byways of loves, absences and distances.) Who knows? mutters my mother, busily lashing sheafs of wheat, a bundle of reeds strapped to her waist. The harvesters go on with their work, with the harvest, with the afternoon, in pursuit of the bread that the generous earth never tires of giving. I'm a little boy who can barely stumble though the stalks of wheat, my legs and face scraped up, my feet black with sweat and dust. To everyone's surprise, the boat rows up to the beach, just a stone's throw away from us, and from it descends a man in a Basque beret, knee-high leather boots, loose baggy pants, a scarf around his neck. . . It is my father, returned from Argentina. Fifty-five years after that episode, I don't remember feeling any emotion. All that is left in my memory is a luminous afternoon, a glistening sea, an unknown man descending from a rowboat, and a wheat field toppled by the wrath of the sickles.

Sergio Mansilla Torres was born in Achao, Chilé, in 1958. Throughout his youth he lived in a rural town, Changüitad, on the Island of Quinchao. He is currently tenured at Austral University of Chilé, where he teaches Philosophy and Humanities.

Cynthia Steele is Professor Emerita of Comparative Literature at the University of Washington. Her other translations have appeared in *Chicago Review, New England Review, Southern Review, Washington Quarterly Review, Agni,* and *Anomaly,* among others.

I'VE RECENTLY JOINED THIS Facebook group where people around the world roleplay as ants—no, not like that. Nothing weird, just unusual. I suspect I enjoy feeling like I'm part of something.

I tried telling my therapist about the colony, but I could tell from the switching railroad tracks of her eyebrows that she didn't understand. So I talked about how I feel like I'm in danger even when I'm safe. How, in romantic relationships, I feel loved even when I'm not. Especially then.

I power up my home computer first thing after work. Sloane'82 posts: *A western tunnel has collapsed, anyant willing to help?*

Dig, go people in the comments. *Dig dig dig.* I type the three letters into the bar and hit send thinking, I did it. I accomplished something.

When I'm not in therapy, I make lists of things I should bring up next session. I saw my ex walking his dog and felt like gnashing my teeth at him but instead I made small talk and exchanged pleasantries. There was a fake bomb threat at the mall where I get almond-milk lattes even though I don't like the way they make my gums taste. At night I dream about sleeping in nests with the other ants, safe in the crowd, underground.

I should probably delete this last one.

An Australian named Robbie Fighter posts a picture of a red lollipop his toddler dropped on their lawn. *Anyant wanna help carry it to the colony?*

Lift, go the group members in the comments. *Lift lift lift.*

I stay up all night, burnt coffee and yellow streetlight, refreshing the page until dawn breaks and mends itself into morning. My voicemail blinks its angry red eye. My boss, or maybe an insurance salesman, like my ex. Or, why not, a bomb prank.

I pay it no mind, entranced by the sheer number of colony members responding. The lollipop must have made it safely underground by now. Everyant has been working so hard, they deserve a sweet treat.

My fingers tremble as they type. I know no-ant needs me, but it still feels good to be part of something.

Lift.

Avra Margariti is a queer Social Work undergrad from Greece. She enjoys storytelling in all its forms and writes about diverse identities and experiences. Her work has appeared or is forthcoming in *SmokeLong Quarterly, The Forge Literary, Baltimore Review, matchbook, Wigleaf, The Journal of Compressed Creative Arts, Longleaf Review,* and other venues. Avra won the 2019 Bacopa Literary Review prize for fiction, and placed third in *Reflex Fiction's* Spring 2020 Competition. You can find her on twitter @avramargariti.

HAND-WRINGER OF THE DAY   how to get out of a chinese finger trap: you don't pull, obviously (and what does that teach you about going against your instincts when something vital is on the line?)   just one of many puzzles i've been stuffing my head with since birth solved rubik's cubes in theory but once they're in these hands   it's spinning hours and misspent days from then on   thousand piece puzzles don't faze me, so how come this one did

i say spin it this way and that   but when you tried to kill yourself, you weren't spinning so well were you   it felt much more monopoly-esque: roll the dice, do what it tells you the other time it was like trying to make a word out of mismatched scrabble squares: ok so there's the pain   here there's a little turbulence   with this one you could spell tenacity   if you were so inclined   this one looks like trauma   that one, like dead-eyed cynicism   put all these bone-white squares together, you've got   perhaps   the so-called easy way out   why not why not, i say

what was the question, how to get out   no, wasn't it: why trap your fingers in the first place   why induce the things you know will induce calamity, quick and categorical like all those times you   jumped rope barefoot and persisted even as it cracked your bare calves played jenga under glaring lights flipped mikado sticks under the influence of mania and rage tackled poker menteur with seasoned liars   answer: because you like things that can make you laugh   and you laugh best when you are scared

it's like relative minors of a major scale   kins from same-same stock but curiously inverted   i've been told i should surrender Perfection   i've seen her   that one's a pretty pretty talker   i've been told i should be looking outward   feel so selfish   how many times have i said i   but i cannot look past my too-tall thicket   is that something i should be saying aloud   anyway the finger trap back to the finger trap   recap: what did you learn today   i haven't been myself in a while   but i could have told you that

don't hug me i'm going to cry   no really don't hug me   don't touch me don't touch me   first my hair, which you seem unable not to rake through   then my skin caressed and complimented for its pulling blackness   but that is a story not for today today i want the aforementioned hush for its own sake   not for some higher purpose   not out of a sense of collective justice (is that something i should be saying aloud)   a nacreous bubble   i am

can contain it all but if you so much as thumb-graze my surface   i will puncture and it won't be pretty   i operate this feeling   like   playing operation with bated breath   counting on that honk that'll advertise my failure for all to hear

careful with that one   it's a tongue full of vinegar   all you'll be getting from there   wisdom says deal with it, talk about it, forgive yourself   but stay away from Guilt   put her in a corner with that bitch Perfection   Guilt is like gum   step on it once, it's sticky steps from here on out   and i like to kiss the curbs

sculpt your intentions around what you are trying to say—what *are* you trying to say   what is wrong with you all of a sudden   you're so good with words   why can't you just say it   *i feel like dying*   why must you take the metaphorical avenues and tricky byways just to call a thing a thing   because your memory is short leash   don't you remember what happened the last time you went on this ride   actually i haven't i'm just taking a break i'm just taking it easy on the agony wagon

you haven't learned a thing   have dillied and dallied   have flimmed and flammed   and learned nothing   the trick is to not try so hard after all   the trick to it is

pinch your fingers together, make them touch   hope the stiffness folds and one of them catches free   least that's what every film you've seen says will work   if all else fails you could still enjoy that useless pull-pull stretching   it feels like pulling taffy you saw that once when you went to the carnival   as a child   and you've been craving sugar since

---

Aïcha Martine Thiam is a trilingual and multicultural writer, musician and artist who goes where the waves take her, and might have been a kraken in a past life. She's an Editor at *Reckoning*, and Editor-in-Chief/Producer/Creative Director of *The Nasiona*. Her work has notably been nominated for Best of the Net and The Pushcart Prize, and her collection *AT SEA*, which was shortlisted for the 2019 Kingdoms in the Wild Poetry Prize is forthcoming with CLASH BOOKS. @Maelllstrom/ www.amartine.com.

WE WERE UNABLE TO find the page you're looking for. This may be because:

- The URL was entered incorrectly in your browser's address bar.
- The page you're looking for has been moved or deleted.
- The page you're looking for never existed at all.
- The page you're looking for vanished mysteriously, like the twenty-five mothers who disappeared from your D.C. suburb.

Unless:

- This is the page you're looking for.

In which case, you may want to:

- Read this 404 error page to come up with ideas for your own website's 404 page.
- Take a screenshot of our 404 error page for a listicle of forty-four inventive 404 pages.
- Seek some comfort in the absence of your mother, who always said the 404 error page was the only place she could show *a speck of goddamn originality,* either because clients didn't understand what it was or didn't care what she did with it. She came up in a time when web design meant hardcoding sites from scratch, HTML, CSS, strings of commands and characters you'd stare at on her screen in hopes that one day they'd become legible. But then *CMS site-builders leveled the market,* and despite her recommendations, clients wanted pre-built Poshbox templates and tacky newsletter pop-ups. So she plugged and played, clicked and dragged, built sites that all looked identical for people who could've built identical sites on their own if they put in any effort. But on the 404 page, she could leave a calling card. A treasure map. A distorted

version of the homepage. A flow chart explaining the 404 page to visitors. That may be why you're here. Because maybe she left a note, one she knew only you would find. A map to wherever she's gone.

If you were directed to this page by a broken link on our site or in search results:

•Contact our administrator here with more details. We strive to keep our site links up to date.

•Try our site search on the homepage to see if you can locate the page you're looking for.

•Don't think about the broken links strewn around your life—the long, curled hairs clogging the shower drain. The photographs on the hallway wall. The small wristwatch left behind, stuck on 11:47. All these underscored indicators of her presence that, when followed, lead to nothing, an error in your own neural network.

It's possible there may have been an issue with a 301 redirect. You may want to:

•Refresh the page to see if it redirects successfully.

•Try visiting the URL again in a few hours.

•Attempt to redirect your father's attention away from the news, where baffled officials shrug, unable to provide answers. It happened late that night, when many of the mothers were asleep or alone, but a few eyewitnesses—mostly distraught spouses and children—describe them simply popping out of existence. *There was a popping sound,* one woman confirms. They vanished, clothes and all, leaving no evidence behind, except those few who wore watches when it happened, watches that fell wristless in the empty space, hands or digits stopped at 11:47, the time of disappearance. On the internet, conspiracy theorists gather evidence of a matriarchal alien abduction. Evangelicals panic about rapture, much tinier than anticipated. Your father sits in your mother's recliner, news stations on the television, social media feeds scrolling on his tablet. He wears her watch, its band joined by duct tape, too small for his wrist otherwise. Whenever 11:47 rolls around, he stares at it like it might reveal something. You try to get him to go back to work, to go on a walk with you and get some fresh air at least. He thinks he can figure it out. *I'm close, I can solve this,* he says. *I can save her.*

If you're only seeing this page in certain browsers or on specific wifi networks:

•Clear your browser cache.

•Reset your modem.

•Contact your network administrator or ISP. Ask if there are any firewalls or security protocols that would prevent our site from displaying correctly. Ask what troubleshooting steps they recommend for issues like this. Ask if you should tell your father what you know, that on the night your mother vanished along with two-dozen others, you woke up and walked to the living room and watched her watching the first reports roll in about the mothers. She didn't notice you framed in the doorway behind her. You wanted to say something, but she was leaning so close to the screen. As details emerged, you watched her wind her watch and remove the battery. She placed the watch on the seat of her chair. You remembered sitting on her lap once as she rearranged elements on a client's site. *Your father is like one of these templates,* she said. *There's so many lives we could build but he wants one that looks like all the others.* You hated her for saying it, for making you complicit in this verbal betrayal, but an embedded script ran in the background of your heart, one of relief and something like joy, that her telling you this might mean the life she wanted still included you, *you* were part of her *we.* But that night, she left alone. She put on her jacket then thought better of it, hung it up. She opened the door to the night and, for her own benefit, hooked her finger into her cheek, pulled it out like a fishhook, making a soft pop that rang in your ears until morning.

If you've refreshed this page multiple times, hoping to see something different, remember:

- The URL may have been entered incorrectly in your browser's address bar.
- The page you're looking for may have been moved or deleted.
- The page you're looking for may have never existed at all.
- The page you're looking for may have never existed at all.
- The page you're looking for may have never existed at all.

Sam Martone lives and writes in New York City. Find him at sammartone.com.

POCO MOTO, WOMAN, THERESE thought to herself, as she pulled herself up from the bed and towards the door. She felt she heard something scuttle away in response to the creak of the wooden floorboards as she padded, naked and content, through the hall. "They flee from me that sometime did me seek!" she sang to the living room door as it opened. Above the mantelpiece, a false widow spider was pretending not to have been weaving a web in the corner of the large mirror. She has found her perfect home, Therese thought, noting how the spider's marbled, mahogany markings complimented the dark wood of the mirror's frame. Catching her own milky reflection through a layer of dust, she was satisfied to note that while her skin retained its luminescence, the strands of grey were starting to dominate the front sections of her long hair. She felt a jolt of shock and delight, too, to see how bloated and distended her abdomen looked, which she now caressed appreciatively, and bit her lower lip.

Turning towards the record player, she scanned for 'Für Elise'. A frisson as the needle made contact with vinyl, an erotic crackle, the titillating opening notes, followed by the sumptuous waves of the melody – all of this made her swell with happiness. The feeling of Saturday morning bloomed inside of her as she made her way back to the bedroom. The actual date and time felt irrelevant.

What to wear for such a blossoming, imaginary Saturday? The oxblood velvet, of course, and the amber scarf, draped like a shawl. The dress was pleasingly strained over her stomach … She felt certain people would ask her about it today. She loved these enquiries, and when people offered her seats on buses, and when people smiled at her, instinctively and knowingly. The communication was both coded and unambiguous. Her position was now confirmed and legitimized, it seemed, and she was now surrounded by quietly protective guardians. She knew that these protectors would defend her, when the time came, from the Apparitions.

She put on her mother's pearl earrings, and collected her gloves and handbag. She hesitated for a moment at the front door, momentarily paralyzed by a brief piercing jab in her womb, a sudden pain that radiated outwards like a mushroom cloud. She understood this message and responded by removing one of her earrings, placing it on the nearby console table. But of course! Someone might want to speak to her to tell her she had lost an earring. A young woman, perhaps it would be, or an elderly gentleman. A good sort of person, the right sort, another Guardian from the Apparitions. It was only ever these people, these days, so she was able to navigate the city with more confidence than she had been able to in the past. The men—the other ones, who used to look at her with contempt, while licking their lips—also knew to keep a safe distance. *Noli me tangere,* she thought, patting her abdomen, *for Caesar's I am.*

She decided to leave the record playing when she left for her appointment, as it pleased her to imagine passers by hearing it, and thinking it was someone, a son of hers maybe, playing piano in her house. She pictured a pale, slim youth with bony fingers. He would be modest, polite and emotionless. When Therese tried, she was also able to picture a daughter at the piano, who was similarly pale, but there was a haughtiness in her mien, and Therese couldn't warm to her. She sensed the girl was talented, but plain and serious in a way that meant no man would ever love her, so Therese couldn't bring herself to either. There wasn't a clear name for the girl.

The air was sharp outside as the door clicked shut. The pavement was strewn with half-wet ghosts of leaves, their veins bashed into the ground by boots and high heels. She decided to walk the long way to her appointment, because she wanted to go via Regent Park, rather than Easter Road. The route had more of an aesthetic coherence, which struck her as important on a day like today, whereas the idea of facing the chaotic bustle of Easter Road gave her a chartreuse sick feeling. She wanted to be in the Edinburgh of James Hogg today, not Irvine Welsh's version. She wanted the drama of the Crags as opposed to hi-vis drilling and Farmfoods delivery vans. Moreover, Easter Road was sometimes rife with Apparitions, and she could not risk encountering one today and jeopardizing everything.

The thing about the Apparitions that made them identifiable is they had perfectly white, symmetrical teeth. Some were the girls from school who had once owned coordinated Forever Friends stationery and had appalling names like Nicola and Lorna. Their mothers took them to Alton Towers and adored them consistently, despite their abhorrent pointlessness. They all picked barren pastel colors for their bridesmaids. On Easter Road, she had once spotted a University Apparition called "Steph," who was supposedly now a doctor, because her father had been a doctor, and he had given her a car before she was old enough to drive. She was instantly recognizable from the gleaming white teeth, incongruous against her insipid grey eyes and sallow skin. The Apparition had done a double take when she had seen Therese, and had pretended not to recognize her, turning her head right round and whispering in the ear of the man who was still holding her hand, despite the fact she was virtually bloodless and not of woman born. Some of these Apparitions would smile before they attacked in broad daylight, others did so silently, in the dark, over the internet, maybe. Some of them employed a modus operandi so mysterious that even Therese wasn't entirely sure in the aftermath quite how they had executed their sabotage, but she had to stay hidden indoors until they were all gone.

There were no rabbits in Regent Park, and the light felt thick. A vagrant on a bench looked at Therese but did not say anything, which she understood as a warning that she must be vigilant and look closely at all the teeth.

"Have you experienced pain since the laparoscopy? How has the bleeding been? Any nausea? Unusual discharge, anything like that?"

Therese frowned. "The crow makes wing to the rooky wood." She replied, and pursed her lips.

The doctor hesitated. "Endometriosis can be very unpleasant but there are other options available to you. I know last time we spoke, you were concerned about your fertility. Further laparoscopy may improve your chances of getting pregnant – you mentioned last time you would be thinking of trying?" Therese stifled a cough. "Hormone treatments are also available and less invasive, if you'd prefer to explore that alternative. The potential impact on your fertility is obviously a concern we need to take quite seriously."

Therese paused and glared at the doctor. "I know your game. Unsex me here, I suppose?"

"Sorry . . . pardon?"

"You want to give me a hysterectomy."

"Certainly not, Therese. Why do you think that? That would only ever be a very final resort. I'm sorry if I gave you the impression bef-"

"You want to go deep into me, to the place from which life flows, and tear it out. Have you been talking to the one called Steph?"

The doctor looked at Therese and gave a quizzical, almost fearful little smile, revealing an immaculate top row of perfectly white teeth.

When Therese returned home the record had stopped, so she went to bed. It was only dusk, but it felt like the dead of night on a Sunday. She rolled onto her side and clutched her stomach. Don't take my devils away, she thought, for my angels may flee too. She would not leave the house again until notified that the Apparitions had gone. She pictured Rilke and he told her to believe in a love that is stored up for her like an inheritance.

Kirsty McGrory is a writer from Edinburgh, Scotland. Her writing has appeared in such publications as *Gutter Magazine, The One O'Clock Gun, The Coffin Bell Journal, The Disappointed Housewife, The Leither* and *The Skinny*. She is a regular contributor to *The Wee Review* and *Pinhole Cinema*.

WATCH YOURSELF, THE BOY is told and the boy must not trip over baby on the floor, must not give lip when no lip is needed and when he's sent to the big tent to help with the guy ropes, watch yourself his mother says, don't go playing with the Lobster Boys and the boy thinks she doesn't have to tell him that, he's not going anywhere near those freak boys with their claw hands wanting to pinch at his thighs and he runs to the big top wondering how can you watch yourself if you are the one doing the watching of you watching yourself?

Where the trees stand at the back of the paddock is where he goes to try and figure things out. Like how to climb a tree in the dark and whether the tree is still a tree if no one can see it and watch yourself, he says as his head smacks against the branch. Watch me, he cries when he gets to the top, his palms sticky and sore. Watch me!

Wonder is the time when the boy turns bigger, strutting in front of the fun house mirror. Hair in places he never had before and watch yourself comes back when the Lobster Boys peer down at him from the loft and when their voices thicken with longing for *what* the boy does not know but clasping is involved that's when the voice says, watch what you say and then another voice shoves that to the side, it's his daddy's voice, come out of the ground, all earthy and woodsy, saying a watched man never plays, and the Lobster boys scuttle around with that thought and then leave him alone.

Why his daddy died, is why his mother tells him to watch himself. A step gone wrong on the wire, and the show of his life is over. The boy swivels his neck from side to side. He can watch from here, there, over and away. Each day he twists his neck further and further until the burn sets in and the swivelling makes him dizzy.

Walk too close behind the grown boy and his head suddenly turns 180 and looks straight at you. Sometimes his eyes hold the shadows of trees, other times they bore right through you. After the evening show, he's the first to walk out of the tent, glass of beer in hand. He should really stay for the applause, he should really take off his bird suit but instead he sits on an upturned bucket in the dark thinking, Lordy, this boy is someone to watch.

Frankie McMillan is the author of five books, the most recent of which, *The Father of Octopus Wrestling and other small fictions* was listed by Spinoff as one of the ten best New Zealand fiction books of 2019. In 2016 her collection, *My Mother and the Hungarians* (Canterbury University Press) was long listed for the Ockham New Zealand Book Awards. In 2013 and 2015 she was the winner of the New Zealand Flash Fiction Day competition. She has won numerous awards and creative writing residencies including the Ursula Bethell writing fellowship at Canterbury University in 2014 and the Auckland University Michael King writing fellowship in 2017. In 2019 she was awarded the NZSA Peter and Dianne Beatson Fellowship. Recent work appears in *Best Microfictions 2021* (Pelekinesis) , the *New Zealand Year Book of Poetry* (Massey University) and *Atticus Review.*

EVERY NIGHT WE FINISH September dinner in 1955 Comanche, Texas. Stand slow with gravy gut, hobble to the parlor for a song. My wife is graced across the circle, luminous with lunar health, voice and verses hopped up on Royal Davids.

Driving home in the pickup, she asks: What ails you? Why not take the cure at the Uranium Sitting Pavilion, just up the road? $2 for a foot-mounding, somewhat more for full-body. Let the loaded soil cover you, two feet deep in death, head angled to the air so you can breathe. Low-geiger farmboy birthright shovels-full, they say it cures asthma to cancer, gout to great depression, same for pilgrim butchers as stuck-pig bankers' sons like you, can't carry a tune 'cept in your digestive midnight privates.

Did you hear the one about Enoch with the diabetes, left foot long gone, whiskey-soured the right? Last month he coughed two bits for a cure, joined the line of penitents' toes in the trough, scanned obits in the *Comanche Chief*, then pulled out his rounded stump and cried: Lordy, where's it wormed off to? Save your sordid piggies 'fore it's too late!

So I think: my dear, that's a thought. Make an appointment for 11:30 next Thursday, neighbors say you don't feel nothing, not even a tingle, maybe an ankle itch you can't scratch. Could I pay extra to feel a few clumps cross nose and throat? Chest heaves as usual in the underneath. The man in the stall next-door snores, while Joe threads between patients in his white overalls, comforting as a soda-jerk in a Philco Television Playhouse bridge-scene.

And here's Perry now, crouched to say: Time to flip you over, friend. Grain-fed sliced American won't grease no grief.

James Miller won the Connecticut Poetry Award in 2020. Recent poems have appeared or are forthcoming in *Typehouse, Rabid Oak, North Dakota Quarterly, Yemassee, Phoebe, Mantis, Scoundrel Time, 8 Poems, After Happy Hour, Concho River Review, SOFTBLOW* and elsewhere. Follow him on Twitter @AndrewMI621.

LASYA TRANSFERS TO OUR school in the peak of summer when the heat makes us more mirage than matter. Our mothers warn us against going out but we want to see that translucence that makes us enquire after her surname.

"That house is *Lord Krishna's mouth*", our mothers say, "containing the entire universe within it".

The air-conditioners are dismantled first. The first time we step inside their house we find it throbbing like the angry vein we sometimes see on our fathers' foreheads. Lasya's Ma gives us watermelon juice to cool down our stomachs and tells us of the family that went to sleep in the icy coldness of the air-conditioner which later became heat and debris and death.

We try not to look at their bruises. They are livid like their house.

Days later, the perfumes go too. Lasya smells of sandalwood-lemon-rose water as she tells us of a newly wedded wife who spritzed on something her husband liked and went into the kitchen. We cry for the husband, who will now love her forever, for no fault of his.

Our mothers mumble on the terrace as they lay out the pickles to dry.

"You cannot save your children from everything", they say, their hands bright red from the pickle oils.

We think of Lasya's bruise.

In the monsoons, we stare at the house until its stillness becomes bright green needles inside our heads. We hear of a man who got electrocuted in an ATM nearby. Our mothers shake their heads as they restock the refrigerators, even as we stick our fingers in the air, looking for sockets, for something a bright electric blue, like her bruise. We shudder at the mute violets and pinks that streak the skies. Our mothers tell us about lightning that strikes elsewhere. We see her looking at us from her room, the windows both her eyes and skin.

We think of that bare house, now swollen with the rains and anticipation, that lushness of nothing. We sleep to the thickening of crickets and want to ask her what drowns out the night in her house?

We have trouble sleeping. We wake up to the pricking absence of a knife, or to the moon-mothball hidden inside the clouds to keep the darkness fresh. We want to ask Lasya if this is her Ma's doing.

In autumn, we meet Lasya and her banked fire of a bruise. It holds colours that the fall has never shown us. We shuffle leaves with our feet as she tells us the stairs are being removed in the house. Something about someone having broken their neck in another house.

These things happen, she says.

Our mothers tug at their *sarees* and wring the necks of banisters when we tell them.

These things happen, they say.

Winter brings with it bright rich soups and frenzied dancing. Lasya tells us the meaning of her name, and that she prefers *Tandava,* that dance of rage to *Lasya,* that dance of grace. We struggle to keep ourselves warm. She tells us her Ma read about the dancing plague which began with a girl like her. Bread can get fungi, fungi brings madness, she says quietly. We wonder at all the things that ferment. We wonder how we will live without bread or rice. We wonder at the rage that household grains can cause.

Ferment. Foment. We fail to grasp how something that relieves inflammation then becomes the cause of rage. Lasya tells us the story of a tyrant who catches fever. A blanket soaked in distilled spirits is sewn on to him. Then he dies once it catches fire. Do you choose the fever or the flames?, we want to ask her.

Next summer, the pregnant elephant dies first. We hear it from the villagers who come into town for the weekend markets. We stroke our stomachs as they tell us of her having ingested a pineapple filled with firecrackers; and then having gone into the water to stand silently for three days as life fizzled out of her.

We who grew up on stories of mad elephants terrorizing entire villages do not understand this. We run to our mothers, who soothe us and nod silently. Do they understand this? We know rage as pineapples bursting with firecrackers, they know rage as the gently laughing ulcers in the womb. Is that what a child does to you?, we want to know.

Lasya's pa dies a few weeks later. Cardiac arrest, the doctor says. All of us, and our mothers, gather at the house. It is buzzing in a way that is almost disrespectful to death. We see new furniture, new utensils, new appliances. Our mothers smile softly at their presence. We stare silently at the absence of their bruises.

Aishwarya Mishra is a writer from Jharkhand, India. Her work has been awarded/published in *New Millennium Writings*, *X-R-A-Y* and *JMWW*.

I READ THIS STORY once, of this man, bed bound for so long the sweat from his head left a lasting yellow halo on the wallpaper. There is a world within yellow. It's hues are a weight only the dying feel.

When I was younger, I loved to mix paint colours. I would find the warmest reds, the brightest yellows and watch them disappear inside vivid greens and effervescent blues. Eventually my beautiful swirl of colours would turn a dull, unremarkable shade of umber. It would float off the plastic pallet and settle inside unprotected nooks within me, whispering into a chest that had long forgotten with hardship came ease.

Hooyo is fussing over the pillows again. I wish she would to speak to me, tell me stories like she used to when I was little, sat between her legs on the living-room carpet as she pulled, tugged and strained against my coils, reshaping them into waves less offending to the eye. Her voice could drown out Warrior Princesses, Charmed sisters, Malcolm and Homer. But these days, her tongue is made of stone. Its stillness kindles flames consuming skin and soul. The scent of unsi foretelling her arrival has been absent lately. A stranger visits my room; I feel her tyrannous presence with each intake of breath.

"Are you ok Ms Samatar?"

Hooyo grips my arm. She pulls the cotton bedsheets tight around me. Back home, there is a photograph in the miscellaneous items draw of our kitchen of her and I. She is in a hospital gown and I'm in her arms, cocooned in a blanket. My face is red and swollen. She once confessed to me she had wrapped me so tight a nurse had been called. It had taken a week to get the swaddle just so.

"Alhamdullilah. God loves patience." she says.

"We still have one more test left to do."

I call him BBC. Each time he speaks to Hooyo, he opens with *I have some news*. His entrance even comes with a jingle. His shuffle of a walk causes his feet to drag against the linoleum floors. Each step feels calculated; he moves in beat with the sounds drifting from machines determined to keep me chained to this room and to this body.

"We'll test for brain activity in the morning."

"Thank you Doctor."

I wish they would stop talking through me. It makes my mind wander; melancholic memories, their hues a lemon yellow, now converse with me as loved ones should. I have created compartments for each thought, separated worry from pointless contemplation. I try to bring them out in turns. But instead, I craft halos of my own. I fade into thoughts I never even knew were there. Today I'm her. The girl perched high above her world; watching, from amongst the clouds, her very self burrowing deep into the ground below. Hooyo says there are locked rooms inside all women. How unbearable to be trapped in mine.

Asha Mohamed is a Somali-British illustrator, photographer and writer whose work can be found in literary magazines such as *AFREADA, TOKEN Magazine* and *Hargeisa Literary Magazine* as well as in the anthologies, *Cut From the Same Cloth* and *Unbreakable Bonds*. Her art and writing centres on self-reflection and knowledge seeking with a focus on how this process is affected by the external world.

SHE WAS STARING AT the carcass of the dead spider that had been glued to the wall for a week as she scrubbed the rim of the toilet. It had become habit to spend a few minutes each morning wiping Telicho's shit from the toilet seat, picking the pubic hairs from where they had wedged themselves under the lid. She would then inspect the handlebars jutting from both sides of the toilet, installed so that Telicho could keep her balance as she sat. Then she would clean the faucet, then the door handle.

When she finally sat down to use the now-clean toilet she couldn't stop staring at the dead spider. She had killed it one evening after she had found it dangling over her shoulder as she was peeing. It was a ghost spider, white with eight legs that stretched from its body like skeletal fingers. It was fall, so the spiders were everywhere—on lamp shades, in window sills. Resting on the tablecloth of the dining room table like they were dinner guests.

Months ago, a spider egg had hatched, the little baby arachnids flinging out everywhere like streamers. Miniscule parachute soldiers. She would lie in bed, watching an OJ Simpson interview and the spiders would crawl onto the television screen, into OJ's eyes and across his mouth as he told the camera that he did not, in fact, kill Nicole. They would float down onto the salmon-colored rug and crawl into the dirty laundry that was piling up on her floor.

She bought bug spray. The 100 percent toxic kind, because she would much rather get cancer later in life than have tiny baby spiders crawling all over her, into the crevices of her body as she slept. The thought gave her chills.

When Fidelia found the bug spray under the kitchen sink she put it out in the garage. It was unsafe to keep toxic substances in the house, she chided, it will make your tía sick. Telicho is already sick, she thought, but said nothing. She could not talk back to her elders; a good niece would never talk back. So, she continued to crush the spiders when she found them falling from her hair.

She asked Telicho if she was finding spiders in her room, too. Telicho shook her head no, turned to Fidelia, who was putting herself through nursing school from the money she earned as Telicho's part-time caregiver. Fidelia wiped the crumbs from the kitchen counter and said no, she wasn't finding any spiders.

Of course Fidelia wasn't finding any spiders, she thought, she was only at the house in the daylight. Fidelia came on the weekdays to cook and clean for Telicho, to take her to doctor's appointments, to trim her gray hair and sweep the discarded locks from the kitchen floor.

Telicho could not do these things for herself anymore. She could not hear the doorbell when the delivery man left the packages of insulin on her stoop, could not rush down the stairs to greet the delivery man, could not slice the package open with a knife and place the insulin in the fridge so that it wouldn't spoil. She could only take the stairs carefully, one by one by one, greeted only by the walker she kept at the bottom of the steps. Telicho could not see the mold growing on the bread on the kitchen counter, could not see the symbols on the buttons of the television remote, couldn't read the words on her favorite magazines anymore. Telicho couldn't see these things and couldn't smell anything since the car accident fifteen years ago that damaged the pre-frontal cortex of her brain. Not the onions Fidelia sautéed for dinner, not the flowers cut from the garden outside and placed in a vase on the kitchen table.

Telicho couldn't smell the essential oils—lavender, patchouli, peppermint—that her niece blended to ward off the spiders. She swiped the oils along the cracks of the windowsills after Fidelia had gone home for the night and Telicho had retired to the TV room. She floated through the house touching the oiled cotton swab in corners of rooms that hadn't been touched in years.

That smell is giving me a headache, Fidelia complained the next day, hand to forehead. She couldn't think, couldn't breathe, couldn't do the homework for her nursing program. The smell had crept outside too, had settled on the porch and permeated the garden. Fidelia wiped the oils from the edges of the windows, removing cobwebs and dust in the process. Do not do that again, Fidelia scolded Telicho's niece like she was a child, not a twenty-year-old who was afraid of spiders.

She flushed the toilet and stared at the dead spider carcass gummed on the wall above the toilet paper dispenser. She washed her hands, listening to the tapping of water rushing through old pipes. She had stopped using the toxic spray on the spiders, the non-toxic essential oils. Each time she found one scurrying across the room or swinging from its silken thread like an eight-legged Tarzan, she swatted it. And she had stopped sweeping the bodies away, stopped scooping them up with old grocery receipts and tossing them in the trash. The house was starting to look like a spider genocide had happened here, bodies collecting in the corners of each room.

But Telicho could not see the ghost spiders, and they did not reveal themselves to Fidelia. Only her. She stared at the dead spider again and decided she would leave it there just a little while longer. She was waiting for someone to take notice; to confirm that it was, indeed, fall, and there were, indeed, spiders invading the house, creeping in at the seams, searching for warm places to die.

Feliz Moreno earned her MFA in Creative Writing at the University of San Francisco. Her work has appeared in *The Acentos Review*, *Longreads*, *Apogee*, *Vestal Review*, *ANMLY*, and *The Sun Magazine*. She is a library associate and lives in Oakland, CA.

1. SHE HOLDS HER FIST like a bird. The knucklebones rattle. If she opens the window, she might fly—over the vegetable garden and over the gorse hedge and over streetlamps and Jim's house and the school swimming pool which smells like fear. But flight is a coward's noun. Her good hand is an anchor. It holds to arithmetic and furniture, swing sets and stars. She is greyscale. She chews the nib of the graphite pencil. It's broken. It is what it is.

2. They counted backwards from ten. *Here we come*! they said, and ran like ponies. She hid in the wash house, between the tub and the electric dryer. She was prey, and inconsequence—a small leaf blowing through a stampede.

3. What is the place between the filament and the light? It is the girl. She holds her photoreceptors like she holds her heart—loosely. She likes to think it could slip through her fingers.

4. The girl is big boned. The doctor said if she were small she might have disappeared, might have turned ghost, or a crustacean that you can see through—the gut bits and the nerves. The girl wears her bones like a badge. *Look*, she says, and animals size her up. She is too big to swallow.

5. There are breaks that chart a history of sorrow. She is broken in eleven places. Her collapsed lung and split spleen. Her ribs, her lumbar, her small hope. *What do you want to be when you grow up*? says the nurse, and the girl says *Whole; I want to be whole.*

6. How many times can it hit her? She counts the blows in twos, like it's as simple as mathematics.

7. There are animals and then there are animals. The girl is a runner. In her dreams she is a colt in the starting stalls, a wind- back toy. She knows the hundred-metre sprint like it is her body. She sleeps with her sneakers on. She is ready, always ready. The nurse with the face like sunshine says she needs to slow down, to breathe from the belly, to think of her toes.

8. The girl with the big bones does times tables in the shower. She catches herself in the mirror and spells her disgust in eleven- times-nine. She grabs at the flesh and wishes it away. Collateral meat. Ground bait for sharks. The girl can doggy paddle or breaststroke but it's not enough. She is a landlubber. The girl is not a girl to the predator below the surface, whose gum eye she cannot meet.

9. But this is not about water.

10. This is about the love that lurks in corners. The girl is sutured together, with strings that action her like a puppet. The nurse says *This will not hurt* and for the first time, it doesn't. The girl wants to go home in the nurse's handbag. She wants to fold into a wallet, or lie straight inside the cigarette tin. But the girl is big boned. She will not fit.

11. The movie ends with the girl running into the sunset. She is running to give you a happy ending. She runs past the dairy and the fruit shop and dry fields of maize. If you wait the credits out, you can see her rise, up and up. It's like the dream, but better.

Thinner.

Less.

Elizabeth Morton is a New Zealand poet and teller of tall tales. She has two poetry collections—*Wolf* (Mākaro Press, 2017) and *This is your real name* (Otago University Press, 2020). She was feature poet in the Poetry New Zealand Yearbook 2017 (Massey University Press), and is included in *The Best Small Fictions 2016*. She has an MLitt in creative writing from the University of Glasgow, and is completing an MSc in applied neuroscience from King's College London. www.ekmorton.com.

I AM A VOID. An empty space. A defined area containing absolutely nothing. Not air. Not light. Not anything. Of course, I am not static. Objects and substances are continually entering me and thereby diminishing me. My borders shrink away from them. But I also grow. Things move away from my edges and I expand to fill the space they leave behind. Sometimes these two things happen simultaneously and rather than growing or shrinking, I move. In this way I avoid contact with objects/ substances. In this way I float through the universe. You would think that as the universe expands I would grow with it, that there would be more empty space for me to be made up of, but no. Humans are filling the universe more quickly than it can expand. They keep making things: self-portraits, tumors, ghosts, more humans. The human condition can be defined as etcetera. The universe is becoming fuller and I am becoming smaller. As I shrink, I hold onto one memory. Long ago, while I was sliding through space, I came upon another void, travelling in the same manner I was. We saw each other and moved towards each other, until we came into contact. We touched and as we touched merged, doubling in size through this connection. Since then, we have moved through the universe together, still gradually shrinking. We are now smaller than either of us were individually when we first met. But we are a we and not an I. That is important. We will hold onto that until all the space is filled and something comes our way that we cannot avoid.

Jackson Nieuwland is a genderqueer writer, editor, and librarian, born and based in Te Whanganui-a-Tara. They are a co-founder of the reading/zine series *Food Court*. Recent work has appeared in *Pantograph Punch*, *the Spinoff*, and *Ibis House*. This isn't even their final form.

CALLUM HIT ME WITH a Lego brick that made buttons on my shoulder but he doesn't care cos he cares about nothing but how much he can get away with in front of our teacher as she's scared to say anything cos of his father with the badge and tinted car and as Callum hits me he tells me me what a stupid hippo my mama is cos he learned what a hippo was after we went to the zoo and he called out to the hippo at the fence saying my mama's name and didn't she look lovely and when I told him to shutup he kicked me with the top of his shoe that stabbed but I didn't let him see how much it hurt but held my shin all the way back on the bus and every day since he's gone on about the hippo using my mama's name as if it was his to use and talked about how much my mama likes grass in front of Miss Mulligan who can hear because it's quiet time but she just gets up and tidies the crayons with her ponytail swaying like a horse and leaves me to ignore him while holding my button shoulder and leaning against the wall wondering if I pushed hard I'd fall through to the other side where the small kids learn colours and numbers and understand none of the things that go on this side of the wall until I hear mama's voice in the room like bells and she wraps her arms around me and kisses me on the cheek hugging me tight and Callum looks at us with eyes full of water as my mama puts on my coat and wraps the scarf around my neck and as she walks me downstairs I tell her about the Lego and my shoulder and the hippo and she listens in that way to make sure I'm finished before saying anything and rubs me on the wrong shoulder and says not to worry although Callum shouldn't have done that and as we get to the bottom of the stairs she kneels down and fixes my hat so it isn't in my eyes and tellls me not to be hard on Callum even though she knows he's being mean and tells me that his mama is very sick and may not get better so he's angry and confused so all I can do is be kind because Callum's just trying to understand something that's impossible to understand—after she told me that I let it roll in my head and said I'd try and she said that's all she'd ever want me to do as we walk outside and breathe like dragons all the way home.

Clodagh O'Brien has been published in Bath Flash Fiction Prize anthologies, *Flash: The International Short-Short Story Magazine, Litro, Literary Orphans, The Nottingham Review, The Lonely Crowd* amongst others. She has been nominated for the Pushcart Prize. Clodagh likes to write in bed and always has too many books to read on her bedside table. She tweets @wordcurio.

AFTER ENTERING THE HOME, the sorrow is placed in the sorrow box. As the family returns, the sorrow box fills, though there is capacity for more. For example, when the two guests arrive there is no overflow. This is not because the sorrows weigh each other down. Rather each sorrow possesses a box of its own. Thus gravity is not gravity in the sorrow box. There are other more powerful forces at play in the container of blows and pyrophoric grief. There is a strange snow that loses consciousness but can not faint. And petals do not drift through the air but tick left and right, keeping time with all the arrested tears. Some say the sorrow box is full of vacillating executions of light. Still, a family without a sorrow box once had a stone thrown through their window. They built a sorrow box for show only. Someone told me the family continued to shed sadness in every room, and from room to room the drifts of wretchedness, heart-ache and regret lay about for any passerby to see.

Rachel O'Neill is a writer, filmmaker and artist based in Aotearoa, New Zealand. Their debut book *One Human in Height* (Hue & Cry Press) was published in 2013. They were awarded a 2018 SEED Grant (NZWG/NZFC) to develop a feature film and held a 2019 Emerging Writers Residency at the Michael King Writers Centre. Recent poems appear in *Sweet Mammalian 7, Sport 47, Haunts by Salty and Food Court,* and *Ōrongohau | Best New Zealand Poems 2019.*

SHOULD SHE HAVE IGNORED him? He smiled. Should she not have smiled back? He asked her where her friends were. Should she have lied? Should she have said somewhere around here, somewhere nearby? Should she not have been alone in the first place? Was a girl allowed to walk in these woods alone? He said he liked her outfit. She said thank you. Should she not have worn this outfit? Not have worn red? When he asked her where she was going, should she have said to visit her boyfriend the cop, her father the pastor, her grandfather the judge? And when she opened the door to the house in the woods, should she have locked it behind her? Should she have realized a lock would make no difference? That safety, happiness, and hope were already gone? Should she have noticed the fruit flies over the bowl of Winesaps, how the flies weren't burrowing but hovering, disturbed, and traveling fast? And what about her grandmother? When Grandma didn't answer her hello, should she have left? Should she have grabbed the poker by the hearth, just in case? Should she have cleared her throat and prepared to scream, just in case? Should she have shouted out the window for help, for an eyewitness, for someone to believe her, just in case? Like the hunter she saw in the hunting blind by the stream. Would he hear her? Would he help her? Would he hurt her, too? And what about the stranger? Should she confront him? Fight him? Try to escape him? Would she stand a chance? Would she even see him coming? Would she notice his shadow in the uncertain, soft light that pooled across the floor?

Melissa Ostrom is the author of *The Beloved Wild* (Feiwel & Friends, 2018), a Junior Library Guild book and an Amelia Bloomer Award selection, and *Unleaving* (Feiwel & Friends, 2019). Her short stories have appeared in many journals and have been selected for *Best Small Fictions*

2019, Best Microfiction 2020, and *Best Microfiction 2021.* She teaches English at Genesee Community College and lives with her husband and children in Holley, New York. Learn more at www.melissaostrom.com or find her on Twitter @melostrom.

THE HOME FOR PROBLEM GIRLS

emmilea o'toole

THEY SENT ME TO a home for problem girls because I kept taking my clothes off in music class, and now here I am.

My fall from grace began in the summer, when I was fourteen. Afternoons, my sister Sandra and I took off our shoes and socks in the stuffy old hall where our parents had sent us for music camp, because the air conditioning was broken and it was too hot inside for sensible footwear. We kept our ankles crossed under our chairs. The teachers either never noticed or never cared about our bare feet.

You'll never know how much I appreciated this tiny camaraderie between Sandra and I, becoming sockless together.

But I couldn't stop at just sockless. Once my toes were liberated, everything else had to come out too. Soon I became naked behind my cello. They called my parents and my parents locked me away in a home with other delinquent females.

At the home, I was reunited with my old ballet teacher Janie, the one with the spiked hair and the fruit bat tattoos, the only adult who ever loved me. I remembered Janie from the past as someone much older. But now, in the home, she seemed to have regressed in age. Despite her professional wardrobe, she looked nineteen or twenty at most.

I wasn't sure if Janie was there as a counselor or because she too was a problem girl. Individual roles in the home were always a puzzle. For instance, many of the wardens also served lunch, and many of the lunch ladies wore business-casual shoes. Janie's roll, in particular, was very iffy. Afternoons, she would stride through the halls in a pants suit, holding a clipboard, pen behind ear, and every once in a while, she would tap girls on their shoulders and say they were making great progress. But she slept in the same room with all us problem girls, which none of the other counselors did, and she didn't always keep her socks on during meals.

Sometimes, at night, Janie would climb into bed with me and we'd cuddle. "You're making progress," she'd tell me in the morning, winking like it was some kind of inside joke.

"Am I?"

She never answered.

There were about thirty of us problem girls in the home, but they and I had nothing in common. They were all druggies or hornies. Me, I was scared to paint my nails lest I accidently get high on nail polish remover once I got tired of the chipped colors, and I didn't have a lot of sex, or any sex, I just really liked becoming naked. It was all about skin for me, not about organs or orgasms. Still, despite our obvious differences, I tried to make friends with the other problem girls. But I remained lonely-ish.

During visiting hours, Sandra came to see me frequently. She had a license now. "You'd get out of here sooner if you behaved yourself," she told me, because I was once again naked, hanging upside down from a clothesline in the visiting room. "You're always making a scene."

"Yes," I replied. "I do make quite a lot of scenes."

"Will you please come down and put your clothes on?"

Obediently I got down from the clothesline and wrapped myself in a sweater, which wasn't mine. At least my nipples were covered.

"I want you to come home," Sandra said. "I want to tell everyone you're all better now. Please, Kittie, get better."

"I'll try," I said, and she offered to pray for soul.

For a few weeks I kept my promise. I tried to behave. Really I tried, for Sandra's sake. I kept my clothes on all throughout dinner. I kept my clothes on during midnight ping-pong tournaments, which were forbidden by staff but mandatory for sanity. I kept them on in the shower. I even kept them on outside, which was hard, because I missed feeling the cold lick of autumn on my bare skin once the weather turned. On occasion I scraped the frosting from cupcakes and smeared it on my genitals, but this was only a tiny rebellion, pea-sized really, and I made sure not to get caught. My behavior was mostly good, and slowly everyone seemed to notice my improvement. The counsellors started treating me better, taking me more seriously and hitting me less, and soon they were talking about discharging me from the home, possibly before Christmas. Those counsellors, they always spoke about us girls as if we were delayed construction projects. "Should be done by December, if all goes according to plan."

One night Janie was licking stray frosting from the insides of my legs, which was not intended to be a sexy activity so much as it was an act of hygiene, for frosting can infect if left untreated. Think of a mother cat licking its babies. As she cleaned me, I broke the news that I would probably be home by the holiday season. "Home for good," I specified. "As in, permanently discharged."

"Progress," she whispered.

"Progress," I repeated, and she smiled. I thought of my parents who'd sent me here, of my parents who were always shipping me off to some boring summer camp or after-school shenanigans activity, of Sandra who loved me but was always preaching at me. "I'll miss you," I said to Janie.

"No, you won't."

"Yes. I will."

"You're beautiful," she said. "Such a sweet girl."

I told her I didn't believe her, and that beauty meant nothing to me anyway.

"Don't sacrifice your future for me," Janie advised, and I promised I wouldn't. But by morning I was running up and down the halls stark naked once again.

Emmilea O'Toole is working toward her MFA in fiction at the University of Illinois and plans to graduate in Spring of 2021. She genuinely enjoys public speaking but is also fond of talking to herself and laughing at her own jokes. Her writing, as of late, focuses on misfit teenagers. If you're a misfit teenager, she has no advice whatsoever to offer you—but you're welcome to send her story ideas through telepathy or Facebook.

A Well-Balanced Routine

I EAT MEGABERRY CRUNCH six mornings per week. My mother serves waffles on every seventh day, but let us set aside the Sabbath. What is unsurprising? I enjoy, like everyone possessed by a mouth, processed berries mixed with crunchy bran and 2% milk. I mean: I have always been human. But, on some mornings, I, with martial discipline, watch with spoon in hand while a portion of cereal softens in milk. It softens, bran flattens, berries deflate, the whole works (milk included) become discolored. Such mornings are called Sundays, and their wonders would be diluted if I engaged in the discipline any more often. Their frisson is more than balanced by the experience of Mondays through Fridays, when I must eat breakfast in haste and fulfill the citizen's obligation to work.

Genesis

Megaberry Crunch was developed in either August or September of 1975 by an independent farmer in a hamlet east of Lafayette, Louisiana. This Boudreaux had an entrepreneurial drive, an experimental bent, and a mourner's need. He ground sticks of sugarcane to powder, mixed that with flour dissolved in the watered-down juice of all varieties of berry. He rolled the product into balls the size of curled up roly-polies and fried them to a light crisp which, after they cooled, sent both his pigs and his children into nonlethal but frenzied wants for more. He baked his bran with brown sugar and fingernail clippings hammered to specks. The latter were provided to him by his and several nearby hamlets' people as a moonshot investment in his fancy. It paid off. Boudreaux sold the formula to the Scabino Corporation and achieved financial freedom. He used a significant percentage of the proceeds to restore the structural integrity of his and the nearby hamlets' public schools. He funded a new cancer research wing at Lafayette's Memorial Hospital, where his mother had recently succumbed to the disease's mammary form.

1976-1991

Before my memory came online, the country endured the malaise of the 70s and turned, with surprising cheer and faith, to the malaise of the next decade. The citizens were helped (modestly, indirectly) by Megaberry Crunch. Sales of the cereal increased each year and, by the mid-80s, seventeen million Americans were calling Megaberry Crunch a satisfying start to their days.

My mother first purchased a box of it in July 1984. My father, apparently unimpressed, moved across town and into a luxury condominium with a younger man newly transplanted from Pennsylvania. He bedded a number of younger men and women in a number of luxury condominiums until six months before his passing, in the way common to his people in that time, in June 1991. He never developed an interest in cereal. I never developed an interest in younger (or, really, any) men and women. I have never coveted interferers.

Unacceptable Approaches to Breakfast

My mother has never forbidden cereal. I have noted, however, her acidic side-eye on me on one or another Yom Kippur. On several weekdays, at least twice a year, she has suggested that I eat a waffle. Sometimes she even sets before me, without warning, a scone.

Mass Production Creates Uncertainty

Everyone knows that the Scabino Corporation could not widely distribute Megaberry Crunch if it relied solely on the fingernail clippings volunteered by the citizens of hamlets east of Lafayette, Louisiana. But no one knows whether the corporation utilizes clippings (or whole fingernails) produced synthetically in a laboratory, clippings of non-human animals (cats are, of course, cheap and available), or the clippings of large numbers of overseas humans (clippings which may or may not have been obtained with express legal consent). Any of these possible sources raises an ethical and scientific concern: how might any of them, when used in place of American citizens' freely granted fingernail clippings, affect a consumer's health? This concern has rarely been enunciated and, so far as I know, has never been addressed in a publication or pronouncement of any sort.

Health Records That Are True but Unsuitable for Use in a Peer-Reviewed Article

Megaberry Crunch, particularly the softened Sunday version, has proven excellent for my digestion. When young, I regularly suffered both constipation and diarrhea. Since I began eating Megaberry Crunch, however, I have been seriously constipated (more than sixty hours) once, and I have suffered medically distressing diarrhea (more than three experiences of liquid excrement in a twelve-hour period) forty times. Thirty-five of those instances were a direct result of overindulgence in barbecue. I will not give up barbecue.

Genesis II

In July 1984, my mother and I briefly lost contact while shopping for new school clothes in a JC Penney's that smelled as though lotion had been watered down and spritzed on the walls. When she said I might look tougher in khakis than in blue jeans, I hid among the parachute pants hanging from a four-armed sales rack. There, under a black and red shelter of merchandise, I became distracted by my miniaturized and smeared face in the rack's semi-reflective steel. My mother must have gone to challenge the restroom. When I emerged, the world appeared to hold only me, the scent of lotion, and several thousand samples of boys' legwear that did not fit my nonstandard waist/length requirements.

I wandered from rack to rack, unable to resist the temptation to slide, as I passed, clothes left and right in order to catch another of my smeared reflections. The landscape brightened and expanded to include a display of shoes (I particularly admired a pair of sneakers with a zippered pouch for storing coins), then make-ups and perfumes (that section was as white as the inside of a new refrigerator).

The employees must have crammed into the break room for cake and ale. I found no one who wondered what I was about, though a man did push a stroller and baby past. He eyed me as though I meant to glom onto his family and even to claim one of his absent wife's breasts for my health and succor.

At the wide rectangular mouth of the mall, where hundreds of citizens entered and exited stores that sold everything but appealed to me in no way (for the old toy store had closed down in spring and the new one would not open till winter), my mother snagged my hand. Anyone, she said, could sneak me into a fitting room and inflict the world. Didn't I know how easily a boy could be turned inside-out and shown his beating heart? Together, we pictured a young, beaten heart on the tile. We quit that day's hunt for pants. We shared a giant mall cookie. Later, at the grocery, she let me choose the new week's cereal. New life began.

Marcus Pactor's second book, *Begat Who Begat Who Begat,* is forthcoming from Astrophil Press in Fall 2021. His first book, *Vs. Death Noises,* won the 2011 Subito Press Prize for Fiction. His work has most recently appeared or is forthcoming in *3:AM Magazine, Pithead Chapel, Harsh,* and *Juked.* He lives and works in Jacksonville, Florida.

BEFORE THE BUTTERWORT LEFT a hollow chitin exoskeleton after sucking the insides dry, you must've noticed his pearly sweat beads, his violet lips on a long stalk, suffused with a striking reddish tint, and wanted to conceal someone essential to you. But Tina was a non-biting midge; she hovered around enchanted while you watched helplessly. You must've detected the neat order of things, the existence of an intricate invisible trap, believed she'd see it eventually, but she chose to be a warrior—warrior not as in riding a destrier, but warrior as in martyr.

You can't help but imagine him break into his evil-butter-smile after he'd had his fill; the discarded red bubble jacket and dark jeans on the floor, while your girl shattered into dust in your arms.

Your nest is milling with people, at the centre of which Tina lay peacefully. You share a chronicle of her loneliness for the week after that day with the mourners, as if in trance. You talk of her half-breaths on the periphery of existence, her dissolving into nothingness. You recount like dream, snippets of your togetherness with your only sixteen-year-old daughter.

Her dad sits, head balanced in a freckled middle-aged hand, the look of a sliding drop. He isn't privy to Tina's call records, the depths to which she trusted her classmate, and denies yet the knowledge that your prescription sleeping drugs in the drawer went missing last night.

In death, the insect warrior is happy in spite of herself, in spite of the series of events that conspired to hurtle her down, in spite of that betrayal on prom night, in spite of the perpetrator roaming free.

After she's carried away, you begin to detest the semblance of regular in your happy family home, in Tina's orderly room—the curtains, fresh dahlia in the vase, books on the rack, all reek of something your world isn't. Chaos. You wade into the turbulence where alligators and frogs live, where the shadowy tree's roots and cypress knobs nestle birds. Tina holds your finger like she used to as a three-year-old in her polka-dotted frock when you descend the crescent swamp between the mangroves. Together you'll troll the mucky brown down; where the jewel bright, blue and red damselflies reside; mud up to your knees; let the will-o'-wisps ignite the flame in your hearts.

With reedmace towering over, you'll hunt out the butterwort from behind the sheaths of defense he's conjured up.

Mandira Pattnaik's work has appeared in more than a hundred journals including in *Ilanot Review, Watershed Review, NFFR, Splonk, Passages North, Press 53, Bending Genres, Citron Review, Claw&Blossom* and *Amsterdam Quarterly.* Her writing has been translated, included in anthologies, and received multiple nominations for literary awards including the Pushcart. Forthcoming work in *Flash: International Short-Short Story Mag, Timber Journal, Miracle Monocle* and *Atlas & Alice.* Mandira lives in India.

SUNSHINE WAS STANDING IN the lake when she discovered the stones, one behind each bare nipple. They felt tender in the cold water so she stood and cupped her palms against each and that's when she noticed them—two strange, tucked-away treasures.

Her mama hated the word *nipple* and instead said *buttons* when she had to call them anything at all. She also hated the words *fart* and *anus* and, for some reason, *toe nail clippings*. If Sunshine's own nipples worked like real buttons, she could unfasten each one and pluck out the stones for safekeeping.

She pushed her goggles back from her eyes and looked again: The nipples themselves were bigger, she saw—two pink, puffy mounds. Beneath them she could push the stones back and forth, just like with her kneecaps, only her kneecaps were there all along and these stones were what JL would call *une surprise*. JL only spoke French to annoy their mama, who insisted that the Turners never mistake themselves for Cajuns. Mama said Cajuns both drank and talked too much to be trustworthy—and whoever knew the difference between the truth and another tall tale? Mama only said these things because of Sunshine's daddy, who was half-Cajun. He told true tales and tall tales, and Sunshine had to admit it *was* hard to tell the difference. He told her, for instance, that a crocodile lived in the lake—though everyone knew there were only gators. But her daddy shook when he talked of it, his eyes buggy.

It was massive, he'd said, its hide black as time itself, with jaws that could swallow a whole house. "Could swallow *you*, Sunny, before you even saw that crocodile for yourself. You'd live out your days in a crocodile belly."

The morning was swollen with humidity. On their walk to the lake, steam had curled off the grass that grew along the ditches. Sunshine had been excited that JL came along, but once they arrived she'd only flopped back on her towel and declared she was going to get so tan that the pale skin underneath her freckles caught up to the color of the freckles themselves. Now, as Sunshine stood in the water, she squinted toward her sister and saw something else she hadn't noticed before: Rising up from beneath JL's olive green bikini top were two breasts.

Little green hills on a flat, pale landscape.

If their mama weren't there, Sunshine could confess to JL about the stones. JL would tell her what she knew from the library books she read in secret, like the name for the stones, and if they should be squeezed out of Sunshine's belly button or if they were the start of something else—of breasts, maybe, or something worse, something monstrous.

The lake was not actually a lake but a wide and deep brackish bayou. The far shore was crowded with tupelo and cypress; once, out in her daddy's bateau, Sunshine had seen a gator leap from under the duckweed to snatch a mama duck sitting on her eggs in the hollow of a rotting tupelo. Sunshine had screamed, but her daddy had only sipped his flask and grinned lazily, like he wasn't at all impressed.

On the swimming side, Sunshine had only ever seen one gator—a three-footer moving sluggishly toward warmer water. Cold springs bubbled up from deep in the earth on this side and turned the water an abrupt, clear jade. Still, someone had long ago tied up a yellow safety rope to emphasize the boundary anyone could plainly see. "Never, *ever* let me catch you swimming under that yellow rope," Mama warned them every summer.

Sunshine obeyed, but she liked to put on her goggles and swim as close to the rope as she dared. She liked to peer toward the opaque, pea green water on the other side and imagine what might be hiding just out of sight.

"Sunshine?"

Sunshine looked up from where she was still touching her chest. Mama stood waist-deep, her face pinched up like she'd stepped on something sharp. "It's time you start wearing a top when you swim, you hear?"

"Yes ma'am," Sunshine said, then sank down until the water was up past her shoulders.

Mama sighed. "Honey, it's okay to be naked with just us girls. But around other folks—around your daddy—you stay modest." She loped back toward shore, red hair glistening.

Sunshine's throat felt knotted and tight, and her cheeks burned. She wanted to follow Mama back to the towels and bury her face against her freckled shoulder. Whenever she cried, Mama knew to touch her back just right, or dig in her purse for a Werther's Original, sticky with age.

But to leave the water would be to walk, stones exposed.

She turned her back to the shore and pulled her goggles down over her eyes. Her daddy had given her the goggles for her birthday last summer. They had a red rubber strap and their lenses were made from the good kind of plastic that didn't fog up. Over the far tree line, the clouds were piled like teetering boulders. The yellow rope wasn't too far ahead. Slowly, she swam closer.

"Sunshine—" Mama called, but Sunshine pretended not to hear. She took a long breath and ducked under.

Along the sandy floor, minnows scattered like arrows, then disappeared in the soupy green water just ahead. She swam closer and then closer. At the surface of the water above, the yellow rope and blue sky wavered like light.

Then just ahead, she saw something—a shadow. She started. Her feet kicked up little swirls of sand. But there it remained, past the divide. It wasn't a gator; it was too large. It was massive. She heard her mother call her name again from far away, but she kicked her legs and glided forward.

Just to see.

Ashleigh is a writer and actress with an MFA in fiction writing from the University of Pittsburgh. Her fiction has appeared in *The Iowa Review, The Kenyon Review, New Stories from the South, Covered with Fur, Places,* the New York Public Library's Library Simplified app, and has been shortlisted for a Pushcart Prize and *Best American Short Stories.* Ashleigh's writing is represented by Jon Curzon at Artellus Ltd, and her debut novel *The Crocodile Bride* is forthcoming in May 2022 on Hub City Press as part of the Charles Frazier Cold Mountain Fund series. Ashleigh lives with her dog, Ernest Huckleberry Pedersen (just "Ernie" to most), in Brooklyn, NY.

PROCEDURES FOR MOVING HOUSE IN THE SIMS 4

WHALE ROAD REVIEW

maria g. picone

GET FED UP WITH tripping over your art easel and violin case. You're running out of space for new paintings, photos, and keepsakes. Never fear that you lack the money to purchase a decent living space. Any level 3 career will do.

Announce to no one that you are moving. Select a house or apartment on your smartphone or personal computer in a matter of minutes. Don't fret about your stuff; it will go into your 'family inventory' for easy placement or sale later. Nothing will get lost. Gauge how much money you'll have left over, the way you paid a deposit in Boulder, discharged any fees, and hired movers to wrap your furniture in plastic gauze and drive it 1.5 miles away from your old home.

Make the change an instant after selecting your desired lot. You won't need to clean, trash odd items from past tenants, or spend the entire moving day doing a precleaning to get a $35 "shucks we're sorry" refund from your new property management company. Coincidentally, they are rated 1* on Yelp.

Once you arrive, snap all your furniture to a grid. If you must reorient your furniture, you can do so by clicking a single button. You can recolor items that don't match using the 'swatch' tool. Use your remaining money to fill out the empty space within seconds. You never have to fit your furniture through awkward 1900s doors without ruining the doorjamb. No need to spend three hours sitting on every chair in the furniture store. Nor will you have to undergo the upselling attempts of a scraggly salesman. The furniture will last until you want it to—no worries about the pleather chair beginning to peel within six months.

If you choose to deplane from your relationship, it's easy. Select whichever Sim wants to go. The household funds will be divided in half, as will the furniture. You can decide who keeps the house and who leaves. It's not like he tells you that you have three and a half days to move out because he's going home for Thanksgiving, like you have less than $400 in your checking account and rack up more than $1000 in postage because you haven't the time to hire movers—not like you have to throw every ounce of your life on a bonfire of vanities to spare his pain. At the end, once the charity comes to pick up your accoutrements from the porch, it will be like those five years never even happened.

Maria S. Picone has been published in *Ice Floe Press, Moonchild Magazine,* and *Whale Road Review.* She won *Cream City Review's* 2020 Summer Poetry Prize. She is a HUES Scholar, Watering Hole Fellow, and VONA alum. A Korean adoptee, her work explores themes of identity and social justice. Her website is mariaspicone.com, Twitter @mspicone.

ALVIN LIVES IN THE eight-by-two-and-a-half-foot space between the walls of our living room, according to his estimates, which may be exaggerated, since, even if he had a tape measure, he wouldn't have enough light to read it. I have no reason to doubt him. Partly because my grandfather's name was Alvin, but mostly because he speaks with the unwavering calmness of those who have befriended their illnesses.

Our landlord didn't tell us about him, which disturbed my roommates. But now, after a few months—it's amazing how a little time can initiate a fresh perspective—we're comfortable enough to say, Hello, Alvin, or, Good Morning, Alvin, or, Thank God for another beautiful day, Alvin, when we notice—I should say, when I notice, since my roommates don't always say Hi–one of his eyes gazing fixedly from the five peepholes subtly spaced around the room's perimeter.

Peephole—the word has such a nasty flavor. I'll call them vantage points from now on.

Admittedly, I thought I was losing it the first time I noticed one of his eyes staring from the wall. So I ignored it and didn't tell Linda, my girlfriend—and roommate—or Phil, my other roommate. I didn't want to freak them out.

But the next day I saw the eye again. This time from a high corner of the rear wall where I had mistaken the vantage point for a spot of flaking paint. The eye blinked, and I waved in its direction. The eye blinked again, and I walked towards it, still waving when I said, Good afternoon. (I have the tendency to make the irrational rational by means of social convention, a tendency that I'm working on with a therapist. I think I'm making headway, though Linda disagrees, claiming I have trouble accepting the reality of things, what she calls the world's inherent strangeness.)

The eye blinked a third time, accompanied by a muffled sound. Like someone trying to speak under a pillow. I realized that Alvin was talking through the insulation and the plaster.

My name is Alvin, he said.

He repeated himself a few times before I understood what he meant. When I did, I said, It's good to meet you, Alvin.

It's good to meet you, too, Alvin said.

We became fast friends, to the dismay of Linda and Phil. After introducing them to Alvin, Linda immediately phoned our landlord, demanding that our, at that time, two months' paid rent be refunded along with our security deposit. But our landlord, a forceful mother of three, responded with her usual sternness, quoting sub-section C of section IX of our lease: any creature–animal, insect, bacterium–residing in the house is the responsibility of renters if not brought to the attention of owner before lease has been signed.

A human being is an animal, said our landlord, and don't act like you didn't know there was someone living in the walls. There're as many people as rats these days.

Then she hung up the phone.

You've gotta be kidding me, Linda said.

It's always in the fine print, Phil said.

Couldn't we call 911? Linda said.

We signed the lease, Phil said. There's not much we can do.

Alvin's eye stared from his vantage point above Phil's bookcase.

Who are you? Linda said.

My name is Alvin.

Since then, Linda and Phil have ignored Alvin's presence. Their ignoring him is understandable in certain respects, but, still, it disappoints me. I believe there is a lot to be learned from Alvin, even if his methods and ideas are somewhat extreme.

For example, when I asked him a couple months ago why he chooses to live within the walls, he said, I wanted to do it because it frightened me. I wanted to learn how to listen.

Oh, I said.

I didn't understand what Alvin was talking about, but I respected the intensity of his commitment. Still, I periodically offer to open a door in the wall for him. Just say the word and I'll get you out of there, I tell Alvin. I'm actually quite good with an axe.

But Alvin refuses my offers. He claims he has not yet heard what he needs to hear. Whatever that is, he claims he will know it when it finally comes, if it ever does. He says that he must continue to wait, even if that waiting takes him to the end of this life, a wait Alvin is prepared for, even if it means that his skeleton is left to lie with the already substantial pile of bones of those who waited before him. Apparently, there have been many like Alvin who listened for a voice that never came. Still, Alvin has hope, even if the hope is small, so small that I would not call it hope.

Recently he has been very quiet. He claims our conversations divert him from his purpose. Now, when he notices me staring, his eye immediately disappears. I hear him shuffle slowly–it's difficult to maneuver between the walls and all those bones. Then, after a minute, I see his eye resurface from another vantage point. But, if I wait, his eye vanishes for good.

An entire week has passed since the last time I saw him. I feel quite low. The only reason I know he's still there is the tears he sheds, the tears whose salty residue lines the walls like those shining paths that mark the progress of snails.

Vincent Poturica lives with his kids on the rural coast of Northern California, where he teaches at Mendocino College. His writing appears in *New England Review, DIAGRAM, Western Humanities Review,* and *7x7.*

I FEEL THINGS HAPPENING around me that are not real. I must be in a dream, or in a movie, or watching a movie on an airplane in a dream. On the other side of the field there are blossom trees in full bloom. They are pale, barely pink, like branches covered in fake snow. I hear the wind begin to rise and think of how in movies, the wind is always a sound at first. I push my hair out of my eyes and see petals fall from the trees in thick waves like something from a Miyazaki film. The sky is that same imaginary blue. My first thought is not of snow but of volcanic ash, of children shaking white dust out of their hair. A layer of white petals on the grass. If the wind kept shaking the trees and the ash flowers kept falling and everything became coated in dust petals they would soon get in our eyes, in our pockets, in our shoes, inside our mouths. You belong nowhere in this spring apocalyptic scene—I didn't build it for you—but soon you are standing next to me looking at me but not straight at me and we are laughing and making handprints in the dust, listening to the wind blow them away.

Nina Powles is a poet and zinemaker from Aotearoa New Zealand, currently living in London. She is the author of *Magnolia*, shortlisted for the 2021 Ondaatje Prize and Forward Prize for Best First Collection, and a food memoir, *Tiny Moons*. In 2019 she founded Bitter Melon, a small press deicated to publishing limited-edition poetry pamphlets by Asian authors. Her debut collection of essays, *Small Bodies of Water*, was published August 2021..

A HUNDRED YEARS AGO this town burnt down. Now there's a dairy and a pub, stumps in the bay where a wharf used to stand, and a little wooden church where Old Nick keeps his traps. He told me rats taste good with beans.

Mum says stay away from that cracker. But Old Nick just washed up here one day, same as us, same as all things in the mangroves: jandals, doll parts, rubber gloves. I hang around the mangroves waiting for Big Daddy. "He isn't washing up here," Mum says. "How do you know?" I shout at her. All she does is sit on the sofa in a dream.

When I told her about Old Nick's rat stew she mumbled, "Eye of newt."

"What's that?" There were toast crumbs down her front, I brushed them off. "Mum?"

"Owlet's wing."

"Well, he says he's eaten kingfisher roasted with taters and carrots."

I don't want to eat kingfisher though sometimes I get so hungry, maybe I could? We eat bread and tins of spaghetti off small plates. I steal fruit—sweet bright oranges. Nasturtiums are out along the roadside, you can eat those. Most everything else has dried up. Dead flax spears clack in the wind. The toetoe are frizzled white, they line the road like ghost-heads on spikes.

"What else you eaten?" I asked Old Nick when he walked past the mangroves.

"Dog," he laughed, showing off three brown teeth.

"How'd you chew dog?"

"Cook it slow," he replied. "Long time, low heat. Meat melts off the bones like whipped cream."

Whipped cream! My stomach growled. "If you ate my dog, I'd kill you. I'd put Mum's pills in your tea, when you fell asleep I'd slit your throat."

"You know about slitting throats?"

"Heard about it," I shrugged. "Seen Big Daddy snap chooks necks. Helped him pluck them, too."

Old Nick clomped off sniggering.

Back before we washed up here, we had two dogs, a tribe of chooks and a bunny.

Water began welling out of the crab holes in the mud. As I watched, a memory grew. I saw Big Daddy's arms. Me curled into them. "Big Daddy," I whispered. "I'm hungry."

The tide slid in like a mirror. I saw a kingfisher's white front reflected in the water, it was hunched on a branch. Ripples pushed against my ankles. I sank into the rabbit-soft mud, the water rising past my knees.

A green streak: the diving kingfisher water-bursting with a sprat in its beak. A blur of wingbeats and it darted out of sight.

"Hey, girl."

I turned to see Old Nick holding a live chook upside down. "Got sick of this one gabbling round. Want it?"

I was out of the water in a flash, snatched the chook and ran. "Thank you," I called over my shoulder. Old Nick's mouth was moving, but my heart beat so hard I couldn't hear the words. He waved, his arm's shadow swept down the road and curved around my feet. *Big Daddy*? I breathed.

Leanne Radojkovich is the author of short story collections *Hailman* (2021) and *First fox* (2017) published in the UK by The Emma Press. Her stories have most recently appeared in *Landfall, ReadingRoom, Short Fiction Journal* and *Turbine|Kapohau*. In 2020 she was shortlisted for the Sargeson Prize and longlisted for the Short Fiction/University of Essex Prize. Leanne has Dalmatian heritage and was born in Aotearoa New Zealand where she works as a librarian. She holds a Master of Creative Writing (First Class Honours) from AUT Auckland University of Technology. leanneradojkovich.com, @linedealer.

with appreciation for Italo Calvino

The City of Serena

IN THE BEAUTIFUL CITY of Serena, every old woman wears a mask. The body may yet appear lithe in slacks, in silks, in exquisitely calculated jackets; the gait still steady in the cleverest shoes. The hair is calibrated to perfection, dyed, snipped. And yet the face—the face!—cannot be made to please the eye, by needle, by knife, emollient, unguent, pressure, laser, poison, paint. And so the old women of Serena go about in vivid masks: the poor in the primary colors; the wealthy in the jewel tones, garnet and sapphire, emerald, all of it fired in the city's famous ovens. Time was, the old women removed their masks at night, in the dark, but now it is the law that they must wear them, even to sleep, even to die. The hands must be gloved. The toes must be sheathed. The old women of Serena may be sixty or ninety, or two-hundred and ten. Despite their wild hues, no one sees them at all.

The City of Infinite Names

Everyone is lost here, even the mice. The old folks wander alone or in groups, searching for home, but the streets have new names, have turned in different directions. The city itself changes name every hour. At one it is Los Santos. At two it is Poteryannyye Serdtsa. Each day is different. Each minute is the same. Every iron statue, every monument identical. The earth smells of salt or of mouse or of blood—but no, that's not it. The women wear keys at their throats like a necklace, but all of the doors have been burned to the ground. Under the dirt lie the bones of the dead. They, too, are restless.

The City of Exits

Every edifice in the City of Exits has a door marked "out." No one is out. No one is in. The houses are vacant, the churches, the synagogues, temples, mosques, the old market, the hospital, brothels, streets. Bones shrink on dishes, flesh stripped off. There are shoes lost in haste. The gates are stuck open. The clocks have all stopped, each marking a different hour of depletion. Birds' nests are splintering cups holding nothing. Nobody knows where the souls of the City of Exits have gone. It is rumored they fled on a Tuesday, or maybe a Wednesday, or some other day. It is rumored they are living in the City of Infinite Names.

Dawn Raffel is the author of five books, most recently *The Strange Case of Dr. Couney: How a Mysterious European Showman Saved Thousands of American Babies.* Other books include two short story collections, a novel, and a memoir. Her stories have appeared in many magazines and anthologies, including *Big Other, NOON, BOMB, Conjunctions, Exquisite Pandemic, New American Writing, The Anchor Book of New American Short Stories, Best Small Fictions* 2015, 2016, and more.

I WANT A LIMO for this, a huge stretch limo like the one Sinatra rode in, a black one, longer than a semi. I'll stick my head out the sunroof and breathe and sneeze from the pollen and smell Tommy's chili cheeseburgers, kimchee on Sixth Street, deep-fried Snickers at the L.A. County Fair, runners' sweat, rubber on racing bikes at the Venice pier, fried catfish, and brine, all in the air. I'll tap my lips so I know I'm there, massage my jaws, ball up my hand, and thump my thymus where the second button of my shirt touches my sternum and leave this morning's slog-dream behind. I'll rise like a pudgy bodhisattva levitating over his cushion. I'll ignore the placards of grief. I won't acknowledge death. I'll test my fear. I'll take Vitamin C, maybe a whole gram a day. I'll float like a kite blown so high I'll see yogis performing asanas on the mountaintop. At eight o'clock it'll still be light out, I'll hear the sound of drums and whistles, incantations, grateful cries from people's windows. I'll finger the air and float back and forth in a sky-blue sack like a Malibu seal. Sirens will go off in the desert for a sale at Costco, I'll buy Dexatrim and an apple-scented room freshener, grab free paper cups of sharp cheddar cubes and soy drinks. I won't be able to sleep. I'll go take in the poppies. We'll park right by sidewalks full of people in shorts and smiles, kids eating Dreamsicles, laughs echoing through the crowd. I want all this in one huge breath. Driver, don't drop me off yet, go around real slow one more time, for one more look, one more breath, so I can remember.

Bill Ratner is a Poets & Writers Readings and Workshops Grant recipient. His poems and essays are published in *Chiron Review, Baltimore Review, Rattle Magazine's Rattlecast, MacQueen's Quinterly, Pleiades, Missouri Review Audio*, and others. Bill's readings are featured on National

Public Radio's Good Food, The Business, and KCRW's Strangers. He is the author of *To Decorate a Casket* from Finishing Line Press and *Parenting for the Digital Age: The Truth About Media's Effect on Children* from Familius Books. He is a 9-time winner of The Moth Story Slams. Bill teaches narration for the Screen Actors Guild Foundation and earns his living as a voice actor.

MY DAUGHTER WAS ALMOST three when I decided to observe the ashtmi fast. It was the first year I'd had a meal to skip: otherwise, late autumn saw me in the kitchen, haphazardly throwing beans and veg into a pan, slow-roasting so that the oven would help stave off the arctic chill. I didn't live in a MetLife ad—I'd never needed to FaceTime my mother for spice reassurance—so unless Amavasya was there with me, I cooked alone. This year she was with my husband. (Did he ever cook? Yes, more than half the time. But husbands, not just my gora babu, have always been incidental to Hindu fasting.) I had decamped for the Mediterranean hills, whereupon I would, we'd discussed, return home to a daughter who understood her mother to be a person, separate and inviolable. Not a tap. So a small sacrifice—in thanks, in recompense—seemed fitting.

It was too early in the month, but then, who was there to challenge me, the girl with the blue wedding invitations, from honoring her daughter on the dark night she'd chosen to reappropriate as her daughter's name? Each day that week, the hotel staff had laid out for us aspirants a feast that reminded me of nothing so much as my mother's table: plentiful, well-made, not to my taste. I drank my tea at breakfast—Hindus are soft-core, you understand—and found to my surprise that I could feel my skin pulling away from me. I was fasting, technically, but so far I was only a banana and a bowl of porridge down. Once the top layer had sloughed itself off, writhing like a nautanki, I wondered whether to toss my skin in the compost bin or wrap it up to carry it home with me. I crushed it into my tote bag and went to commune.

The morning felt quotidian. I scribbled notes to myself, trying to capture what meaning I could hear around me. It felt, to be honest, like home: not where Amavasya and I wind ourselves together and mutter to ourselves in a language no one else can understand, but the genuine article. By lunch there was a straightness to my back I hadn't made use of since conception. As a girl, I'd been a champion faster, or, as I'd covered my tracks, in training. Just inside the studio door where I'd assumed the mantle of Miss Swapna was a garbage can filled, and then, I assumed, periodically emptied of sandwiches my mother filled for me, eggplant and peppers and tomatoes and other nightshades that would rot in the trash far away from any children starving in oft-brought up slums of my ancestral home. Though I knew the furthest a brown body would get to principal was principal of a provincial ballet academy, I wanted to fail ready.

The skin underneath my cast off epidermis was hot to the touch. I thought to myself, *Amavasya has a fever,* and then corrected myself. The auras of those who had also paid to inhabit the mountaintop expanded to fill the available space, so I slipped on my shoes and descended. At sea level, I slipped amongst the crowds and watched, as is part and parcel of the rite, youths eat sweets, throw themselves with abandon into the waves. As I teen I'd swam until my skin turned purple, too dark to be seen at night, and climbed up onto my roof in my leotard, practicing camouflage, but for the pink satin encasing my toes, slithering up my ankles. At home, up north, my daughter found me without opening her eyes, casting her arms about for my hair strewn across the pillow, pulling herself in with it, nose to breast. When I got back, I told the youths, I'd promised these breasts to the waves as jetsam. I flung myself about, spun as fast as I had before letting my head fall from the stage, fulfilling the vow I had made to myself then: this is what it will feel like, to be free. When I heard my own voice, saying my own words, I realized that the ashtmi fast was never a sacrifice. It was a test.

What is belief in karma but a belief in a panoply of second chances? I dragged my milk-filled body up the mountain, ready to commit to the reshaping we had promised ourselves, each one smoothing the others' chatter marks, celebrating the others' light. When I unlocked my hotel room I realized I'd thrown the bag with my skin inside of it into the sea, with nothing to show for my offering to Varuna. Nothing imminent, at any rate. When I returned home I pleaded with him: *O God of the West, I have given you my daughter. Just let me have another skin.* But it soon became clear I did not need one. Amavasya was happy enough to drink from this raw and bruising malai. It was only ever I who needed to be other than myself.

Rashi Rohatgi lives in Arctic Norway. Her writing has appeared in, amongst other venues, *The Toast*, *The VIDA Review,* and *Electric Literature.* She has served as a reader for *The Rumpus,* an intern for *Ayesha Pande Literary,* Reviews Editor for *Africa in Words,* and fiction editor for *Boston Accent Lit,* where she convened the Accent Prize. She is a former AWP and Binders mentee and a Bread Loaf, VONA, and Tin House alumna. Her novella, *Where the Sun Will Rise Tomorrow,* won the Galaxy Galloper Novella Spectacular Award, and was published through that now-shuttered press in March 2020. *Jaggery Lit* called it "fearless and breathtaking." She is currently at work on a novel.

RHODA'S HUSBAND, DON, SAYS maybe he should put out an ad seeking a partner better suited to life in the end of days.

This is after he comes home with a trunk full of dry beans and rice, and after Rhoda says she would wither and die on a diet of dry beans and rice. "What about butter? And flour and sugar and eggs? If I'm going to hunker down and hide, I need pastries. I need coffee and wine. Otherwise, what's the incentive to staying alive?" And after Don says, "The incentive is survival. Also, what if the power goes out? That butter will become rancid. The oven will be useless." And after Rhoda says, "But what if the power doesn't go out and we suffer needlessly?" And after Don gives her an exasperated look and says, "There's no baking in doomsday prepping."

Rhoda's problem, according to Don, is she's governed by appetite, and appetite is fickle. She's unpredictable even to herself. They'll go out to their favorite Italian restaurant because Rhoda wants ravioli, but once there, she'll deliberate for fifteen minutes over the veal marsala, the chicken saltimbocca, and whatever special the waiter describes with what Don considers to be overly precious words.

As Don stacks the dry beans and rice next to his other stores—hefty bags of oats, a vat of peanut butter, stacked boxes of saltine crackers—he says to Rhoda, "You want too much."

Rhoda considers all that Don wants.

She envisions Don scrutinizing prospective end-of-days partners' resumes for inconsistencies. "Says here you're detail-oriented, yet the next line is missing a period and 'responsible' is spelled with an 'a.'"

She pictures him sitting across from these women and gauging how matter-of-factly they look him in the eye when answering his questions, whether they fidget their hands, tug at the waists of their jeans to tuck in bits of belly that would otherwise poof out like pillows from clumsily-made beds.

He will be looking for someone without impulses to restrain or hide.

But also, someone who would be good at hiding when the world comes to that, as Don believes it will. Someone who can keep still and keep her mouth shut whole days. Someone whose desires are discreet. Someone easily satisfied. Or maybe: someone for whom satisfaction is not necessary, for whom survival is enough.

Rhoda imagines his first interview question will be "Cake or pie?" If the candidate says cake or pie, she's out. Because the right answer is neither. The right answer is sugar has no nutritional value. The right answer is sweetness is nonessential.

But Rhoda thinks the look on Don's face as he talks about what he still needs to purchase for their pantry and what he needs in a partner in these times resembles that of a child anticipating the tinkling music of an ice-cream truck. One who doesn't speak the language of doomsday prep might think "frugality" and "practicality" and "going without" mean "compote" and "cream" and "toasted meringue."

Michelle Ross is the author of the story collections *There's So Much They Haven't Told You*, winner of the 2016 Moon City Short Fiction Award, and *Shapeshifting*, winner of the 2020 Stillhouse Press Short Fiction Award (forthcoming in 2021). Her fiction has appeared in *Alaska Quarterly Review*, *Colorado Review*, *Electric Literature*, *Witness*, and many other venues. Her work is included in *Best Microfiction* 2021 and 2020 and the *Wigleaf* Top 50 2019, among other anthologies. She is fiction editor of *Atticus Review*. www.michellenross.com.

'SALVATION' BY THE BLACK REBEL MOTORCYCLE CLUB

FURIOUS GRAVITY (GRACE AND GRAVITY)

jessie rothwell

YOU'RE SITTING IN YOUR car on the crest of a hill in Hollywood that overlooks the neighborhood below, the 101 freeway running through it, and, beyond that, downtown Los Angeles. It's sunrise, and you've only slept a couple of hours in your car a few blocks away from here on a narrow, shaded street that doesn't have street lamps nearby so it was really dark at midnight or so when you drove there to set up your sleeping bag in the back seat and try to rest and put the image of bedbugs out of your head. You were sleeping at a motel when you think you saw evidence and felt evidence of bedbugs so you checked out of the motel and called a guy you'd been sort of loosely dating around that time and of course he didn't want you to come over because maybe now you had bedbugs in your stuff. You should have known not to call him because of course he wouldn't want you to come over, you were never close with him and you knew better than to expect anything from him but you were so panicked and desperate, you called him anyway. When you hung up, you debated going to another hotel but you knew you shouldn't do that because of money, so you did what you had to do and drove to a spot where you could sleep in your car (though if you'd known at the time about Korean jjimjilbangs being open 24 hours you would have gone and paid $15 to enter one of those and then you could have slept on a mat on a heated floor).

As soon as you know you're going to sleep in your car, you know where you're going: to that street around the corner from your old apartment in Hollywood, at the base of the hills that surround the famous sign. It's a safe neighborhood relatively speaking even though your car got broken into once in the six years you lived there. So you get to the block and it's springtime so there is vegetation around, because actually there's vegetation around all the time in Los Angeles, and you get out of the car to get into the back seat and you can smell the jasmine so sweet and sharp in the nighttime coolness and there are palm trees and other green hanging down close to the car and it feels oddly like you're in paradise and it's such a disjointed feeling, here you are, actually homeless, with nowhere else to go at almost 1 a.m., so you get your sleeping bag out of the trunk, where it always is because your car is loaded with almost everything you might need in any given situation (water and granola bars in case of an earthquake) because let's face it, it's more likely that you'll be in your car than anywhere else when the shit hits the fan.

You take off all extra clothing once you're in the backseat, get rid of your jeans and again try to get the picture of bugs infesting everything you own out of your head, and you crunch up in something like the fetal position on your backseat but the seat isn't even—there are indentations in the two end seats and the middle seat is higher, so in ten minutes you're already uncomfortable and restless, and as you are shifting around you hear car doors and then voices laughing and talking outside and you see people walking from a car to their house right next to where you've parked and you pray they don't notice you but of course they don't because everything is dark.

At some point, finally, the world gets blurry and fades. And then it seems like a few minutes passed but was probably a couple of hours and you're awake, listening to so many birds, such a loud refrain and you try to identify some of the bird calls hoping that will lull you back to sleep and it probably would if you weren't so stiff and uncomfortable from the backseat so you decide to move and you pull yourself up and you put on clothes and you're not sure what time it is but it's before dawn so you realize you can't go to the laundromat quite yet, which is the first place you're heading so you can hopefully get rid of any possible bug infestation. You get back in the driver's seat and the air is lovely and fragrant and the world is so still and you start driving again and instead of going the route by your old apartment, you turn so you won't pass it because you know it would make you too sad if you passed it, so instead you drive up the hill that now you are perched on, overlooking downtown and it's getting close to sunrise, so you sit there, watching how beautiful this city is right now, and listening to "Salvation" by Black Rebel Motorcycle Club on repeat. Robert Turner is singing *Feels like nothing's really holy,* and never has a lyric been more apt for the moment and the light starts to emerge over downtown because that's the east and you aren't ready for such beauty, the way the sunlight starts to reflect on the blue lit buildings and cause them to burst into gold leaf.

And now Turner is repeating the refrain *Do you feel alive? Can you feel alive? Do you feel alive? Can you feel alive*? And you wonder.

Jessie Rothwell is a writer, storyteller, composer, singer, teacher and concert curator. Her writing has appeared in *The Rumpus, Barrelhouse,* the *Grace & Gravity* journal series, *Breadcrumbs Magazine,* and on Minnesota Public Radio's Classical blog. Jessie's music has been performed on both U.S. coasts, and, when there's no pandemic, she sings with several groups, most recently with the Balkan women's vocal ensemble Orfeia, and the band Mezhdou. She is a recipient of the Jenny McKean Moore writing fellowship at George Washington University, and holds an M.F.A. in music composition from the California Institute of the Arts.

LET US IMAGINE TWO birds are feeding on a rotten tree.

Let us imagine the descending cadence of decadent notes as they hook curved beaks into decaying bark, their ivory-tipped tails mimicking slivers of silver light.

Let us imagine my father's voice occupies the air. Except it is not my father's voice. My sister presses record on the tape deck again, and I speak his accents and inflections into the microphone as the black ribbon whirs and spools. Its tight black circle is like the stain of a coffee cup ingrained in the table. I have become an expert at imitating my father's call, snaring his intonations and tempos. We play it back and for a moment I feel my feet swaddled in his large steps, his grey speckled stubble scattered like stars.

Let us imagine it is my father's words that flutter from the speakers, not just feathers at the window. The crackle of my voice inhabits his.

Let us imagine he is here.

Let us imagine the huia had not climbed to the top of a tree and glided into the distance. For a moment pretend one scratches in the leaves outside your window and calls for its mate, the notes swoop into your room as you pluck them from the air and wrap them in flax leaves. Bury them with the hot rocks of your heart. Let us imagine the only memory of their song is not just a recording of a man whistling.

I clear my throat like native bush, stumble over words as if they are thick roots of harakeke. My father's waiata is extinct—that is me you hear singing.

That is me you hear singing.

Let us imagine him singing.

Tim Saunders farms sheep and beef in New Zealand. He has had poetry and short stories published in *Turbine|Kapohau, takahē, Landfall, Poetry NZ Yearbook* and *Flash Frontier.* He won the 2018 *Mindfood Magazine* Short Story Competition, and placed third in the 2019 and 2020 NZ National Flash Fiction Day Awards. His book, *This Farming Life,* was published by Allen & Unwin in August, 2020.

I find pieces of myself everywhere, and I cut myself handling them.
-Jeanette Winterson

THE MAN NEVER MET the woman who lived in his walls, his floorboards, his attic, his heart. He'd only felt her presence when he discovered her nest. Dirty clothes, garbage bags, discarded food wrappers, a pile of rotting apple peels, insulation pieces she'd plucked from walls and pulled around herself for comfort, for warmth, for no reason at all. He imagined the itch from synthetic fibers against her smooth skin. Surely there was a freckle on her lower back. Some flaw that made it all possible. The nest smelled of iron, powder, life, rot. There was a worn circle where her body had remained curled and silent while he moved about living in the space below. All those wasted moments, he thought. He'd never been careful enough, his mother had said, even in his birth.

The man never saw her face, but he gave her green eyes because he'd once read of a mermaid with green eyes the color of the sea just before dawn. A lighthouse keeper had called them emeralds, so the man thought it suited her. He gave her red hair because he liked to imagine the morning light that peeked in through the rafters stirring her and reflecting like gold off the woman's soft head. Not bright red but woodsy red and deep. He gave her ample hips and milky arms because he was, truth be told, a lonely soul. Lonely enough to imagine a beautiful woman living in the rafters in a nest in the attic of his rental house. He knew she felt the same longing, that's why she'd chosen him, even though his mother said no woman ever would.

He'd discovered her at his morning cereal. A box had been opened. Cut with scissors. The man opened each new box with his hands, grabbing and twisting at the plastic until it burst, sometimes sending bran flakes onto the floor, which he ate anyway because no one was around to know. The woman, when she was sure of his absence, crawled down from her hiding place and opened a new bag without finishing the last sugary dregs from the last. She had grown tired of his insistence on wheat-squared nothingness. It annoyed him at first, her lack of order and attention to the clear system he'd established, but then he was so grateful for actual evidence that a woman had finally come. For him. He forgave her trespasses. He thought himself noble.

"There's a woman living in the walls of my house," he called to the ceiling. "She keeps a nest in the attic." The mice heard him, but they already knew the news. She must be a woman because he needed her to be and a man would never think to use scissors for a task when his hands would do.

He named her Dill because he liked the earthy smell of it in his soup, the way it never quite broke down like other herbs but floated on the surface. She always remained green, regardless of how small you cut her; she refused to be integrated into the broth.

The man thought often of the 911 phone call he never made.

"What is your emergency?"

"There is an intruder in my house. A woman. I call her Dill."

"Is the intruder still present? Are you safe?"

"She's gone."

"Would you like me to send the police, sir?"

"No. Please send Dill back."

The man wasn't sure how Dill could slide into the narrow spaces of his heart, his mind, his body, but she had. He felt her first in his fingertips, then his wrists, then clearly in the sweat on his brow. He'd called her an intruder and it was the truth. She broke in, broke everything, and left a mess he couldn't mend.

He couldn't tell anyone, of course, not in the beginning, and so he sat quietly tucked inside his cubicle at a downtown accounting firm. His numbers added up to logic. They said he had a gift for sorting out the most complicated of financial matters. Usually it was a missing receipt, a column that had shifted when no one was watching. The man kept his eyes keenly on the numbers and the numbers obeyed him. But if his mind drifted to Dill, if he day dreamed about what she was doing at their home in his absence, maybe putting in a pot roast for their meal or fluffing the couch pillows, he'd look down at the tills of paper growing from his adding machine, curling around his ankles and have to begin again. The affair with Dill wasn't good for his career. When he dropped by an obligatory happy hour at the pub next to his office, he mentioned her. He couldn't hold back his happiness any longer. Jacob raised his glass. Serena snickered, "So, we get to meet this one, huh?" and drops of beer came out of her nose while she laughed. On the walk home, he jabbed holes into his underarm with his work pen.

When the man talked out loud to Dill, which he did often now that he was sure she'd gone, it was to coax left over pieces of her out from wherever they might be hiding. A whisper, a toenail clipping, a hair of unknown origin. He collected them all into a copper tin carved with his mother's initials, *EMR*, which he knew Dill would like for its shininess and light. "It's bright in there, isn't, Dill? Can you see the sea? I hear the ocean, too. Sleep, baby, sleep." And Dill would begin snoring. She always took up too much room in their bed, splaying herself sideways across his body, pinning a leg or an arm, so that he was afraid to move and make her vanish.

He had no choice but to begin adding pieces of himself to his collection. How else were they ever to be properly united? He began with the obvious that could be easily disconnected, a scaly elbow patch, the pad of his pinky, a nip of back fat. It soon became inevitable that substantial pieces would have join Dill, too. If he held back from their love, it would fester not grow. A railroad track of clean slices up this thigh, like the ladder she used to climb into the corners of this thoughts. He cut DILL into his belly; the relief was a wave of lust. One morning he found a small glass vile with drops of her left on the bathroom counter. That's when he knew for sure. His mother had always been wrong.

The man sharpened a blade, which she'd put back in the wrong drawer and it'd taken him weeks to recover, and piece by piece he joined her in their nest tucked away in the rafters of his rental house.

Melissa Scholes Young is the author of the novel *The Hive and Flood,* and editor of *Grace in Darkness* and *Furious Gravity,* two anthologies of new writing by women writers. She is a contributing editor at *Fiction Writers Review,* and her work has appeared in the *Atlantic, Ms., Washington Post, Poets & Writers, Ploughshares, Literary Hub* and elsewhere. She has been the recipient of the Bread Loaf Bakeless Camargo Foundation Residency Fellowship and the Center for Mark Twain Studies' Quarry Farm Fellowship. Born and raised in Hannibal, Missouri, she is an associate professor in Literature at American University.

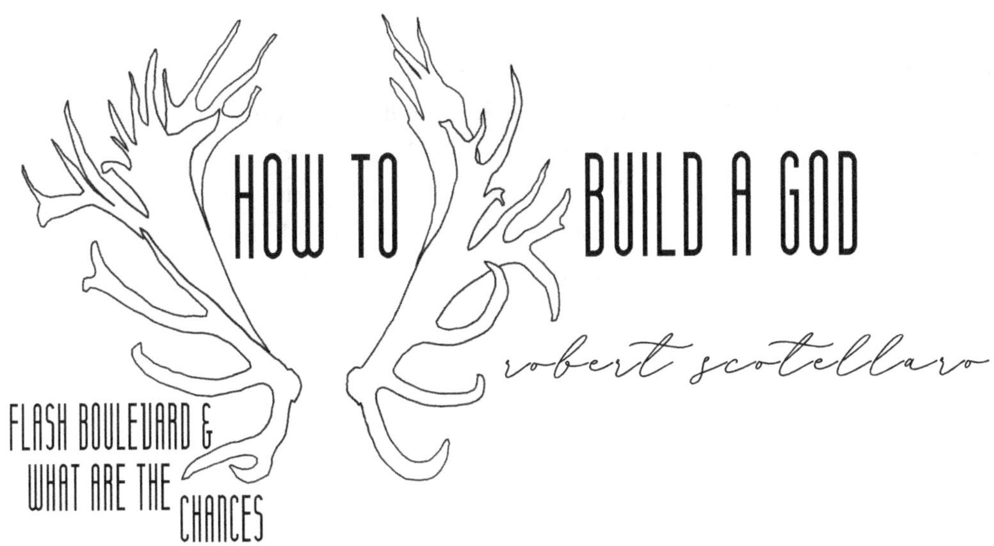

A FRIEND COMES OVER with a book on how to build a god. He has read many such books he clings to. Books with heft and wings, which never leave the ground. My wife is by the window playing an intricate piece on harp, the lovely notes in contrast to the crows outside with their harsh, monosyllabic utterings. She waves when he comes in: a midway grace between an uninterrupted pluck.

"Nice," he says, and she smiles. The crows, with their harsh esthetic seem less impressed. He was a riveter at the Oakland Naval Yards years earlier and I wonder if that skill will come in handy with such god building. But metaphors are wimpy when it comes to such hardy applications. They are mist and vapors, when you need a hammer's grip.

He reads a passage, slowly, looks up at me. "I'm just sayin'," he says. He has all his ex-girlfriends' names tattooed down one arm, with a black tattoo line through each: a permanence highlighting impermanence.

I try to recall the name of the piece my wife is playing Go through an alphabet in my head to retrieve it. Think it begins with a "D." Perhaps: "S." Hell, it could be any one of them. It suddenly means so much. Getting this or that right. *Knowing.*

But the crows, the crows seem to understand something we do not. That sticks. Branch to branch, perhaps. With a single screech against the silence. The only page they turn.

Robert's poetry and flash fiction have been published in over 300 books, journals, and anthologies, including W.W. Norton's *Flash Fiction International, The Best Small Fictions* (2016 and 2017), *Best Microfiction 2020, NANO Fiction, The Laurel Review, Gargoyle, New Flash Fiction*

Review, The Journal of Compressed Creative Arts, and others. He is the author of seven literary chapbooks, several books for children, and five flash fiction collections most recently *What Are the Chances?* (Press 53, 2020). He was the recipient of Zone 3's Rainmaker Award in Poetry and winner of the Blue Light Book Award for his fiction. He has, along with James Thomas, co-edited *New Micro: Exceptionally Short Fiction* (W.W. Norton, 2018). Robert is one of the founding donors to The Ransom Flash Fiction Collection at the University of Texas, Austin. He currently lives in San Francisco with his wife, artist and art historian, Diana Scott.

SHE PUT SOME COLD mashed potatoes on toast. She made gravy from a powder packet. She washed her things in the sink and dried them off in a brown towel rubbing the crotch of her good underwear like a wet puppy's ear after a bath. Connie called three friends to ask after Dee Dee. He was gone again with her keys. Dee Dee always lost his set. He took her keys last night when they got sloppy and screamed into their own hands at each other after his show. They had messy period sex. She said that going to work tomorrow was out of the question. She put out his cigarette and clicked off the light. Before Connie dozed off she asked Dee Dee to bring her pizza and a hot water bottle to bed in the morning and she would make him mashed potatoes for lunch. His unspoken list of easiest things to throw up after he copped.

Connie was tired of using wadded up toilet paper all day but couldn't leave the apartment without locking up first. Feeling trapped and dingy she decided it might be a good day to start keeping a diary; to have imaginary interviews with herself like she did as a kid; to record her savings and keep track of her most loyal johns; so that someone would use it to write a story about her one day. A book that her best friend, Art, gave her at the abortion clinic two months ago brought on the idea. It was a thrift store copy of *Lady of the Camellias* by Alexandre Dumas *fils*. The black-haired girl on the cover had a face like wet wax dipped in cream and large, potent flowers snaking around her ghost tits. Art said she would surely be bored lying around these next days off and it was time to read about a hooker for inspiration. Connie told him to wait at the bar down the street if he was so fucking embarrassed of her. They both looked around the waiting room and Art rolled his eyes at her with fake patience. Connie was feeling mean and scattered as ash after they took out the not-yet-baby she called Camille. Art thought it strange and then he thought it wise to give the problem a proper name. He braced himself for Connie screaming that name the next time she was wasted, but it seemed better than the nothing she

usually howled at.

When Connie began reading from her consolation prize gift, the part of the book she liked best was Marie Duplessis wearing white camellias pinned to her bust when she was available for male company and red camellias for her days off. Connie laughed so hard at that passage that her hot toddy spilled all over the baby blue chenille blanket and she soaked her briefs through the pillow-sized pad she called the *grief catcher*. Art agreed it was no *dream catcher* to be sure when they met for cocktails her first day back on the street.

She looked around for her nylon mint-colored slippers with bouncy rosettes sewn on top and hummed, *red camellias mean day off*. Connie scrunched her toes to nudge the slippers on and put a big sweatshirt over her robe. She stuffed her remaining hundred and forty-eight dollars, minus whatever Dee Dee helped himself to when he snuck out in the morning, down her pilled pocket and went out into the freezing hallway. Using an old bar of soap she wrote, *Will Rip Your Dick Off* on the painted black metal of her front door and shut it without locking. She ran down to the drugstore cursing the biting sleet on the cracked marble front steps while reciting her list: pads, pack of white French-cut briefs, Love's Baby Soft spray, razors, gravy packets, and Pall Malls. On the way in Connie grabbed a plump bouquet of red carnations and on the way out she swiped a pack of Juicy Fruit. Her feet were wet and blue when she got back to her place. She left the message up on her door until Dee Dee showed his idiot beauty of a face again.

It began snowing faster outside and the steamed up, old bathroom window looked like kids were throwing old milkshakes at her all day. She briskly shaved in the near scalding bath. Her body was so cold it hissed against the wall of heat. Connie liked the faint vinegar smell of brand new, *red camellias mean day off*, underwear. She sprayed her pad with Baby Soft. The bright sting of the perfume meeting with the freshly cut flesh hurt well enough to please. Connie put her damp hair up in a high bun tied in place with a red ribbon and drew in a breath she could feel for once. Connie threw the Dumas book in her grey leather purse and grabbed a carnation from the vase. She stuck it in the buttonhole of her fur-lined denim coat and let the doorknob self-lock behind her this time

.

Sophia Shalmiyev emigrated from Leningrad to NYC in 1990. She is an MFA graduate of Portland State University with a second master's degree in creative arts therapy from the School of Visual Arts. She lives in Portland with her two children. *Mother Winter* is her first book.

I WANT TO TELL Jack I am not a good girl. I want to tell him when he's at our kitchen table, writing a postcard to his wife, in his slipshod hand, all flashy off-kilter letters, and a sloppy X to end. She fled the city when the first quake hit, and there's no chance she'll come back—*she's always been the one with sense,* Jack nods. He's stocked up on shots of the city that was, from a tourist stand they once flogged in their cabs, bolted to the seatbacks, and he sifts them out of a shoebox, one a week, like coupons for memory. *Spots we grew up in,* he tells me, *spots we took the nippers, even spots we…got up to mischief.* He shoots me a devilish wink. The muddle of berry jam and vegemite he's paddling onto chunks of bread leaves the latest message tacky, but he's happy with it. You've got to have a project, the way he sees it.

His project, most days he's not driving shifts, is to comb the suburbs hunting for junk to trawl home. There's no shortage. There's street after street lined with offcuts of furniture, cast off bric a brac, the abdicated slump of old mattresses, homely with ground-down springs, the silver-brown watermarks of sex or birth or heat. The arms and legs of oak props and panels, the white metal faces that no longer tick, the fringed lamps shimmying like a chintzy joke. Come into my parlour, where everything's dust. Tablecloths scalloped and murky with fingerprints, the tatty knots of curtain half-hooked to splintered rods. The crooked trash we used to need to live. He keeps on tugging it home. *Free to a good'un,* he'll report in when he comes back towing a haul—he needs us to know he's a cut above the looters. His takings are all above board. Just another family trucked out, left it all behind. *The whole shebang. You'd hardly credit it. Sign up saying help yourself. No smiley face though.* He doesn't get smiles from us either. We hardly have the space for it all. But we've let him wedge his leanto with it, curio cabinets with no walls to tack them on, the copper dents of a firescreen though we don't have a hearth. A set of chipped enamel tiles sitting in a stainless tub, curlicues of crunched deco sheen. I don't know what it means, this hoarding. Perhaps he imagines he's storing up the makings of a fitted out base so his wife will come back. *She's always been the one with sense,* he says, *but I'm the one with hope.*

So much hope that he scurries the crumbs off his polo, and wobbles into his boots, determined to get to the postbox, feed his note into the slot. And I go with him, keen to block him spotting the latest leftovers piled on the berm, hitching home with more shards. He likes my company, though he half suspects I'm tagging along to thwart his fossicking. Sometimes he pulls a dopey dawdle like a toddler wowing over some new speck—you can just see him as a kid poking fingers at a flickering insect or oil-spill on the pavement. I swear when he starts to dally round a junk pile, grubbing at the crisscross and fishing something free, he shoots me a cheeky-boy glance just waiting for his telling-off. He puffs at my stroppiness happily, and turfs back whatever it was he'd forked out. His grizzle never lasts. And we go on, cagey, to the box where he plants a big kiss on his latest postcard, a cheesy smack on the script before he slides it in. We can hear it flap down into dark. He gives two knocks on the side for luck.

I want to tell him that I'm not a good girl. I want to, all the slow route home. I want to as we pick through upturned chunks of footpath, as we veer and backtrack to skirt the fresh wire, to bypass the mix of taped-off buildings, some gutted, vacant, some half-spliced back up. I want to when he pulls his trademark move, leapfrogs an orange cone, to prove he's still a spry bugger. And when he says, do you good to write too, you know. *You ought to be trying it. Doesn't bloody matter what. There shouldn't be a lock on that head of yours. Pick anyone to talk to. Even hubby, love. He'll hear you, I know it. You just scratch it down.* He claps his rough hands, one-two, a just-like-that diagonal. *And send it off.*

It's me that points out, then, a spiral of floor-rug that's been lugged over somebody's letterbox. His eyes light up, and he's over at the huddle, pulling out a flap to suss its condition. It's thick, baroque, its blue pile not even flooded. *When they've squared your new digs—when hubby's home with you,* Jack tells me, *this beauty'll be just the trick. Consider it a housewarming gift.* I don't say a thing, but Jack is too keyed up to notice. So I let him roll it tight, and we do a clumsy dance lumping it home. Like the freight of a body. He's so stoked that he forgets to ask the question.

I'm not a good girl. The last thing I wrote was a letter to my husband, on the day of the quake. Telling him I was leaving him.

Tracey Slaughter's latest work is the short story collection *Devil's Trumpet* (Victoria University Press, 2021). Her flash included in *Best Small Fictions 2021* is from the novella *if there is no shelter* (Ad Hoc Fiction, 2020) which was runner-up in the Bath Novella-in-Flash Award 2020. Her work has won many awards including the Fish Short Story Prize 2020 and the Bridport Prize 2014. She lives in Aotearoa New Zealand, and teaches Creative Writing at the University of Waikato, where she edits the journals Poetry New Zealand and Mayhem.

JUANETTA PASSED THE ABANDONED house every year since third grade and paid it no mind. She didn't pass close because now she was in high school, she walked in the street. But one afternoon, when the street was freshly tarred, she was hurrying beside the hedge along the property and without warning pitched forward and vomitted.

She ducked into the yard to think. Her sister had a baby at fourteen and looked like she was following in those footsteps. Mama never said, "None y'all girls worth a damn," but inside her head Juanetta heard those words in her mother's voice.

As she cried on the stoop of the house, hidden from passersby, she noticed a flurry of activity inside the hedge. She had the feeling of being watched. Sure enough, at the end of the yard, a sparrow tilted its head from the branch of a mulberry tree. Slipping sunfloweer seeds from her bookbag, she scattered them across the hard-packed earth and waited for the sparrow to come down. It hopped, closer. . .closer. Just as she might touch it, it gave a loud cry and a flock rose from the hedge. Snapping like a sheet, it dropped so quickly she lost sight of her sparrow among the dozens. But when the last husk was turned over, the bold sparrow rose first. With a full throat, it led the flock back to the hedge.

When she checked, there wasn't a sparrow to be found, but along the hedge, fresh hoed earth sprinkled with green shoots. Like beans, she thought. Germinating in a dixie cup on the windowsill at school. Alive. In the time it took to retrieve her bag, the shoots had sprung into a row of collard greens, and in a blink of an eye, they were silver with frost. Perfect. "I can practically smell them cooking down with a turkey wing," thought Juanetta, her mouth watering. But when she tried to pick them, her chest tightened with fear. What had the science teacher said about eating vegetables grown in the city soil? There were bad chemicals in the air and water, lead from the cars. Poison.

She stared at the greens, hungry, unsure what to do, when a long clear cry came from the mulberry tree. Gathering up the greens, she hurried away.

There was nobody home. She cleaned the sink, then rinsed and inspected each leaf like she'd been doing it her whole life. She jumped when the pot buckled with heat, and tossed in garlic and onion before the oil burned. Then leaves.

Mama was overcome. "Lord, if I don't smell greens! And how they fresh too?" But then she stirred the pot and frowned. "Why you didn't use the turkey wings?"

Juanetta had no answer for why she changed her mind or how she'd known about the iron skillet. Mama's lip curled. "That old spider gonna leave a rusty taste."

But Juanetta turned the cornbread out on the counter, and it tasted fine. She explained how she wiped the skillet clean with oil and kept it in a hot oven.

Mama fixed herself some of everything. "Who you ever seen do that?"

Again Juanetta had no answer, and Mama didn't speak more, though she hummed a good deal. Juanetta decided to put off telling her about the other business.

The next afternoon she didn't hear a peep from the hedge. When she checked the other side, the soil was ash-colored and stingy as the rest of the yard. Nothing growing but food wrappers. She rubbed her belly, then sat eating sunflower seeds. Soon she felt eyes watching and there it was. The bold sparrow in the tree. It summoned the flock to Juanett"s scattered seeds, then led them back.

When she checked, there were no birds but once more green shoots growing in dark, loose soil. She blinked and a row of tomato plants appeared, the plum-shaped fruit glistening like someone had only just watered. She weighed one in her hand like a little heart, wondering if it was safe when the sparrow cried out from the mulberry tree as it had the day before. She picked the whole crop and hurried home.

Mama leaned over the sauce, the edges of her hair crinkling from steam. "Did you add sugar?" Juanetta shook her head. "Would"t a fatty pork chop be nice?" But nothing was needed, not even hot sauce. Hungry Mama, thought Juanetta, as her mother mopped the pot with the last piece of cornbread.

All winter, Juanetta fed the sparrow and its flock and found something growing. Even after the snow came, she harvested cucumber, pole beans, corn, celery, and things she didn't have a name for, like romanescu and rutabega. And every day, when she got home, she prepared supper. As the days multiplied into weeks, there was more food than two bellies could hold. She read cookbooks from the library and by Christmas stocked the freezer and put up preserves.

Mama didn't say so, but Juanetta saw she was glad she didn't work all day to come home and have to cook. Glad Mama. Hungry Mama. Meal after meal, she licked her fingers, sucked her teeth, never mentioning Juanetta's belly. Juanetta thought her secret was safe because now they were both fat.

But we ain't elephants. One spring day, eight months from her first hankering for greens, Juanetta stepped out of the yard with potatoes and a baby.

"Fingerlings," she told Mama. They looked like their name. Chubby child fingers roasted deep brown in the skillet. Skin peeling like wax.

Mama eased into the kitchen chair, smiling at them odd taters dressed with pads of butter and began to eat. . .and eat. . .and eat. . .had popped an itsy-bitsy fingerling in her mouth, was polishing off a smidgen of greens knit to her fork, when there was a whimper from Juanetta's jacket.

"You all right?" Mama said. "Sound like your stomach trying to tell me something."

"Well," says Juanetta, looking for a way to bring up the baby. "You know how I always be bringing home food."

There was a flutter under the jacket.

"You got something else?" says Mama, washing everything down with a glass of cold water. Juanetta wasn't sure whose heart was pounding against her chest. Nothing left to eat, it was now or never. She pulled the tiny thing from her jacket, and Mama leaned forward, smacking her lips.

"You got *that* today?"

"Yes, Mama. I went to dig up potatoes and there it was."

Mama knew Juanetta was lying and decided to teach her a lesson. "Well, what you waiting for?"

Juanetta stood up, scared. "What you mean?"

"I mean split it like a chicken."

Juanetta took a step back.

"Roll it in flour! Fry it up!"

Juanetta clasped the little sparrow to her chest and told the truth.

Mary McLaughlin Slechta is the author of a game book-style novel, *The Spoonmaker's Diamond* (Night Owl Press), and a poetry collection about grief, *Wreckage on a Watery Moon* (FootHills). Places her work appears include *Black Lives Have Always Mattered* (2LeafPress), *Thumbnail 4: Flash Fiction, Slab, Main Street Rag, Red Savina Review,* and *Mom Egg Review.* She received the Charlotte and Isidor Paiewonsky Prize from The Caribbean Writer and is an enthusiastic Kimbilio Fellow and editor with *great weather for Media.*

Beijing, 1990

THE MORNING SUN BASKS the city in the color of apricots. A man rides his bike through the secret alleys. A woman sits behind him. Her arms are around his waist, and her mouth is soft and red. They live in different cities and work at different companies. No one knows how they save up leftover coins to buy stamps. The woman's letters consist of short updates. The man's letters overflow with poetry. They are on their way to a memory.

The man stops in front of their old high school. They sit on the steps and walk on the fake grass. Memory rushes to kiss them, leaving the blurred taste of exams and rivalry on their lips. They talk about the future.

The woman wants to go to America. She is not afraid of pain. Pain is as sharp as loneliness, as necessary as blood. Once, her father left for Japan to earn more money. He left with a pocket full of good intentions, but her mother went quiet, anyway, like a candle withered to smoke.

The man does not want to go. He does not want to molt into a bird and travel over a blue mouth to a rough, alien land. Who would ever want to be a stranger?

But the woman wants to go to America. Her father said she should. Her father did not go to Japan to lose his two front teeth and his ink hair and his apple laugh for nothing.

The man does not want to cut out his tongue. He does not want to lose the faces of his people. His blood runs peasant. This is how the land binds him.

There are only endings in China, she says.

There is still loss and sorrow in America, he says.

They separate.

In the afternoon, the woman visits her family in the countryside. The sun hangs blood orange. The fields glow summer pears. Her sister is not there. She is at a party, somewhere, and drunk. The woman cannot look at her father, his eyes heavy with shadows. Instead, she watches her mother use all the remaining vegetables to make dinner. Holes and stains eat their clothes. The house hurts. The chair roughens against her shoulders. She misses her grandma. She wants to get out of this place.

The man has nothing left in the city. He goes home and passes by the countryside. His town rests along the river, to the east of the mountains, near the ocean. His father greets him. He used to be a manager of a business. His mother makes all of his favorite meals.

They talk about America. America is young, his father says. America is free, his mother says. Tiananmen Square won't let go of their dreams. Later, as the sun struggles against the horizon, his mother sits next to him on the porch. Their voices are too difficult, too tender for words to be heard.

When she leaves for bed, the wind hums something full of heartache, and the dragonflies echo this song. The man thinks about his friends and his family and his childhood. He thinks about the woman. He goes back to Beijing.

They meet at their old high school and walk on the midnight street with the world at the edge of their heart. The woman shows him his letters of love declarations. The man takes out the folded pages from her journal. She smiles. He likes how soft and red her mouth is.

They cannot afford a real wedding. They must take pictures in fancy clothes that do not belong to them. The government hands them a piece of paper.

They kiss.

The photographer never captures it.

When they go home, they lay in bed. She listens to the radio. He tickles her. Then, they marvel at English. They wonder if eating hamburgers is a national sport. They dream America will love them.

Grace Q. Song is a Chinese-American writer residing in New York. Her poetry and fiction have been published or are forthcoming in *SmokeLong Quarterly*, *Monkeybicycle*, *Passages North*, *PANK*, *The Journal*, and elsewhere. Her work has been included in *Best Microfiction* and *Best of the Net*. She will be attending Columbia University in fall 2021.

IT WAS THE SUMMER of spray tan / burials / the summer we decided not to bare the toxic / relationship to ourselves anymore / apathy shaken free / as swimsuits off our sweating skin / diving into wild waters / like learning other bodies / could deliver us our own / to feel the squeeze of freezing water / forcing out our last breath / mocking our unfamiliar mortality / to feel our feet / against the slip of stones / the sand / we wiggle off our toes / before flip flops wield us off again / on new ways / to find ourselves / long before I'd struggle for sixteen years to sleep / we'd stay up all night / our wildness exposed / in cahoots with the moon / a stolen piece of the heavens //

It was the summer we palmed our packs of du Maurier and Export A / an addendum to our sadness / or adultness / no one knew for sure / what we were waiting for / we moved frantically / in jeans biting at our waists / a frenzy of hips / sucking our teeth like girls on a diet / like the urgency to shrink beyond ourselves / was our only momentum / the summer C95 / stopped being the cool radio station / and on Saturdays we'd get a dime bag from the local guy / stretching the night out long like taffy / ignoring the open mouths of garage doors / calling us by name / choosing to leave / our starched streets / in old cars with open windows / in search / of a sky we could sleep under //

Sometimes I catch the scent of those summers / washed over in a whiff of open windows and salty bodies / preserved in resin-coated images / I keep them awake with me / charting out a map of moments like stars / burning out too fast / a whole sky bursting / into empty night / sometimes I remember it was that way / for us too / someone always dies / someone always gets married too soon / someone skips the stone / and forgets the count / doesn't matter / it

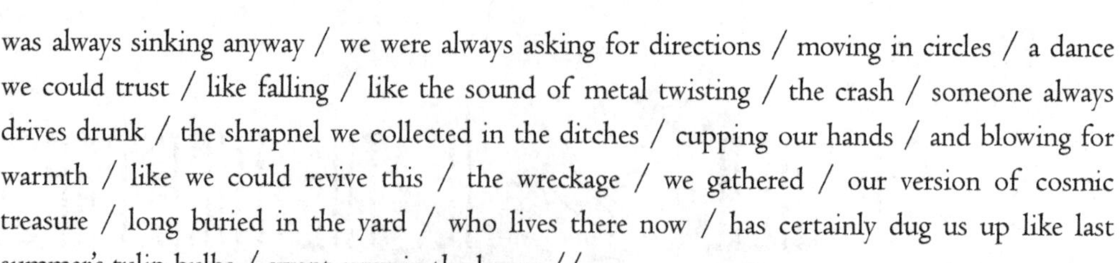

was always sinking anyway / we were always asking for directions / moving in circles / a dance we could trust / like falling / like the sound of metal twisting / the crash / someone always drives drunk / the shrapnel we collected in the ditches / cupping our hands / and blowing for warmth / like we could revive this / the wreckage / we gathered / our version of cosmic treasure / long buried in the yard / who lives there now / has certainly dug us up like last summer's tulip bulbs / swept away in the leaves //

Jaime Speed lives, works, and plays in Saskatchewan, Canada. A fan of reading, gardening, throwing weights, and dancing badly, she has recently been published in *The Rat's Ass Review*, *Dear Loneliness Project*, *Hobo Camp Review*, *Anti-Heroin Chic*, and *OyeDrum Magazine*, with work forthcoming in *Psaltery & Lyre*, *Channel*, and *They Call Us* along with collections by Ship Street Poetry, Gnashing Teeth Publications, White Stag Publishing, and Indie Blu(e) Publishing.

AT NIGHT SHE CLEANED the offices of a law firm that mostly dealt with divorce. She was glad she never married. She found scribbled notes of what the divorcees said on the phone. The rage, threats, tears too loud even on a piece of paper.

On the desks, she could peek at photos of what remained of the marriages. Cars, children, beach houses. She wanted to drive the cars to the beach houses. She would lift one arm and wave to the kids waiting. She found herself dressing for it sometimes—a new blouse, sandals with a buckle.

Each desk was slightly unkempt in a cozy way. The broken pencils, the twisted metal clips, the torn Post-its waited for her every night. She picked up the plastic cups with remnants of coffee. Holding them to her chest for a moment, she imagined conversations. She rushed through bitter arguments with a lawyer. She closed her eyes and listened to her voice, louder and more confident than she knew. Mostly, she refused this, that. Whatever was offered was too small.

A note on the desk of Andrew Miller, Esq quoted a woman refusing a settlement as ridiculous. Andrew Miller, Esq. looked terribly off-putting in a photo with his Labrador. If she had a dog, she would not keep it stuck in a frame in an office. A yellow Post-it note, underlined twice, reminded John Franklin, Esq, to take home the mail. The mail was still there, held by a rubber band. It wasn't the first time. John Franklin, Esq.,was growing old. She moved the bundle closer to the side of the desk, so it would catch his eye before leaving. After work, she was more and more often tired and forgot her purse. She had to walk back. When that happened, if she saw letters left behind by John Franklin, Esq. she picked them up and posted them on her way home.

She now paused and looked out the window leaning on her mop, fixed her gaze on the tall building across the street, the small balcony crammed with plastic toys. They seemed to glisten in the light from the street lamps.

In the hallway, she glanced at herself in the mirror, her eyes alert. Age was a kind of disfigurement, she thought. For an instant, she saw herself as before, back when she used to go out in the evening on weekends, to a movie and a bar afterward. Sometimes she had a drink with a girlfriend, and they laughed loud.

Marcos, the other office cleaner, was much younger. Made calls from the office phones, careful that it was not too often. Sometimes he fell asleep, curled up on the leather couch in the meeting room. He told her that dinosaurs once had wings, and he was pretty sure humans did too. That was what made us suffer melancholia. That's why he had pain between his shoulder blades, at the soft spot where the wings used to be.

She told him that the doctor wanted her to take many tests for her problems. She had no pain nor a doctor. But that was the one story Marcos paid attention to. He liked that she said that when lying in bed at night, she had a cough that stiffened her neck and arched her back "like an upside down cat stretching." He liked it when she said that. He was never tired of it. The sharp lights in the office had the feel of an ER. She told him that she might go to the ER tonight. She imagined nurses fretting over her, and she would make offensive remarks about the taste of the medicine.

Marcos was done sweeping, and she had carried the garbage bags to a large blue bin. They were now standing side by side in front of the mirror in the hallway. He was looking off and away, not at himself.

"Mirrors can be used forever by the same person and keep nothing at all," she said.

"That sounds good." Marcos smiled. At that moment, one eye half closed, long fingers lazily combing his hair, he looked weathered. Looking tired made him almost handsome.

She wanted to take his reflection out of the mirror like a picture from a frame and put it away in her pocket.

"We are in a space ship here," he said, looking outside. They were working at a very high floor, surrounded by the sky. He moved his arms like floating. "No gravity. Watch." It did look like he was flying away. "I'm a Pterodactyl. Look at my wings, so strong." Marcos always spoke of going back to Guatemala. The smell of the streets. The taste of the food. He wanted to be a bird and fly back. He wanted his wings again. He made the shriek of a prehistoric animal, running around the office.

Sometimes he reached to take her hand, and they made a couple of silly dance steps. They laughed.

Marcos became a little monkey in her dreams. When he jumped down to her on the bed, he became a man again, making love with little grunts.

Sometimes on leaving the house, she turned at the door to remind Marcos to feed the dog. And check the water bowl, to see that it had enough. She said it twice to make sure, as he was young. She had no dog, and Marcos was not sitting in front of her tiny TV. But still, he said OK, and rose to do as asked. First, he pulled her to him like a dancer for one last hug before she went.

Rosanna Staffa is an Italian born author. A prize winner of the 2020 TSR Nonfiction Prize and Honorable Mention for *The Tiferet Journal* 2019 and New Millennium 47 Writing Contest Award. Her writing has appeared in such publications as *The Sun, Tampa Review, American Fiction 16: The Best Unpublished Stories by New and Emerging Writers, JuxtaProse #21, The Examined Life Journal #8 ,Gargoyle #72* and *Brevity Blog*. Her plays have been seen on stages all over the country and in Tokyo. *The Innocence of Ghosts* was performed Off-Broadway. She is a McKnight recipient.

WHEN THE BOMBS BREAK the earth, it feels like your house is coming down on your head. And on your family. And you thought you were so young, and had your whole life ahead of you. And the fact that you never left Serbia didn't matter because there was so much time ahead. And the fact that you only studied and dated stupid boys. And all of a sudden, with a pilot's hand movement, with some muscle and joint contraction, with a screech of release and a smell of burnt metal, there is a whistle in the air above your head, and you're ticking the rest of your life away listening to that whistle growing meaner and louder. And the fear is unlike any fear you ever felt before, any fear you ever read about in a book. And you don't even care anymore if God exists or not, if there's heaven or an afterlife or reincarnation. You just want to live.

And when your house shakes from foundation to roof, and the crystal chandeliers swing viciously, and the glasses and porcelain break, and your great grandmother's armoire that stood in the same spot for a century slides toward you, you wonder if you're still alive. And when you feel your heart is fighting to break out of your chest and jump and run and hide, and you're all drenched in sweat and tears, and your mother is pulling her hair out like in those heroic epic poems you studied in school, and your father is on his knees peering out of a broken window, you realize you are still alive. Then you hear another whistle. Groundhog day. And even if your sweaty palms are on your ears, you still hear men and women and children screaming in the streets, you hear cats, and babies and dogs wailing alike, and cars starting and someone swearing at Christopher Columbus, and at someone's fucking American mother, and at Milosevic's mother, and you hear doors slamming, and someone's running.

Then the lights go out everywhere. A whole new layer of terror. And then you think if you're still alive, you won't be for much longer. And this must be how the grave looks like from inside. Then you hear seconds in your head, filled with lead like bombs, but they seem like minutes now. Then like hours. And suddenly everything silences. And you're thinking, this is it, I'm dead. It wasn't too bad, it didn't hurt too much. Until you hear a siren. But you don't know what it means, because, when in your twenty years of life did you ever hear a siren, and it's not like they teach sirens in school. And when a neighbor chants: "Curfew over," and his voice is first louder then fainter, and the lights go on again, on the street, then in the house, and you see your mother weeping. And your father grabs your shoulders and asks you, Ana, are you are okay. And his hands are bloody but you can't speak. And your mother hugs you so tight that you can barely breathe. And then she releases you, and you see her mouth move but you can't hear her.

Marija is a U.S. Diplomat serving in Brussels, Belgium. Her stories have been nominated for a Pushcart Prize, anthologized, and published in *Prairie Schooner, Doctor T. J. Eckleburg Review, South 85, Barely South Review, Gargoyle, Epiphany, Lunch Ticket* and *Inertia,* among others. Her work won the Neoverse Short Story Award, a prize given by a transmedia company, and her novel-in-stories was a finalist for the Washington Writers' Publishing House competition. She was a 2014 'Undiscovered Voices Fellow' and taught creative writing at the Writer's Center in Washington, DC. She also worked for *The New Yorker* as a fact-checker, translator, cultural and linguistic consultant, and wrote *Translating the Gorilla* piece: https://www.newyorker.com/books/page-turner/translating-the-gorilla. Marija grew up in Serbia, has a MA from American University, and was an actress before she turned to writing, appearing in an episode of *30 Rock* opposite Tina Fey. She is currently looking for an agent for her new upmarket novel *American Sorceress*.

.

KIM SEEMS ANTSY, AGGRESSIVE. She asks if you've ever stared at a turtle.

You try to remember. The smell of burnt plastic comes from somewhere unseen. "Sure I've stared at a turtle," you say. "Hasn't everyone?"

Kim leans forward on her elbows, drawing her voice close to the hot sidewalk cement like she's chatting with the heat, urging the warmth upwards. "No. I mean have you really truly *stared* at a turtle *in nature* trying to *get back* to nature?"

This is specific. This excludes pet-store staring or friends with pet turtles plunked in old fish aquariums. This excludes the number of times you've been high and hallucinated turtles. This excludes the faded turtles on the yellow plastic shower curtain which hang in your Boyfriend the Bassist's bathroom.

When Kim narrows the options, you realize that you stared at a turtle once near the mailbox and maybe other times in roadside ditches as well.

Kim shakes her head and smiles like she's got you. "That's the illusion of turtle. Your eyes followed a tor-*to-ise* which is not the same thing."

You insist it was a turtle. In its shell.

Kim repudiates your claim as well as your tone. "Fuck insistence," she snaps.

You want to know how Kim can be an authority on whether you stared at a turtle or a tortoise. Can she see through time? Does she live in your body?

"I *just know* you," Kim says. "I know you lie. You'd say anything to find common ground with a friend you've been ignoring for weeks. You'd gush over her shitty haircut. Or say you stared at a turtle. And then swear your perfect little life on it."

Your perfect little life. It is. Too easy.

And then Kim leans her palm on your knee. It is summer; your skin is a landscape of fire ant bites and rosy mosquito lips. "I know you *so well*," Kim whispers. The feel of her hand is softer than the Bassist's—but the pressure she puts on your knee is more relentless, insistent.

"Let's go," she says.

And you follow.

You rise from the sidewalk and follow Kim to the vinyl wall behind the gym where janitors sneak their cigarettes in a way that feels familiar. A bike stand serves as a landmark. Somewhere in the cafeteria, the Bassist is holding your seat.

You stand with your back to the wall, and lean forward, letting your hair inch across the tips of your leather sandals, as Kim counts down from ten, her voice far, hollow.

*Seven. . .six. . .*The blood pools in your head, a tender thickening, a known pressure.

The Bassist is probably wondering. . .

When Kim says *Ze-ro,* you flip your head up and press your back against the wall. You hold your breath and close your pumpkin eyes as Kim's hands circle your neck, the firmness of her palms meeting in a butterfly shape at the center of your throat. She presses hard, cuts off a supply of blood, air, light, sky—flashmarks beneath your eyelids, the pulse of blood in your temples, the world of high school blurred, broken.

It is comforting to let go, to remember how it felt—how it always feels—as it comes off again: the knees weakening, blood leaving your lips, Kim's freesia lotion, grass somehow touching and not touching your body—the worried eyes of the Bassist asking where you've been. And what happened.

"I found a turtle outside," you'll say. Then you will touch his cheek and settle into the seat he saved for you. "I found a turtle and decided to watch it."

Alina Stefanescu was born in Romania and lives in Birmingham, Alabama with her partner and several intense mammals. Recent books include a creative nonfiction chapbook, *Ribald* (Bull City Press Inch Series, Nov. 2020). Her poetry collection, *dor,* won the Wandering Aengus Press Prize and is forthcoming in July 2021. Alina's writing can be found (or is forthcoming) in diverse journals, including *Prairie Schooner, North American Review, World Literature Today, Pleiades, FLOCK, Southern Humanities Review, Crab Creek Review,* and others. She serves as Poetry Editor for *Pidgeonholes,* Poetry Editor for *Random Sample Review,* Poetry Reviewer for *Up the Staircase Quarterly,* and Co-Director of PEN America's Birmingham Chapter. More online at www.alinastefanescuwriter.com.

Goth Nanny

THE BABY SEES BLACK eyeliner circling dead eyes that teach skepticism, or something more sinister, a desire to detach from society. The buggy is covered in black satin. Goth Nanny likes to hang out by the cliffs, along the sharp stone edge, in view of the murderous sea. She communicates with the baby using a sign language of her own design, one heavy with menacing gestures. A smirk drags down the blood red corners of her mouth as she reads pavement-thick Ann Radcliffe novels. Later they will go to the graveyard, the only place where Goth Nanny smiles wide. In the meantime the baby sits up and shakes the nanny's thermos of espresso, enjoying the sloshing sound it makes, and noticing (because this baby will be an audio engineer), the distinct difference between the crashing waves below and the secret splash inside the cold metal cylinder.

Ladybug Nanny

The baby lives with the awareness of impending flight. Early on this baby has learned that cuteness does not equal goodness. Fly away home, the nursery rhyme goes, introducing the baby to images of fire and missing children. Sometimes Ladybug Nanny arrives home in triumph, looking like a chubby red sportscar, carrying diapers and ice cream and Prosecco, but the baby is not fooled. This nanny was hired to stay, not leave, and there is no reason to praise her return. Fortunately the baby is an entrepreneur who uses everything life throws at her. "Fly Away Home" will launch the realty business that grows into a brokerage, then into a construction firm, and finally into a village of minimalist red buildings on stilts that address urban density while gently persuading people to fear flood over fire.

Spider Nanny

The baby is in love, just as the mother predicted, though the mother's friends are horrified. Social workers are called in but disappear with a chilling consistency. Everyone admits that the spider silk layette is beautiful, and even the judgmental neighbor leaves her linens to be mended by Spider Nanny. How can you beat eight eyes?, the mother asks, determined to shame all those who dare criticize her. I hired a nanny who would help my girl for life, one who would show her how to handle men. The friends look around without speaking. Nobody knows who the baby's father is. Nobody ever mentions him, not at birthdays, not even at the big graduation party, after the baby has completed her fancy fashion degree on a weaving scholarship.

Octopus Nanny

The baby never wants for anything. Each arm of Octopus Nanny holds something different: a bottle, a hammer, a plush heart toy, a thermometer, an astrolabe, a pacifier, a cell phone, a baby. They spend half the day at the city aquarium, the rest on the teal loveseat. The parents feel unneeded, unwanted. Sometimes, in the dark, they wince at the sensation of tentacles kissing their skin while strong arms anchor them to the bed, forcing their union. Often the mother wakes, screaming, then runs to the nursery, where the baby is neither drowning nor suffocating. He sleeps the sleep of babies while Octopus Nanny lurks in the temperate nursery aquarium. Does she ever sleep? The mother struggles with jealousy and resentment until the day she realizes, while listening to Jacques Cousteau, that the octopus had no choice but to become a nanny. Motherhood would have killed her. The mother races to the nursery to apologize and finds the baby playing with eight different piles of toys, turning effortlessly from one to another, never losing his place. Someone has been teaching him to multitask, preparing him for his life as a construction manager and single dad.

Punk Nanny

The baby likes to gum Punk Nanny's stiff lavender mohawk. The baby takes a biscuit and dips it into the mug of milky tea that seems always to be cradled in Punk Nanny's right hand. She hangs from the chains on his black leather jacket. Punk Nanny is patient. His clients always speak early, in polite sentences, though he himself says little. It's all in his smile, his mother explains, when she drops by with carnation bouquets and strawberry tarts. He was born to be a nanny, like all the men of our family. Punk Nanny's mother flicks her wrist so that her many diamonds catch the sunlight. She is about to leave for the airport. She and the baby's mother shake hands, smiling and nodding, but something unpleasant hovers between them. Is it competition? Distrust? Perhaps it is merely the yearning to stay with one's own child, which neither woman is able to do. The baby senses something is wrong, but instead of crying, she rises on two sturdy legs and walks for the pure joy of it, refusing to choose a career path.

Jan Stinchcomb is the author of *The Kelping* (Unnerving), *The Blood Trail* (Red Bird Chapbooks) and *Find the Girl* (Main Street Rag). Her stories have recently appeared in *Atticus Review, Ligeia Magazine* and *Fractured Lit.* A Pushcart nominee, she is featured in *Best Microfiction 2020* and *The Best Small Fictions 2018.* She lives in Southern California with her family. Find her at janstinchcomb.com or on Twitter @janstinchcomb.

IN THE LONELY, FOGGY summer mornings before I met Stephen, I would sometimes wake up early and look out my bedroom window to watch an older girl walk a reticulated python down my street. She wore a pink cotton robe cinched over pajamas—her hair up in a messy bun—with the python cleanly slung across her shoulders. While they walked, the snake would scan the world, its head perched on her upraised hand. Neighbors, walking their dogs, would cross the street to avoid them. It wasn't until later that I learned she was Stephen's sister.

A week before I met him, Stephen's sister's python—Balthazar—bit him three times on the upper thigh. He showed me the scars the first time he undressed, guiding the tip of my finger to brail the bubbled tissue. He told me how Balthazar required daily socialization; otherwise, he could turn wild again. Stephen told me how his sister walked Balthazar to the park most mornings, where they'd sit on a bench and watch people do Tai Chi. The night Balthazar bit Stephen, his sister had been at summer camp for three days, a summer camp that didn't allow snakes, but did allow each boy she liked. Stephen had been having trouble sleeping, and since it was the middle of July, he'd also been postponing his chores—one being to walk Balthazar. When Stephen began pulling the snake's long, slowly waking body out of his deep, glass tank—to go on a moonlit stroll—Balthazar snapped down three times on Stephen's left thigh.

After biting him, Balthazar slithered away through the dark house and stayed lost for two days, until Stephen's sister came back from camp and found him curled up inside the washing machine. She only needed one hand to pinch Balthazar behind the jaw and slowly coo him back, while the other gesticulated to her frantic mother—begging her not to have her snake put down.

I remember Stephen's sister walking Balthazar best on those foggy, pre-Stephen mornings. How I started to wake up early just to try and glimpse them. I never told him I'd seen his sister, or the snake who bit him. When I met Stephen—him leaning against the wall at the mall, legs slightly spread, smoking like the child he was—he still had a slight limp from the swelling. The more I saw the scars in the back seat of his old minivan—the more I watched them fade—the more Balthazar enthralled me, and the earlier I'd wake up just to see them walking by. Just to see her scratching Balthazar's chin while Stephen somewhere snored. The more I saw the scars, the more I wanted to have that effect on someone. I wanted to make a temporary mark. To play a role in a story that would, with time, fade away.

I never met Balthazar or Stephen's sister. I never even learned her name. But I would sometimes lie in bed, alone, with my mouth wide open, one hand pinching the back of my neck. I would sometimes bite him, too.

John Elizabeth Stintzi is an award-winning queer novelist, poet, and artist whose work has appeared in *Ploughshares, Kenyon Review, The Malahat Review,* and many others. JES is the author of the novels *My Volcano* (forthcoming Spring 2022) and *Vanishing Monuments,* as well as the poetry collection *Junebat.*

IN THE FIRST HOUSE, a bungalow on Victoria Peak, Rosa sleeps on top of two washing machines. When the wash cycles sync on *rinse & spin*, the laundry room shakes and sends vibrations through her body. She pretends she is back home in Manila, sinking into her mother's favorite massage chair. Her teenage bones only feel the ache many years later.

In the second house, a condo overlooking the harbour, the wife tells Rosa she's probably the only maid in Hong Kong who gets to enjoy grade-five Wagyu beef. You're one of the lucky ones, the slender Chinese woman says, gesturing at the spread of leftover food on the dinner table. As Rosa hunches over the hotpot on the kitchen counter, fishing out slices of meat with a pair of chopsticks, she wonders if her little sister Tala will ever get to eat Wagyu beef. When the couple is done watching TV in the living room, the wife offers Rosa what's left of their honeydew. It's air-flown from Hokkaido, the wife says. Rosa declines, having already snuck a piece while slicing it up earlier.

In the third house, a refurbished walk-up in SoHo, the husband enters Rosa's room one night when the wife is away on business. The pudgy expat asks Rosa for a massage. I can't sleep, he says, my body is aching from work. He does not leave when she tells him to. Don't worry, he says, I won't tell anyone. Rosa believes him—no one will ever know what happens in this room because no one will ever take Rosa's word over his. Rosa climbs on his back and gives him a massage until his sweat soaks through her thin mattress. When he finally leaves she sleeps on the bare floor so she does not have to lie in his scent.

In the fourth house, a penthouse in Central, the bored housewife opens a bottle of Chardonnay at noon every day because the husband comes home smelling like other women. While Rosa watches over the son at the park, she video chats Tala, who is studying to become a nurse. My baby sister's all grown up now, the first in our family to go to college, Rosa says, I feel like a proud Mama hen. Tala rolls her eyes, which makes them both laugh.

In the fifth house, a 40-year-old flat in Wan Chai, the widow confiscates Rosa's phone, releasing it only after the day's chores are done. You need discipline and focus, she says after slapping Rosa for folding the laundry imperfectly, then once more after grabbing Rosa's hair by the root and grinding her face into the dirty spot she missed on the coffee table. During their whispered phone calls late at night, Tala tells Rosa to call the police. *Pasensiya,* Rosa says, not yet. You have just graduated and you will need the money while you look for a job.

In the sixth house, a seaside maisonette on Lantau Island, Rosa watches the young couple file for divorce, and helps the ex-wife pack her belongings. Rosa's back hurts each time she picks up a box but the ex-wife is too exhausted from crying to help. Maybe I should've been like you, the ex-wife says. Maybe it's better to be single all your life. Rosa nods and smiles as she slides the ex-wife's wedding album into a box before sealing it with tape. She is reminded of Tala's wedding day last year, and will forever be grateful to the young couple for allowing her to take two weeks off without pay so she could fly to Manila. Tala had jumped on her at the airport and shouted: Your hair is so grey now, *ate*! You have lines around your eyes! The man standing behind Tala, who was to be her future husband, had to pry her out of Rosa's arms because their excitement was attracting too much attention. Don't go, Tala said when Rosa entered the departure hall for her return to Hong Kong. *Pasensiya,* Rosa said, I'll be home soon. You're married now and you'll need the money to buy a house and raise a family.

In the seventh house, a spartan duplex in Sai Kung, Rosa walks the dogs and tends the garden while the retired couple spends their days sitting by the pier. When the tan young man who is building the house down the road first waves at Rosa, she dares not wave back. Talk to him, Tala says over video chat, you've lived your whole life for others and now it's time to live for yourself. The retired couple ransacks Rosa's room and throws her clothes out the window when they find their money and jewelry missing. Rosa dares not tell them about the tan young man who had laid in her bed that morning and stroked her hair until she fell asleep. The retired couple are placated when Rosa promises to pay them back if they do not report her to the agency. She gives them the money, a full year's savings, but they report her anyway, and do not even call her a cab to the airport on her last day of work.

In the eighth house, a four-bedroom in the heart of Manila, Rosa sinks into her late mother's favorite massage chair, which Tala insisted on keeping. Tala's baby girl Chesa is asleep in Rosa's arms, and the living room is filled with the aroma of Tala's cooking. Rosa sees her life's work on the walls: Tala's framed university certificates and professional licenses, photos of Tala and her husband on their wedding day, photos of Rosa's mother playing with Chesa. In the eighth house, which is to be the final house, Rosa kisses Chesa on the forehead and sings her a lullaby, as her mother did to her as a child.

Marcus Tan's work has appeared in *No Contact Magazine*, *Prime Number Magazine*, and Ethos Books anthologies *Kepulauan* and *Unhomed*. He is from Singapore and currently resides in Hong Kong.

MY AUNTIE CHEEKS MOVED in with us when I was around the age memories start to stick. She brought with her no belongings and made no requests except one:

"Put me there," she said, pointing the yellow nail of her forefinger to underneath the kitchen sink.

Fortunately for her, the sink was relatively large for such a small apartment. Auntie Cheeks tucked herself neatly into the cabinet, bent knees on either side of the drainpipe, neck crooked below the crackled porcelain undercarriage of the basin. She was flexible and petite, her skeleton thin as pins, and every joint seemed to rotate one hundred eighty degrees.

"It's perfect," she smiled. She had caves in her grin, and the teeth she managed to hang onto were more marrow than bone. Within weeks, the dankness turned her brown leathery skin into gray sheets of parchment, but she didn't seem to mind. "Best room in the house," she'd say, laughing with her cloudy black eyes.

Back then, any woman with white hair was an auntie, but no one could tell me how we were related. My dad said she came from my mom's side, and my mom said she came from my dad's. My parents rarely agreed about anything.

But Auntie Cheeks didn't look like anyone in my family. I asked her once if we were really related. She snapped, "Of course we are. I looked exactly like you when I was your age." I didn't believe her. No one that old was ever my age.

I spent many afternoons bare-stomached on the dirty linoleum playing with Auntie Cheeks. I'd scratch on the cabinet door like a cat. She would immediately push it open and say something like, "Did you bring me any marshmallows?"

I always tried to have something sweet for her, even if it was just two cubes of sugar or a packet of ketchup from the fast food restaurant down the street. Auntie Cheeks made me taste everything before giving it to her. "To prove you're not poisoning me," she'd say. But my offerings were so small, and I ended up eating the whole thing myself. Even when I managed to procure a bigger treat, say a Twinkie or a popsicle, Auntie Cheeks still never seemed to get her share.

I asked Auntie Cheeks what she did while I was at school. She said she spent the day massaging her face, that's how she stayed looking so young. I asked her to massage my face, just to see how it felt. She twisted forward and threaded one arm through the U-shaped drainpipe like elbows entwined in a lovers' toast. She put her cold hands on the sides of my face. Her fingers, like the rest of her, were short and narrow. Intense pinpoints of pain bored into my temples, piercing the middle of my eyebrows, and pinching underneath my jaw.

"See? It keeps you young," she said tearing at my flesh with satisfaction and humming a happy tune.

Auntie Cheeks liked to sing, especially when my parents were fighting in the other room. Whenever my parents started to scream at each other, my Auntie Cheeks would pick up my feet and sing as she cracked the knuckles on my toes to her own special rhythm. Sometimes I joined in, but never loud enough for my parents to hear over the sound of their own shouting.

I only eavesdropped when they argued about Auntie Cheeks. Once, I heard my mother say something about wanting to be able to keep the Clorox under the sink like normal people. And my dad often complained that he was sick of living with three crazy women.

One day after school, I brought Auntie Cheeks a piece of chocolate I found in a heart-shaped tin on the floor of my dad's station wagon. It was more bitter than the chocolate I pocketed from the bins at the supermarket. My mother found the tin on the kitchen counter and asked me where it came from. When I told her, my mother's eyes pinched. She said, "Why are you bringing garbage into the house?"

I told her it was because Auntie Cheeks was hungry. My mother said, "Auntie Cheeks can starve for all I care."

The cabinet was closed, but I knew my Auntie Cheeks heard her. I stood in front of the sink. My mother grabbed the tin, ran to my parents' bedroom, and slammed the door. I heard my mom yelling into the phone. Auntie Cheeks popped open the cupboard door and said, "How about a song?"

After that day, every night when I went to bed my mother would say that Auntie Cheeks might not be there in the morning. I'd cry myself to sleep, trying to figure out where Auntie Cheeks and I would go if my parents kicked her out. But Auntie Cheeks was always there the next day, asking for a squirt of syrup, or an orange soda, or a spoonful of pistachio ice cream.

My Auntie Cheeks was still under the sink when my dad finally left. When I told her that my mother and I had to go live with my grandparents, I promised to take her with me.

"Can I live under their sink?" she asked.

The cabinets in my grandparents' house were filled with pills, herbs, and slimy jars with labels I couldn't read. I said Auntie Cheeks could probably stay under the pullout bed my mom and I would share in the living room.

"No, I like it here," she said. "I think I'll stay."

My eyes and nose started to leak. My Auntie Cheeks wiped my face with her strong hands. "Go and give your grandma a good face massage. It will keep her young."

The morning we left our apartment, I scratched at the cupboard like I always did. Auntie Cheeks didn't push the door open. I put two heart-shaped candies on the linoleum. One said, "U R Sweet" and the other one said, "Dream On".

Renée Jessica Tan's work has appeared in various anthologies and publications, including *Flash Fiction Online, Everyday Fiction,* and *365 Tomorrows.* Her short story "Baghead" was read live at Symphony Space in New York City and featured on the Selected Shorts podcast.

WE WENT DOWN TO the river yesterday to watch our beaver do his business. We have a beaver of our own, we said in wonder, here on our own land, just a little walk from our own house.

We used to want things, I distinctly remembered we used to want things, but I could hardly remember what those things might have been. The beaver did its thing for a while, and we watched. It was really going to town on our trees.

I said: this beaver is a poet, but his poetry is at the expense of our trees.

He's so consistent, you said.

Pretty soon, it was a lot of our trees in the river. It occurred to us then, there were actually two beavers, and there had been two the entire time. One beaver may hide another, as the poet says. But only one had been out of the water at a time, so you couldn't really tell.

I said: These beavers are kind of like us, you know? Like there are two of us and there are two of them—what a pair of pairs we are together.

Here is the figure the two beavers suggested to me:

There is the first beaver and there is the idea of the first beaver. There is sky which lies somewhere south of the sky—the final sky.

You took my hand. Your right hand, in my left hand. And I wondered, really wondered, where you ended and where I began—was I myself or was I somewhere within you, lost or hidden or unknowable or something.

Here is another figure for your diary:

A person hold hands with another person; two people spend the afternoon watching

some beavers gnaw down some trees. It's an entire life if you're willing to modulate your expectations.

I feel the sensations on your skin. I feel my damp left hand reach out and take your dry one. And at that point, the river began to overflow and divert.

Oh shit, I said, the beavers are really doing their jobs today.

You said: We should seek higher ground.

But we did not move. I felt the water creep under your butt, just as you feel the water creep under mine. We lean back in the damp grass and in doing so, we get even damper—pretty soon everything is damp.

By then, the stars are out and for every star we see in the sky, there is another, bubbling up just beneath it. And beneath us, the final sky, our bodies floating away on it.

Kaj Tanaka's fiction has appeared in *New South, The New Ohio Review, Hobart,* and *Tin House.* Kaj is the reviews and interviews editor for *Gulf Coast.*

Stone

THE WORD FOR MOUNTAIN is *beinn.* The word for home is *dhachaigh.* The word for wall is *balla,* sheep *caoraich,* laird *diabhal. Rathad* means road, *deas* south. The word for leaving is *fàgail.*

She needs no language to know when to shine the brasses, whiten the step, fetch the dishes. Mistress likes her hard work. Master likes her silence.

The gardener teaches her limp English. *Leaf, lily, lip.* He touches his chest. *Heart.* Lightly touches hers.

The word for heart is *cridhe.*

Wood

A Borders man, he slams in posts and hammers rails. He wraps fences round the old places, Appletreehall, Dearly Burn, Parkhouses, Stintyknows, Kippilaw.

He speaks mostly to the sheep in their new fields. *Caoraich,* his mother called them, a spit in her throat. His youngest boy has her eyes, soft as smirr.

Wire

Piccadilly, Regent Street. He humps through mud, shattered leg useless, a creature from his granny's tales, more seal than man. As well die doing, as die in a hole. He finds another break. His fingers fumble, but he fixes the line.

At Oxford Circus, he rests against a fire-step. Reads the sign. *Danger! This trench is in full view of the enemy.*

Shells burst overhead, a thousand whistles blasting.

Something, somewhere, snaps.

Electricity

The clamp fills her mouth, heavy as a boot. *Nnnnrgh, nnnnnrgh.* They have talked her into this until she cannot say no. They soothe her as if she is a horse, tightening straps, placing pads by her eyes.

She's always been a nervous girl. Her mother blames her father, those flaring rages. In the Blitz, she was a firewatcher: burning buildings, blistered skin, bodies flaming like falling angels.

Now fire sparks again, extinguishes, and everything goes quiet.

Silicon

"Do you need to wave it around like that?"

"It's how you move to where you're typing." He places his hand over hers. "See? That little arrow?"

He talks her through mouse, double-click, icons. He's overcomplicating. Her eyes have that familiar, middle-distance look.

"Watch." He taps the first words he thinks of.

Baa, baa, black sheep, have you any wool?

"Oh," His mother smiles. "You loved that one!"

Plastic

On her shiny new lunchbox, Pingu is building an igloo. Her ears hum. So many children in one room.

"Snap!" A black-haired girl plonks the same box next to hers. "Do you like Pingu? I *love* Pingu!"

They pout tiny mouths into honking penguin beaks – "Noot, noot!" – until the giggles take them. They will laugh together for the next forty-three years.

Bit

"Say hello to your new granddaughter, Morven."

Half a world away, Morven's grandparents coo. The picture mosaics, the sound burbles.

"Sorry, Dad? Connection's blippy."

"… said, that's an old family name."

"No! How lovely!"

"Let's see. Her great, great…" counting fingers "… great, great grandmother."

"We just wanted something different!"

"She'd have used the Gaelic form. Spoke nothing but, until she came south. I did Google it. *Mhor,* yes, that means great. And *beinn, beinn* is the word for mountain."

Sharon Telfer lives in East Yorkshire, in the north of England. She has won the Reflex Flash Fiction Prize and, twice, the Bath Flash Fiction Award. Her flash has been selected for the 2019 and 2020 'BIFFY50' lists, and for *Best Microfiction 2019*. Her debut flash fiction collection, *The Map Waits*, is published by Reflex Press in 2021. She is a founding editor of *FlashBack Fiction*, the online litmag showcasing historical flash, and tweets @sharontelfer.

WE SIT ON THE CEMENT of our grandfather's boxed garden and wait for the roll of an aftershock. The January air of California is the coldest we have known. Charcoal smolders white and turns to ash in the belly of the hibachi. Chili oil pools—thin and red—in the corners of an iron skillet. Jiichan's face is showered in sunspots; his eyes squint at a brown egg in his hand. We boil water in a tin kettle over the grates of the grill and Auntie makes rice the old-fashioned way. City camping, our grandmother calls it. The earthquake hit in the night. It shook dishes from cupboards. Brought bricks loose from the fireplace. There is no electricity; the phones are still down. We do not think of our house or our parents or the fights that also break dishes. Sirens moan in the distance.

Near the garden wall we crush cans because our grandfather asks us to. I place three cans in a row: two beer cans and a cola. My brother lifts a metal pipe—the width of a baseball, the length of a bat—and brings it down on each can. They crumple, one-by-one, into aluminum puddles, sticky to the touch. We hold discs up and try to spot the sun through creases in the metal. They are the moons of Jupiter, the suns of a new galaxy. My brother smashes his lips and makes the sound of spaceships. I hold two orbs, one to each corner of my head, and say I am a mouse. The kind that steals cubed cheese and never gets caught in the snap of a mousetrap.

My brother asks for more cans. I place them in a line. The crunch is satisfying. It makes him giddy; it makes him show more teeth. His hair, black like mine, falls in his eyes each time he brings the pipe to meet the ground. The aluminum scrapes cement as I peel them up and toss them into our bin. Our bin fills. It feels like hundreds. They spin like tops, clink like treasure. The ground shakes, a soft rumble, a gentle sway. We barely notice. We are not afraid. We are a factory. We are making coins, filling a vault. It is the time when we feel most like one and half children rather than two. Twins, the kind joined at the crook of their necks or along the line of their hips. We shake the barrel for our grandmother. We beat its sides. Baba, we say, look at them shimmer. She runs her fingers through our hair and tells us we did good. She tells us to wash up, to come and eat.

We eat from blue camping bowls. Jiichan wraps rubber bands around our hashi and we spear sausage and nibble at the edges. We sit, shoulders touching, rice stuck to shirt collars and the sides of our faces. We lean together, our arms pushing hard into the other. Tell them, you tell them, our weight seems to say. We wish for one more day. We wish for more chili-red eggs and bonito flakes. We wish our house had a garden, tall and green like Jiichan's. We do not know how to tell them that we wish to stay, that we would be good kids if they kept us. The kind of kids that would listen, that would wash before dinner. The kind of kids that would crush cans as long as they would like. We are still and quiet. We listen to the sirens grow close and loud.

Jacqui Reiko Teruya received her MFA from Boise State University where she taught fiction and served as the Associate Editor for *The Idaho Review*. Her story "How to Spot a Whale" was winner of *The Masters Review's* 2018 Summer Flash Fiction Contest, and was selected for *Best Small Fictions 2020* (Sonder Press). Her story "Every Bird a Rival" was the second-place finalist for the 2019 *CRAFT* Short Fiction Prize judged by Elizabeth McCracken, and she is the recipient of the 2020 Glenn Balch Award judged by Hester Kaplan. Her work has appeared in *Best Small Fictions 2020, The Masters Review, CRAFT,* and *Passages North*. She lives in Boise, Idaho where she is currently at work on a novel.

VIOLET AFTER THE DIVORCE, wanting for newness. Deciding to leave England, to go somewhere else. To go to Mexico, Honduras, and Nicaragua. Violet in an aeroplane on her own. Violet walking on the smooth floors of the airport.

Violet as expat, migrant. Moving to Granada, Nicaragua, learning Spanish properly this time. Violet taking lovers, taking walks, taking painting-classes, taking another shot at life, and then another. Violet becoming freckled. Her hair greying. Violet taking a long hard look at herself. Violet liking herself.

Violet visiting Masaya Volcano National Park. Violet loving that place. Seeing the lava. Laughing on the bus down, even past the chicken factory stink. Violet's big teeth catching the sunlight when she laughed. Violet meeting somebody called Sofia, speaking with her. Violet and Sofia taking walks together, taking tea together, crying together, cooking for each other.

Violet and Sofia drinking Maracuja juice on their balconies. Violet and Sofia making love, sometimes. Sofia dancing to the BeeGees and Violet snorting hot tea, laughing. Sofia dancing more when Violet smiled, and then even more when Violet was quiet. Violet reading the news. Violet trying to understand. Sofia and Violet talking about Ortega.

Violet beginning to feel very tired. Violet trying to read long books. Violet not reading, and not going outdoors very much at all. The sun slipping through the sides of Violet's blinds, lighting her living room through curtains. Violet emailing her family with silly pictures, jokes from the internet, anything to say hello.

Violet feeling very tired, one day. Opening her curtains, and looking out at green. Violet not opening her curtains the next day. The last day. Violet feeling very slow and very tired. Violet lying on the floor, tired and in pain and watching a lizard climb the wall the whole afternoon, it felt like. The lizard flickering. Violet dying on the cool floor, in the afternoon, with light coming in through the closed yellow curtains. Violet found, hours later.

Violet dead.

Violet as email login, as lost password book, address book, phone call. Violet mourned. Violet laid out on a strange bed. Violet in an urn on Sofia's lap on the bus. In Sofia's hands, against her body as she walked. Violet in the green of the National Park. Violet in Sofia's palm on the slope of the volcano. Violet as smoke on the breeze. Ash. Violet as empty urn. Taken home. Violet as volcanic glass, strands, strung across the landscape, like pale hair.

Phoebe Thomson works in a school in South London. She recently graduated from an MA in Creative & Life Writing at Goldsmiths, University of London, which she completed through the Isaac Arthur Green scholarship. Her writing has appeared in publications including *Litro Online, The Mays, Eyot, Cadaverine Magazine, It's Freezing in LA!*, and Vivienne Westwood's *Climate Revolution Pamphlet.*

I'M ONLY GOING TO take one, she said, already a guilty edge to her voice, as if some part of her felt it was wrong to take even one and she was rationalizing, anticipating my condemnation of her.

But less than a minute later, she found another one she liked and quickly picked it up and said, one more's okay, a rhetorical question posed to no one in particular. She nodded slightly in the direction of her daughter and said, just one for me and one for her, that's it and suddenly it seemed as if she'd adopted C for the sole purpose of moments like this, to be allowed to take one more of something when she was already pushing her limit, as if her daughter existed to double her quota, to increase two-fold her right to possess things. Then again, to raise a child requires selflessness, perhaps even a relinquishment by half of one's self and to raise a child alone, as she had, required more sacrifice still. I couldn't help but think that if every person who visited the beach took two rocks, by year's end there wouldn't be any rocks left.

So when she said one for her and one for C, I felt prematurely relieved, not knowing that within seconds she would pick up a third rock, this one rose-colored and gray with a band of white around its circumference, this one as big as the first and second combined. Like a gambler who slides one stack of chips into another with a bang, she knocked two of the rocks together and said which one, as if she were planning to adhere to her second self-imposed limit and choose between them. The rocks made a sound like two pool balls colliding; I half expected to hear an eight ball rolling into a leather drop pocket but there was nothing except her voice saying, in reference to her latest acquisition: it feels so good in my hand, like it was meant to be held. She held the rose-gray rock in her left hand and the first two awkwardly in her right before abruptly thrusting all three into her jacket pockets.

Should we go back, she asked, glancing in the direction of our daughters. Sure, I said, and we walked back ungracefully over the rocks. I was slightly alarmed by the rapid escalation of her desire and its fulfillment, her instant disregard for the limits she herself had set. Then she said, what I really want is a bigger rock, which confounded me because in fact I'd just been marveling at how very big the rocks were that she'd put in her pockets, at how very large her appetite for them had been. I felt a wave of guilt for being a resident of the area who had invited her there, only to passively witness her taking rocks from the beach as if they were owed to her, as if the earth were at last making amends for crimes it had committed against her. She seemed not to think of it as taking but as replenishing. I did nothing to discourage her from taking the first or second or third rock. I simply watched, surprised, as she took them. In truth, I was tired of correcting white people's behavior, tired of functioning as a moral compass on their journeys through the wilderness of life.

She wanted a beach with sand so we drove to one that had a long jetty made of beautifully colored boulders. We walked out to the end and I said jokingly, well here are some bigger rocks but even as I laughed, I beheld a horrifying image of her hiring a crane to lift one of the most beautiful boulders out of the beach and into her truck and her driving away with it, taking it back to the city with her. I felt an acute sense of relief when this didn't happen. As we were leaving, I saw a slim, blue-gray rock bearing a delicate line of white—like a jet stream—across its front and, because she was especially fond of striped rocks, I bent down to show it to her, naively assuming she had finished plundering the town and she exclaimed, oh it's a very preppy one!

And without deliberating or making any effort to appear to be struggling to decide, she put the rock in her pocket with the others. I was startled and speechless and prayed, in my tortured, Catholic way, that the ghosts of the land would perceive my speechlessness not as passivity or weakness but as a silence I had observed in their honor and I wondered, between the two of us, who was worse.

Jennifer Tseng is an award-winning poet and fiction writer who believes in Kundiman forever. An assistant professor of literature and creative writing at University of California, Santa Cruz, you can find her on Instagram @TsengIsland.

MOM HAS AN ENTIRE fortress of pillows that she readjusts around her body.

"Barricading my skin against bedsores. Stay in one place for too long and you'll have to order another ass from Walgreens." Amber prescription bottles layer her bedside table. She marks the empties with a black X, doesn't throw them away until a refill has been secured.

Rustling toes mow through bed sheets as Mom drags up another mini-vodka with her feet. The bottomless cascade of that clear liquid is her Niagara Falls. She is queen of the mini-island. Bottles are stashed away in pockets, beds, pillows, shoes, drawers, seat cushions. She buys tiny airplane-size bottles and layers the counter with them at the Walgreens every Monday, Tuesday, Wednesday, and Thursday.

"I'm not a weekender," she tells the clerk. "The Friday cattle who line up here are absurd, like accountants and flags." No matter who's behind the register, Mom is told that the larger bottles are much cheaper. She's not an idiot. She loads up her empty purse with them, holds her hand up to her mouth as though it's a secret and whispers to the clerk, "Hide the evidence. You get it, right?" Every time they laugh as though this is some kind of code that every customer, whether living in a cardboard box or a three-story house with kids doesn't access.

"Elvirus, I've been calling you," she says, as though I can't hear the wheels of her guttural, somnolent chant, rutting over and over in my head.

"We're going shopping. Light Mom a cigarette and get her a glass of ice for her vodka." She doesn't call me by my chosen name and speaks in third person after a few drinks. "Don't forget her lemon, Elvine," she thrums through a bloom of smoke.

By the time I get back with her glass, she's dressed in one of her slinky 70s dresses.

This mimicry exhibits all the features of someone's mom, but not mine. My mom only goes out for liquor. Her hair is combed. She isn't wearing her shredding nylon nightgown, with coffee-splotched stains and cigarette holes anymore.

I stare in the mirror. I still look like her kid. My bangs are crooked and I wear stagnant knock-offs with shoulder pads, budding breasts polyp through Mom's darts, pleated jean skirts and shiny pink, green and red blouses with moving motifs of lava lamp patterns, fringe and bell-bottoms from the pioneer days of Mom's closet. I have a gift for reassembling the backwash material with scissors and safety pins.

"Do we need to lock the door?" Mom searches her purse for a key she doesn't possess, as we walk out into infested air, thick with all the lives before it.

Mom and I slog through Harwood Avenue to catch a bus five blocks away. She wavers on a slight incline with her head and upper torso two steps ahead of the rest of her. She doesn't drive anymore. I was eleven when I drove us home after Mom had one of her panic attacks, slammed over a curb into the yard of someone's rummage sale. She didn't hit anybody, but faces unhinged from the broken-down armoire, bicycles, toolsets, clothes, toys and astrology books they'd been rummaging through.

Mom's hands were claws. Too much white hovered around the persecuted gray of her eyes. I had to unclench her fingers from the steering wheel and sit on top of her. When we got home, she shut the door to her room and didn't come out for a few days. Dad whispered, 'menopause', but I knew this was no kind of pause.

We got off the bus in front of the 'old bag' second-hand store.

"These clothes are married to a history you can feel. They didn't come from cheap labor in China. Check the labels," Mom says.

I'm fourteen, don't check labels. I rake through racks to find something normal that will fit me. Some lady with a skin-rippled overlip keeps threading silent eye-pong accusations in my direction as she folds sweaters and talks to the woman behind the counter. They have the exact same haircut. "A mutt is a mutt," she says. "You don't have any idea what you're getting. You remember that guy who had the same mutt for like ten years and they find him mauled in his backyard. I mean, that's the chance you take when you go to one of those shelters. With a pedigree, you can check out the parents of the litter and know what you're bringing home." The other lady looked bored like she'd heard this shit before. Overlip glanced over at me. "You can only take six items in the dressing room, honey. Six." She held up six ringed fingers.

Mom was already in a dressing room. I could see the maxi dresses looped over the door. It was either nightgowns or slinky dresses and I loved when she dressed up even when she wasn't going anywhere. That meant Mom was back in the world with us.

This place wasn't an easy score. The women were checking my every move. "Here, honey, let me help you. What size are you? Six?" So much for a free one. Mom never helped. She wasn't the Mom who talked with women. She could care less what transpired between us. Her universe placated one being. Mom bought me a pair of jeans and some sandals and said yes to all the dresses. After we got back on the bus and walked the few blocks to get home, Mom unzipped the dress she was wearing and had two more on underneath. She ripped them off. "That feels much better. I was getting hot. Honey, can you get me a few lemons?"

"You stole those dresses?"

"No one else could have pulled these dresses off, Elvatross, let's be definitive. I was saving the ladies a few hangers."

Meg Tuite is author of a novel-in-stories, *Domestic Apparition* (San Francisco Bay Press), a short story collection, *Bound By Blue,* (Sententia Books) *Meet My Haze* (Big Table Publishing), won the Twin Antlers Collaborative Poetry award from (Artistically Declined Press) for her poetry collection, *Bare Bulbs Swinging,* as well as five chapbooks of short fiction, flash, poetic prose, and multi-genre. She teaches workshops and online classes through Bending Genres and is an associate editor at *Narrative Magazine.* Her work has been published in over 600 literary magazines and over fifteen anthologies including: *Choose Wisely: 35 Women Up To No Good.* She has been nominated twelve times for the Pushcart Prize, won first and second place in *Prick of the Spindle* contest, five-time finalist at *Glimmer Train,* finalist of the Gertrude Stein award and 3rd prize in the Bristol Short Story Contest. She is also the editor of eight anthologies. Her blog: http://megtuite.com.

HORSE MOUTH AND AQUARIUMHEAD

LOST BALLOON

elizabeth turner

THE WOMAN WITH THE horse mouth sighs; she tries delicately, but with that mouth, whatever comes out is a snort. Her gait is even rather equine—her head posts up and down as she strides. She is waiting for the man with the aquarium head—no further instructions other than *you'll know him when you see him,* and if he's been given any instructions about her, they'd be the same. She doesn't know what an aquarium head will look like—rectangular with attachments? Like the treasure chest at the bottom of many tanks? But when he finally arrives, she knows. His head is green tinted glass, like something found on the beach, and beautiful. He's filled with water weeds, wavy grasses, fish darting about, and behind all that was a pair of moony human eyes. She whinnies, trying to portray a sense of recognition and excitement, but she knows that all he probably sees are her yellowing teeth. He takes her hand and leads her away. *I am walking down the street with a man with an aquarium head!* she thinks, and then wonders how he breathes. When he turns his head to look for cars, she sees the gills pinkly flapping behind his ears. She blushes above her horsey snout and shoves a sugar cube in her mouth. She wonders how he eats, and where they are going. The man with the aquarium head takes them up a hill and down another to a bench overlooking the city; smog curls around the middles of buildings like tutus. She is sweating a little and bends to drink from a hose placed to fill a communal dog bowl. Then he hands her a book—*Spells to Counteract.* He pats the seat next to him. On a small pad of paper, he writes, *how did it happen to you?* and pushes it towards her. The woman with the horse mouth ruffles the pages, sighs again, and dollops them with greenish spit. *Work. Jealousy,* she writes. *I dated the boss. I didn't know there were witches there.* The man with the aquarium head nods and writes again, *Everyone was a witch? No,* she scrawls. *Just two. A man and a woman. We had a company performance of A Midsummer Night's Dream.* Bubbles pop at the top of his head as he starts to laugh. The woman with the horse mouth begins to laugh, too; she whinnies and snorts.

They didn't even get the right animal! The man with the aquarium head reaches into a pocket and pulls out a canister. He shakes it at his new friend. Standing up, she unlatches the top of his head, and the greenish glass sparkles in the sun. She sprinkles in flakes of food. The bench is in the shade and the city fuzzes in the late afternoon. She knows just when to stop.

Elizabeth Horner Turner's work has been published in *Cutbank*, *Fairy Tale Review*, *Gulf Coast*, *Lost Balloon*, *Pink Plastic House*, and *semicolon literary journal*, among other journals. She's been previously selected for inclusion in *Best Small Fictions*, and awarded scholarships to attend the Sewanee Writers' Conference and Tin House Writer's Workshop. Her chapbook, *The Tales of Flaxie Char*, was published through dancing girl press. She lives in San Francisco and can be found online: @lhornert.

nothing, nothing can be more bitter
than the sea I carry inside, alone and blind,
the ancient Oedipus sea groping me
for all ages,
when my blood wasn't yet mine,
when my skin grew on someone else's skin
when someone was breathing for me as I wasn't yet born.
—Xavier Villaurrutia

THE POSTMARK TOLD ME the letter took only a week to reach me. Inside was a photo of Álvaro's painting. On the back it read, "Come." I stared at the image for a long time: a twilit sea with the dying sun shining on small wave crests. It wasn't at all a typical landscape to promote tourism. In the center of the canvas, a stout tree sprouted in pitch-dark waters—as if they were contaminated.

It wasn't just any tree. A ceiba born and grown among the waters, with tall branches soaring heavenward. A sacred symbol native to my old lover's hometown. An island surrounded by a strange black ocean. According to ancient beliefs, the ceiba was a portal to thirteen heavens.

My fingers traced the letters beckoning me: "Come." The caress woke something deep inside me.

I put away the photo without even planning a trip. As I languished in the eighth month of pregnancy, the same malaise ran through me every day. Two beings were brewing inside me, the child and the stranger I became. I stood in front of the mirror to scrutinize my reflection.

Every month, something changed. Something became different. Something was left behind. I lived incognito in an uncertain body.

I met Álvaro years ago when he came to exhibit his paintings. Our affair lasted during his few days' stay in Mexico. Afterward, we wrote to each other. I promised him I'd make a trip to his island. He assured me he'd return—we made efforts to turn the sea separating us into a retractable space, as if we could adjust its size for our benefit.

Álvaro once told me the Caribbean wasn't the same in his village. It scared him there. I chuckled incredulously. For me, the Caribbean meant the turquoise waters of Isla Mujeres or Tulum. He insisted it wasn't the same and glanced at me as if he knew something I didn't.

That sea ended up lingering between us.

After the initial photo, a more palpable sample of the painting came in the mail. A piece of canvas with the ceiba bursting. From then on, every three or four days, more pieces arrived.

I began wondering why he sent these. Perhaps I'd brought it on myself: I'd beckoned my old lover. I spent my time longing to be purely one and indivisible. Freedom had that brown face and hands scented with the aroma of sea. As landscapes with palm trees crossed my mind, I recalled the smell of oil, the sound of the breaking waves. Fragments of Álvaro's love.

My OBGYN had told me I could keep working and do my normal activities. But after a sneeze, I couldn't hold my pee. I didn't feel like going out.

I thought about Álvaro and his island to get away from myself, from my house, from my husband's cheesy requests. Apparently undaunted, he endured my mood swings with the condescending smile of a husband who tolerates his pregnant wife's temporary insanity. At night, I rolled over to my side with my back to him and hugged a long pillow which I placed between my legs. Something grew between us. A darkness. A silence.

Sometimes the swimmer in my womb made a movement like a delicate wave or a precise nudge. Then we were a larva together, waiting for the moment when my baby would break out of my body.

When I began locking myself in the nursery, my husband thought I was finally waking up from my lethargy. He'd already reproached me for my indifference, my lack of interest in preparing that space. I told him that the packages I received were for the nursery's decoration and forbade him to come in. He happily promised he'd not intervene in my creative work. "Surprise us," he said. He said "us" to refer to him and our baby, even though he knew how much it bothered me when he talked like that. They had an autonomous existence, foreign to me. They'd already pierced the walls of my uterus.

I shoved the cradle aside and piled up the baby shower presents, toys, and everything else in one corner. Sometimes my husband knocked on the door and tried to peek inside, but he was content to give me new gifts, which I put where they didn't get in the way.

He'd say, "We've got our first swimsuit" or "We bought a sterilizer." He cast his curious look. I snatched the gifts from his hands.

I began putting together Álvaro's marine puzzle on the floor. I followed my instinct. I wasn't interested in reproducing the painting in the photo. Instead, I wanted to create my own landscape from those black waves, barely touched by the sun. I scanned in all directions, trying to guess where the ceiba would sprout.

Piece by piece, that dark tide continued to arrive in the mail. I didn't expect the painting to be so large. I was no longer able to guess where the shore or limit would be. I lost myself at sea, with my legs sore and swollen from my baby's weight. All my joy was in the shady nursery, in the reflections of the ocean light climbing up the walls. I needed every corner, even the windows, for the ceiba's arrival. The same thing happened to my baby. In the last days of the ninth month, its movements were less frequent: it ran out of space.

One afternoon when I was alone, I called the apartment super. I handed him lots of toys and clothes.

Álvaro's shipments ceased. Nothing of the sacred tree. Maybe the thirteen skies wouldn't open for me, but I'd built the arteries of that sea, its new, burning heart. Its sway was lulling me. I was able to alleviate my anguish of not belonging to my own body or its fruit. I dozed off in the last rays of the afternoon sun and the warm breeze that brought salty aromas.

I left the bedroom to do an online search for that exact place where a clean, dark sea was located. I needed an explanation from a marine biologist. I'd postponed the search until now, but I really wanted to know. Images of beaches with black marble benches appeared on the computer screen. That was why the water seemed contaminated. Wide waves looked tainted with oil, but they were clean. As my curiosity was sated, almost immediately I was paralyzed by an electric bite. The pain ran down my back and tortured my groin, opened a canal with a thousand daggers.

Like a tree beset by the storm, I arched my body, picking up my sap and tying my branches in a trembling embrace to contain myself.

The swimmer in my womb began kicking and breaking through with a painful need for air, for space. He fought to break the dikes that had contained him without love all these days. The source of his life was broken. He reached the end of his journey and opened a lightless portal in the middle of a marble night while liquid dripped between my thighs swirling in dark waves.

Socorro Venegas is a Mexican writer and editor. Her latest book is a short story collection called *La memoria donde ardía* (2019). She was a resident writer at The Writers Room in New

York and received a fellowship from the Fondo Nacional para la Cultura y las Artes y del Centro Mexicano de Escritores. She has managed editorial projects for the Fondo de Cultura Económica and the Universidad Nacional Autónoma de México. Translations of her short stories have appeared in various venues, including *Bodega, Compressed,* and *Sudden Fiction Latino.*

Toshiya Kamei holds an MFA in Literary Translation from the University of Arkansas. His recent translations have appeared in *Clarkesworld, The Magazine of Fantasy & Science Fiction,* and *Samovar.*

1.

SATURDAY, I SAT TRYING to thread the Serger, which takes four spools and had just run out of one, four spools and I'd tangled the other three. I'd get through one color-coded map, balancing tweezers, wrapping thread through pullies in a way that made me nostalgic for Newton, lost in the cause-and-effect of it, before you got tired of waiting and barreled into me, pulling at my hand with one of yours, balancing a bottle of milk, and almost saying, "bed." So I'd lay with you for a couple of minutes and get up and try again. We did this until I had the machine working.

2.

I asked my mother to teach me to sew, but she said she didn't have the patience for it and never bothered. She let me pull safety pins of elastic through casings (I know the word, "casing"), pulled cotton dresses over me, inside-out, and pinched and pinned until they knew the area under the curves of me and only me. She did this when I was two. When I was seventeen. She did this to my wedding dress in lace and satin, and it was stunning. She hemmed the dress by hand because she didn't trust the machine not to revolt.

3.

After the divorce, I mailed the dress back to my mother, with a pad of expensive paper. It never arrived. Of course, it never arrived. Years later, I married your father in a pair of New Rocks, a button-down shirt, a short skirt, and a bit of silver in my hand.

4.

At daycare, a woman who reminded me of my grandmother taught me to sew, by hand and in overlocking strokes, the same technique my mother used to hem. I've used this stitch to bind books, but I'm fine hemming dresses on the Brother. And sewing on knit, too. Still, I always fold the rough edge under first, so the line is clean from all directions.

5.

You've never been to daycare, because neither your father nor I can suffer it. Instead, we have $56 in the checking account, and he's given up Los Angeles for a lake with fields, limitless in three directions.

6.

A man I loved but did not marry—a man I loved, but who was not your father—gave me Calculus, Russian poets and an old metal Singer. He didn't know to teach me how to keep a seam from fraying. But velocity, acceleration—how to repurpose anything until it was both well-used and new, and how to say "light" but mean "birth"—these things I learned from him.

7.

I wanted the Serger working because I'm afraid of dying on the plane and leaving you motherless. I am terrified that you will grow up without me, never knowing me, always approaching but never reaching, lonely and unravelling. I wanted to ruffle long sleeves into a summer skirt and hear you say "shirt" and pull at the marker-covered clearance-rack tee that you were wearing until I put the dress on you, right-way out.

8.

I top-stitched the sleeves to hide the four-colored scar of the Serger seam holding them to the dress, but for some reason, they won't lay right. They flop over your shoulders constantly: There I am. There I am again. I let you wear it anyway.

Sherre Vernon (she/her/hers) is a seeker of a mystical grammar and a recipient of the Parent-Writer Fellowship at MVICW. She has two award-winning chapbooks: *Green Ink Wings* (fiction) and *The Name is Perilous* (poetry). Readers describe Sherre's work as heartbreaking, richly layered, lyrical and intelligent. To read more of her work, visit www.sherrevernon.com/publications and tag her into conversation @sherrevernon.

There Are a Thousand Ways to Love a Snake but Only One Way to Kill It

shreya vikram

SMOKELONG QUARTERLY

MY DAUGHTER'S HAIR IS black. It gleams with oil, hot under the sun, hot in my fingers. When I braid it, I lace the sections so tightly her scalp bares itself, dark brown and naked. Each time a strand loosens from its root, I rub it in between my palms so that it forms a ball, which I hold in between my toes. When I am done, the ball is half the size of a fist. *Mama it hurts,* she says, whining softly, holding her scalp as if to protect it from my hands, but she should know better by now.

My daughter's hair is black and browns under the sun if she exposes it in the summers. I keep her in, I boil sesame oil with fenugreek seeds and curry leaves. I pour hot spiced oil onto her scalp. I dig my fingers in and press till she stiffens and strains against my touch. In the bathroom, she sits at my feet, her naked body hunched while I scrub shikakai into the oiled mass of her hair. Back and forth, back and forth her head bobs as I scrub, as if it is only vaguely attached to her neck. The shikakai burns her eyes if she keeps them open. *My eyes,* she shouts, scrambling for water so she can rinse the burning from her face. *I can't see, I can't see.* She is a blinded girl, a needing one. She should have kept them closed. Keep still, I say, taking the water away from her and pouring them over her eyes myself. Her face is turned up towards me; she can see again.

My daughter's hair is a black sheet that falls to her hips, browning under the sun, a living breathing thing. After I braid her hair, my daughter kneels; she presses both her hands together, her head bowed, then places her forehead onto the floor in prayer. May your hair never stop growing, I tell her. This is what I pray for my daughter. That she may rest in her grave, her hair a joyless growing mass, cocooning her corpse in black.

My daughter's hair is a black straight corpse that falls to her hips, browning under the sun, a living singing thing, with life. When I present my daughter to the family, I let them awe over her hair, I turn her around so they may see the length of her braid, admire its thickness. Yes, I say. Yes, she has been blessed. Of course, she will never cut it, how could she? Shikakai and oil, that's what it needs. Yes, I wash it myself, I do. I braid it each day. Look at it, half the length of her body and the thickness of her fist, heavy with oil and snaking down her back, an alive thing.

My daughter's hair is fine, easily torn, a black straight sheet that snakes to her hips, pulling at her scalp, browning under the sun, a living dying thing. When there are lice burrowed in the black, we sit for hours underneath the sun, browning. I use a comb with bristles as sharp as knives to hunt for the pests. They tumble onto my palms and I split their bodies in half with my nails. When there is a particularly big one, I show them to her and we awe over it together. Her scalp is free of lice afterwards, streaked with wounds inflicted by the comb. There is no beauty without disaster, I tell her. I peel the ugly skins of overripe pomegranate, point out the crystal-seeds that fall out. I place them on her tongue, one by one. Do you want this or not? What will you do for it, daughter? The lice lay dead beside us, browning. My fingers are stained with red by the time we are done.

My daughter's hair is parted down the middle, a black straight snake that slips to her hips, browning under the sun, a lying dying thing. Once, she asks me to undo the part, to smooth her hair back, to forego the braids and let her hair sway in a ponytail. I boil the oil, I scald her scalp, I scrub the shikakai into her eyes. What are you thinking, I ask her. What are you thinking.

My daughter's hair is cut. Look what it has attracted, this lying dying thing. Yes, I warned her not to do it. Yes, I showed her what happens to the women without hair, their barren scalps. Yes, I have tried to braid it, to soak it in oil and pull each tiny strand behind and tie it in place. My daughter sits where I have placed her, she faces the mirror and looks herself in the eye. Silently her hair grows, a headless snake, mask undone. A blinded girl, this one, dying under the sun.

Shreya Vikram is a writer based in India. A Dorothy West Scholar, she has been recognised by the Adroit Prizes for Prose and the Young Poets Network. Her work has appeared or is forthcoming in *Ruminate, Hobart, Mid-American Review, Rumpus* and elsewhere. She is a Submissions Editor at *Smokelong Quarterly.* You can find more of her writing at shreyavikram.com.

COFFEE LID THE COLOUR of a pinched lip, a spring so avoidant I'm attracted to it. This rain is wet-whispering a menacing taunt. Because a tornado took our barn in 1983, I am untethered by wind. Wind, like me, is too much. Too feminine. Too dramatic. I don't like the wind, I say, as I make origami hearts on the living room carpet with a kid who isn't mine. We bought the rug thick, so we could sink into it as a family on a Sunday afternoon. In this spring that is still winter, I order blush that arrives in a small white box, and the more I weigh the more lingerie I buy hoping to dizzy up with lace a desire the world doesn't feel. I pick up my phone between lines. I scroll to feel the weight of me lift. I know he's beside me but he isn't really. He's with his followers. I can never be as simultaneously far away and close as they are. I am just here, in parallel play, with our phones out, and our bodies on pause. The kid hands me a flat bronze heart, the wind throwing elbows outside.

Zoe Whittall's fourth novel *The Spectacular* will be out this fall with Penguin Random House in the U.S.. Her last novel *The Best Kind of People* was shortlisted for the Giller prize, and has been optioned by director Sarah Polley. Her previous novels include the Lamda-winning *Holding Still for as Long as Possible,* and debut *Bottle Rocket Hearts.* She has published three collections of poetry, *The Best Ten Minutes of Your Life, Precordial Thump,* and *The Emily Valentine Poems.* Her work has appeared in *Granta, Cosmonauts Ave, The Believer* and more. She is also a Canadian Screen Award-winning TV and film writer, with credits on *The Baroness Von Sketch Show, Schitt's Creek, Degrassi* and others. She lives in Toronto.

THE APOCALYPSE IN STAGES OR YOUR FIRST KISS

miranda williams

I. Terra Firma

THE END BEGINS WITH disintegration of the foundation. The ground, unnoticed until destroyed, crumbling like dried wedding cake. Grass and yellow desert shrubs peeled apart by warm sands and footprints, stripping the earth bare. Then, there's only dust covering the fevered flesh.

You are fifteen and you don't know who you are, but that's okay. He's going to tell you. You wear dresses the color of chewing gum, jeans that bind your legs like Saran wrap around sliced meat—you need to look hot but not slutty. You stand curled because boys like vulnerability. You thought you were a bouquet of flowers but you are only an empty glass vase.

II. Flora

Without the ground, the flowers flourish. They sink their vines into dark gaping crevices and slither until there is only mounds of verdant limbs, strangling the trees and smothering vegetation until it withers. Blossoms erupt from their skin, but the people devour them gratefully.

He arrives with honey coated hair and caresses of freckles. Sunflowers could grow from his palms and he exhales galaxies. You realize this is what you've been awaiting. He is in a band. You want to be his music. He plucks your vocal cords and presses the keys of your ribs and it is tantalizing. You're frantic for more. Can imagine foaming at the mouth. Reaching. Sprawling.

III. Fauna

The males of every species die first. And without them, the females riot. The bears claw at each other's wombs and the does grow antlers to tear through toughened fur. Nature turns herself into a jungle—sweat and war and blood. But then, there is peace and it is like they never fought.

On your first date, he picks you up in an old Corolla and it's somehow endearing. You are simmering in fruit-scented perfume and your arms are glazed with lotion. He flirts with the girl at the ticket counter and says she has pretty eyes. You boil. Through two hours of gunshots, headshots, bodyshots, you imagine all the ways you could hurt her. He takes your hand.

IV. Cultas

People don't panic. They thought it would end with zombies, aliens, robots but it is only earth. So, botanists smear pesticides on choking branches, zoologists shove articles of femininity and hysteria, and the others stampede to the office or tend to children, ignoring all the collapse.

He pulls you to the backseat of his car and smacks your lips with his. You start with eyes open but close them because that's how it's supposed to be. He tastes like nothing. Just wet—sticky summer dew or saliva. You're stuffed with tongue and teeth as he presses your skull to the window. Leftover needles where he shaved burn your cheeks. Flies writhe in your stomach.

V. Plaga

They call it the living dead, body-snatcher, soul-sucker. Paralysis is the first symptom. Motionless vessels litter the streets. Are they people or only bodies? Parts they don't need turn to ash: nose, legs, arms, eyes. Then, they are but organs, and those rot too. It all returns to earth.

The car's seats are soft and worn. You focus on that. Your hands are cold and splotchy like old vegetables. He takes one of them and puts it on his dick: you can feel it through his jeans. His fingers crawl up your shirt and seize your breasts, pinching and pulling the tissue. You stay still because you are supposed to want love. His mouth never leaves yours. You are being eaten alive.

VI. Mortem

The survivors are few. They roam the earth like plastic bags in wrathful wind. The only sounds now are buzzing and billowing. Buildings crumble to piles of splintered wood and abandoned books and rusted billboards. Then, there is only earth, but day and night still continue.

He pulls away. Crimson gloss stains his lips, and his milky sweat melts with yours. He is smiling when he says "that was fun," and he puts your hair behind your ear. It gives you hope. He drops you off at your house and waits until you've unlocked your front door. He doesn't speak to you again, but you keep grasping. Grasping at nothing. Like a child reaching for fairytales.

Miranda Williams is a twenty-two-year-old writer from New Mexico who now resides in Arizona. She received her BA and MA in English Literature from Arizona State University where her research focused on feminist and queer theory. Her work appears in *Blue Earth Review, Five on the Fifth, Third Point Press,* and *Ghost Parachute,* among others, and has been nominated for the Pushcart Prize. Additionally, she is the co-founder of *Ember Chasm Review,* and is currently writing a novel inspired by the movements of jellyfish, Rachel Ruysch's paintings, and the horrors of working at a movie theatre. Find her on Instagram @mirandaiswriting.

IN MY STUDY—WHERE I keep all the things I cherish most—there are two distinct times that I think of as the golden hour: once in the evening, when the sun picks up the dust in the air before nightfall, and once in the heart of the night, when if I'm still awake the world begins to feel slippery and narrow, confined to the cast of the lamp above my desk. Last night, I stayed for the transition from one to the other, waiting through the long fallow period of early darkness—too close to daylight to count as a golden hour, too sober—with a book. I kept the lights on in the room, watching the sky turn pale and then dark. Around midnight I grew restless and stood to sort through some of the remaining boxes and folders stacked around the periphery of the room. Eventually I came to a sheath of Sarah's contact sheets. By then it was much later, so I turned off the lights and brought the stack over to my desk to sort through in the familiar, lonely cocoon of the evening.

Though, already—a lie. Or a set of half-truths. Lately I have grown more vigilant about the obligation I feel even when I'm alone, to go back over the past with a needle, undoing and re-embroidering. Came to suggests an accident, when I have been nothing but deliberate in the Solomonic task of dividing our apartment, parceling up the things that are Sarah's and mine to hand over, or file away, or throw out. Lonely suggests an ache, but sometimes I suspect that I'm most at home in solitude, that for all of my years in the company of friends and lovers I have sometimes kept them around for the heightened sanctuary of calm I feel in the hours of their absence.

A couple of days ago, I called my mother's friend, a woman whom I met the first time when I was thirteen. At the time, she lived in Vancouver, in a blue-walled apartment cluttered with photographs of her children. Her home was densely furnished, as if she had taken care to fill every open space with some token of her existence—while she and my mother embraced, I sat on the living room couch between the department store pillows, feeling suffocated. She was a piano teacher, with a few students who were studying at Juilliard or Eastman and one who had gone on to become quite successful. While we were there, she and my mother sat down at her upright to improvise a duet based on a song they thought I would remember, a Japanese children's tune they had both learned growing up. Though I did not recognize the notes, I was startled by their ease together and their virtuosity—my mother was then an accountant at a small firm that mostly worked with hospitals and charities, and, though I was aware that she had a history before this particular life, I had thought of it as a phase that she had passed through before arriving at a more solid and well-defined present. Before we flew home, the woman gave me a stack of postcards, one of which I have beside me even now, in the top drawer of my desk. Over the years, we kept in touch—I sent her letters, mostly about the mundane dramas of schoolwork or friends, and she replied with advice and worries from her own life, writing with a candor and honesty that I now recognize as surprising. She had no daughters, despite trying three times before her divorce. For many years she sent me dresses on my birthday until I told her that I had given up on gendered clothing, and then afterwards, she sent me hand-me-downs from her children—which I imagined her taking out of their closets over the protests of her three sons.

I called her in part because we had not spoken for some time, and in part because after Sarah moved out I was fine for three days and then went utterly to pieces. By the time I left for college, we had become a form of confessional to each other: she called me after her eldest son, who had spiraled suddenly and precipitously into a depression, had tried to jump off the second floor of a nearby parking garage; she had gone to visit him in the hospital, where he had been taken after fracturing his pelvis, and she called me from a payphone in the hallway, to tell me that she felt a sense of disembodied irritation at the thought of bringing him home, where he would be even more of her responsibility. At a different low, I told her that every path I had taken seemed to be bottoming out, useless. She laughed into the phone and said that when her most successful student had played, for the first time, at Carnegie Hall, she had bought a ticket but walked out before the actual performance: she felt a sour sense of failure even just looking at the ten-foot-tall poster with his name.

Catherine Wong studies language and computation at MIT. Catherine's fiction and audio has shown up in *Shenandoah*, *Bayou*, *The Chicago Quarterly*, and *Nancy from WNYC*.

ON THIS VISIT HOME, Little Uncle has a sparkling white Nissan SUV. Last time it was a used sedan; the time before, a motorcycle. One day, I pile in with my aunts and uncles, riding shotgun because they insist.

The village has paved these roads since my last visit. Paved might be a generous description: my head keeps bumping against the ceiling of the car. We speed past a gray-haired woman behind a wheelbarrow, her face leathery from the sun. Little Uncle honks every few seconds at chickens, children on bikes, men with canes. We pass a woman about my age driving a sleek car. The sunroof is open, and the wind accentuates her long hair. A man is in the passenger seat. None of my relatives comment. Perhaps a woman driving her man around is normal these days.

Little Uncle parks at the curb of a stranger's house in the middle of nowhere. Everywhere here looks like the middle of nowhere. Not until we take out the fireworks and fake money instead of the fruit and food from the trunk do I realize our destination. We are heading to an area overgrown with shrubs, with a gravel road to the right and two man-made fish ponds nearby. No fences or edifices mark this cemetery. We wade through weeds and reeds, the stalks scratching my bare legs. Although I am more than a head taller than my aunts, they move with a speed I cannot match. Their feet avoid the mushy spots in the grass; my sneakers are soaked within seconds.

At the first of the four tombstones, we form a semicircle. I recognize my last name at the top, but I can't read the characters that follow. Your great-grandfather is here, Little Uncle tells me. I do not know my great-grandfather's name, or anything else about him. I would ask, but I do not want to betray how little I know, or how little I will remember. On each person's tombstone is an entire family. The male descendants are listed on the right, the women to the left. My folks come twice a year, at least, on holidays for elders that don't exist in the States. Today is not one of those holidays. They are making this trip for me.

It is my second time, and still the ritual amazes me. *Grave sweeping.* My aunts and uncles grab the stacks of fake money and yellow squares of tissue paper. As with much of Chinese life, my family works with a duty and efficiency I admire. Their fingers dig into diamond-shaped holes within the squares for traction. Their wrists flick to rifle off stacks of paper at a time. Each rainbow-colored bill I try to toss flutters away, the faces of Chairman Mao flying too far from the tombstone. I am also too slow. I give half of my money to second aunt so they don't have to wait.

Little Uncle ignites the multicolored heap with his cigarette lighter. I am the only one who has to step away. The smoke stings my eyes, the paper curls up into smoke, the smoke into air, and the air into nothing. Little Uncle takes the end of the red accordion-shaped packet to the nub of his lighter. This time all of us retreat from the tombstone, Little Uncle plugging his ears before the impossibly loud popping. Fireworks are our music for respect.

We take turns to bow in front of the burning heap of multicolored paper. The husband of third aunt does not bend his knees as deeply as my other relatives do; he is not blood-related to my great-grandfather. I thrust my hips back and fling my arms especially high up, as with a chair pose in yoga. My limbs are too long and too awkward to be graceful.

When I turn around, my relatives are already stepping over the reeds. The next grave has my great-grandmother. The one after that is my grandfather's. My father didn't make it back in time from America, but he wired over money for the tombstone. It is among largest in the cemetery: shiny black marble, not the worn granite of the others. "Your grandfather would have been proud to know how tall you've become," my relatives say. When my second aunt picked me up from the train station, she asked: "Why don't you find yourself a nice girl here?" A tall man, especially an educated American, has his pick of women in China. I made my excuses. "Many Americans don't marry until their late thirties," I said. She didn't argue with me; she didn't insist that I was Chinese, claim me as her own. Instead she was speechless, unable to fathom how Western culture could so corrupt my family values.

Through the drop, burn, and firecracker ritual at each grave, I want to pull out my iPhone and snap a few pictures. It is not often that I come back to China. But I don't want to look like a tourist.

Either heat or boredom is getting to my relatives. They rifle away the money more quickly, letting ever-larger stacks fall from their hands. They bow their bodies up and down faster, as if we are in a video on 2x speed playback. At my grandmother's grave, the last of the four, there is not enough space for us to fit; her tombstone is hardly visible beyond the bush. Little Uncle backs away from the rest of us. He retreats to his cell phone. No one reacts. Following the lead of my other relatives, I do not bow at my grandmother's grave either. The shrubs have left too little room for her. My grandmother died years before I was born, after my grandfather had gone to work in a factory and she took charge of the farm. Allegedly, the neighbors killed her over a fight for the water to irrigate the rice fields.

My aunts chitchat as they throw the paper down. I understand enough of their local dialect to pick up on the gossip: which daughters have married, which ones are about to have children, these questions they keep asking me, the ones to which my answers do not change. No, no one, I have no plans. How many more years can my lies tide me over? My relatives are steadfast; they will always be happy to bring me back here, to my ancestors. The issue is with me, how long I can bear coming back, empty handed.

My shirt sticks to the sweat on my chest. Here we stand atop of the family we have lost, and here we hope for the family we might have, that I am to have. There is the space below my name on my grandfather's tomb, the lines I am to fill with my future wife and children.

Little Uncle waves to me. "Let's go." My phone buzzes. He was snapping pictures of us and uploading them to our family WeChat. In the photos, we have the same creases around our eyes. I am in black shorts and a loose T-shirt. My relatives show less skin, in pearls and polos and slacks, but they, too, are in Western clothes. At least in the picture, I blend in.

I wash my hands at the outdoor sink next to the car, but still my relatives surround my body. They pick off the burrs that escaped my notice, those that have buried themselves into my shirt. I take one in the palm of my hand. It looks like a black alien head, the ears ever so thin but well defined.

Victor Wei Ke Yang is a writer by way of China, Canada, and Kentucky. He is a 2020-2021 Boston Artist-in-Residence. His stories and essays appear in *The Boston Globe, Longreads, The Rumpus,* and *The Southern Review,* among others. He was a finalist for the Chicago Tribune's 2020 Nelson Algren Short Story Award. He graduated with an MFA in fiction from Boston University and is working on his first novel.

HEAVENS KNOW WELL THAT when I said I wanted to hit it big before 30, I did not mean to be hit by a car. That night, the driver had charged out onto the road from the canopy of mango trees beneath which a shed thrives on beer & aphrodisiacs served by women who paint themselves in defiance of the night. I shielded my eyes from the biting yellowness of the headlights and took a step away from the tarred path.

Perhaps I was not quick enough. The car sent me hurtling. I suspect that my stomach swallowed the screech of the car tyres against the road because I don't remember hearing one. A pain, sharp as a blunt knife, crept into my hip like an afterthought. The constellation danced before my eyes like fireflies. Silence blossomed in my head; the people pooled—each recommending whatever First Aid they remembered from Physical Education. Each outshouting each; their voices, like the sound of sandpaper over wood.

I woke up swimming inside my head. All the sounds I heard were as intelligible as the language of gargling.

For every time I opened my eyes afterwards, I embraced a bodied mirage: doctor peering; nurses shuffling with bees for hands; my brother bent over by the bedside like a mullah succumbing to sleep mid-prayer & finally, my right arm, much shorter, finishing as a bandaged stump.

For the rest of the days in clinic, I was assaulted by the smell of the toxic relationship between antiseptic and vomit in the hallways, and the optimism of the therapist who, with calculated gesticulation, chirped on about the cut being below elbow and about me not letting the stump limit me. I knew that he meant well—I still know it—but I also think things like that are easy to say when one has all of their hands to illustrate their point.

Abdulbaseet Yusuff is a Nigerian writer. His works appear or are forthcoming in *Brittle Paper, Rattle, Glass: A Journal of Poetry, Up The Staircase Quarterly, Pidgeonholes, MoonPark Review,* and elsewhere. He's contributing editor at *Eboquills.*

NONE OF HER CHILDREN have shown up for her birthday and Soraya sits at the window, watching the empty driveway, upright in the walnut wood chair that her father had ordered from the most expensive retailer in Lahore for her wedding, what was it fifty years ago, and ignores the hard-boiled egg and the orange and the glass of pomegranate juice on the tray in front of her, same tray she had carried soup and water to her mother on she can't even remember how long ago, feeling the burn from the heater on her small feet resting on the marble floor, and reaches for the single lovebird in the cage beside her—the silver coop with a blue bird her husband had given her on their twentieth anniversary with that sparkle in his eyes and a *Happy Anniversary, darling* even though it was the same year she had lost her mother and happy was the farthest thing from her mind but he had been feeling guilty, turned out, about his new, secret, wife and his affections had become louder and more elaborate until all three of her kids had started saying they wanted a love like their parents' and wasn't she so lucky and her heart had fluttered at the sight of the delicate bird feet trembling on the perch and she had believed she was lucky too but that bird had died that December and soon after her father was gone and then her marriage when the letter from her husband's new wife arrived which, even now, is pressed into an old copy of Sense and Sensibility on the bookshelf behind her, buried between her teaching notes, and which she had kept after all the deaths so every time she stood in front of the classroom of eager girls, the pages reminded her not to forgive her husband and to restrain the silly chirrups of teenage hearts by telling them everything died at its most beautiful, that they must believe only the words that slice the heart (truth was never meant to be kind) and which she glances at now, seeking that little blue edge that sticks out from between the pages as she holds the bird's neck gently between her knuckles and rubs her thumb against the red patch on its head nearly as soft as the hair on her daughters' heads when they were little, before they had layered on hair color and rebellion and shaved and cut and changed entirely how they looked in an effort, she feels still, to rid themselves of her, and she had been left with her son who was the only one who had remained loyal—that sweet thing, sitting quietly by her bed day after day after her husband moved out—and who, though he comes to see her less and less, pays for her to live now and had wanted to give her his pocket money then thinking it was the bird dying that had made her cry and cry and wrap her blankets around her as if she was building herself a cocoon, and who is across the city somewhere with a woman he has come to love more; he was meant to sit in the other chair beside her today, looking out the window with her as she told him about all the dreams she had when she was a child, how she had wanted to train the birds to deliver letters when she was young, how she wished her mother had warned her about endings, how she had given up the habit of looking forward and abandoned her yearly walk to the kitchen to hang the Scenes of Northern Pakistan calendar the maid and the cook so seemed to like and could he find a new one for them, and slowly her knuckles squeeze the small neck between them and with her other hand she holds the wings flapping strong and getting stronger—she knows they will be the strongest right before the end—until the claws scratching at her lap start to fail and she tells herself *this is just how life goes, Soraya, this is just how it is* and stares out the window. It is Tuesday, no Wednesday. Perhaps even Thursday. Tomorrow she will break off another small piece of gold from her wedding bracelets and ask the girl who brings her food to her to go to the market and buy another bird.

Hananah Zaheer is the author of *Lovebirds*, a flash chapbook from Bull City Press in 2021. Other writing has recently appeared in places such as *AGNI, Smokelong, Virginia Quarterly Review, McSweeney's Internet Tendency, South West Review, Alaska Quarterly Review* (with a Notable Story mention in *Best American Short Stories 2019*) and *Michigan Quarterly Review,* where she won the Lawrence Foundation Prize for Fiction. She is a fiction editor for *Los Angeles Review.*

(Basalt)

THE STONE GIRL APPEARS more air than mineral with her cavities and pores of hardened lava trapping dissolved gases, the aftermath of a volcanic eruption. Over time, she oxidizes into hematite, taking on a rust-red that mars her grey-black surface. When a child picks up one of her pieces from the dry stack rock wall surrounding a garden of mulch and hyacinths and drops it onto the driveway, not a single piece chips off.

(Travertine)

To some, the stone girl appears more fibrous and concentric, a cream-colored mass of calcium carbonate. They look at her and think yes, years ago, she precipitated to the bottom of a hot spring and now with the water evaporated, she emerges in solidarity, strong enough to forge ancient Roman temples and aqueducts.

(Something else)

Before the sculptor carves into her, he knocks off her limbs, positioning the point of a chisel against her elbow and swinging the mallet in one stroke. Her arm breaks off. When he is satisfied with the general shape, a stump with a few rough edges, he measures the width of her nose, the curve of her lips, the length of her eyelids with calipers, and draws lines marking the removal area. He softens his strikes so he can remove the small parts with precision—excess flesh in her cheeks, the bit of her temporal bone that protrudes a centimeter too far, the bump in her nasal bone. He pushes a riffler across her scalp and carves out locks of hair that extend past her shoulders. She has hair now.

He leaves the sculpture uncovered before retiring to bed, a twin-sized mattress on the floor, next to his toolbox of chisels and wall mirror.

The stone girl watches her reflection as the sculptor snores. She thinks she has never looked so symmetrical, so delicate, and she wonders if this is what having skin is like. Or maybe this newfound fragility is because she stays awake the entire night, waiting for the sun to strike at dawn, for its rays to heat her face.

When the sculptor wakes up the next morning, he notices a crack down the girl's face: a jagged line between her eyes, off-center and slanted, tearing through her philtrum and off to the edge of her chin—she resembles a Picasso painting. *I can work with this,* he thinks as he picks up his chisel and attempts to pivot his artistic muse—embrace the asymmetry, work with serrated and pointed and straight edges rather than curves that start and end at the same place. But when he strikes the mallet onto the end of the chisel, a chunk of her face cracks off, falls to the ground, crumbles to unevenly sized chunks and dust. The other half of her face stands upright, its remaining eye staring at him, as though to ask what he'd do next.

Lucy Zhang writes, codes and watches anime. Her work has appeared in *The Cincinnati Review, Hobart, West Branch* and elsewhere. Her work is included in *Best Microfiction 2021,* was a finalist in Best of the Net 2020 and long listed in the *Wigleaf* Top 50. Find her at kowaretasekai.wordpress.com or on Twitter @Dango_Ramen.

ESSAY

INCLUSION

AN INTERVIEWER ONCE ASKED me, "If flash fiction were an animal, which animal would it be?" I considered a chicken because you can peck at the stories. Perhaps a badger because short shorts sometimes have to be more tenacious than their larger brethren. I thought a fish was apt because tiny stories often swim together. I almost decided upon a cat because a cat can fit perfectly in your lap, and even as you pet it and listen to its purrs, it stares at you with a mysterious menace.

In the end, I decided upon a coyote that strangely appears in your backyard and stares into your kitchen window. You lock eyes, and the world is suddenly a little dangerous, a little less predictable. Something wild has briefly entered the safety of your domestic space and changed it forever with its feral threat. Perhaps my favorite metaphor for flash stories, though, comes from flash master Molly Giles: they are fireflies, flickering in the darkness of a summer night. The definition of numinous, otherworldly beauty. Ephemeral and captivating at once.

Of all of the forms of fiction, "flash fiction," which is typically defined as being a story less than 1,000 words, is the only one described with a metaphor. As James Thomas, the editor of several seminal anthologies of flash fiction, tells the story, he was talking with his wife about what to call these short stories of under 1,000 words. He'd been calling them "blasters," but that moniker didn't ring with any poetic allure. Right at that moment, a bolt of lightning struck, and the dark night lit up with a flash. "Call them flash," his wife said. And the name of a genre was born.

The irony is that flash, despite being the smallest of fictional forms, breeds sub-genres and an ever-flowing list of new names. Flash stories are often called miniatures, short shorts, or postcard stories. There is the drabble (stories that are exactly 100 words), micro-fiction (stories under 400 words), and hint fiction (stories under 25 words).

The great writer Yasunari Kawabata described his shorts as "palm-of-the hand" stories because they were so small they could fit in the palm of your hand. In China, they're known as "smokelongs" because they could be read in the length of a cigarette break.

All of these different names—these forms nested within one other like a series of Russian dolls—support a theory of mine: constraints don't limit creativity; they spark new layers of creativity, each layer subtly different, nuanced, unique.

I think that one can best write a story with a metaphor of its shape and essence in mind, whether you're writing a story that is a tangled web or an airy breath. So here are 13 metaphors for flash fiction, which I hope illuminate the form in similar ways as that lightning bolt did years ago.

1. Dorothy Parker said, "Brevity is the soul of lingerie." A flash story is the lingerie itself: an invitation to come hither, a promise, a hint.
2. Flash fiction is like a tiny island, created from an unknown eruption at the earth's crust, enhanced by the expanse of the sea around it.
3. Flash fiction is like the moment a turtle pokes its head out of its shell.
4. Flash fiction is like an afternoon nap. Short. Dreamy. A respite from a tough day. A strange and intriguing interlude. And when you wake up, you're in a different state.
5. Flash fiction is the moment you hit the brakes.
6. Flash fiction is like a brook flowing through the woods. It's easy to step over, and it's not big enough to be on any map, but then when you pause to observe it, you see life teeming within it.
7. Flash fiction is like the tip of a needle.
8. Flash fiction is like a bonsai tree, compressed, yet sculpted to create movement, proportion, asymmetry, and poignancy. Some trees slant. Some trees cascade. Some are windswept or weeping. "Bonsai art is the display of a landscape—without the landscape," said the bonsai artist Nobu Kajiwara.
9. Flash fiction is like a rare seashell you find on the beach. It's delicate, yet it's traveled though many waters, only to be mysteriously left on the shore, a found object.
10. Flash fiction is like the faint rustling of a ghost, present, yet absent; alive, yet dead. It has something to tell you, but you have to listen in a different way.
11. Flash fiction is like a submarine, able to go to places beneath the surface of life in a way that other boats can't.
12. Flash fiction is like a pill: small and seemingly harmless, yet full of powerful substances that might heal, might kill—or might just alter your senses.
13. Flash fiction is like the light of a sparkler, spritzing dashes of light into the air for only a minute.

There are many more metaphors, of course. I've heard flash fiction compared to a snow globe.

You can peer into a strange miniature world, you can hold it in your hand, and with one simple shake, the world changes. Flash is like a cooking extract or a homeopathic remedy. It's the rich soil, the silt, found in a river's delta.

Dr. Seuss was entranced by the possibilities of tiny worlds. In *Horton Hears a Who!*, Horton the Elephant hears a small speck of dust talking to him, and he discovers that the speck is actually a tiny planet, home to a community called Whoville, where microscopic creatures called Whos live (and presumably read tiny stories).

Flash allows for drama that floats in the air like a dust mote, but, as Lia Purpura wrote in her essay "On Miniatures," the miniature isn't just a smaller version of something larger. "Miniatures transcend their size, like small-but-vicious dogs; dense chunks of fudge, espresso, a drop of mercury, a parasite. Miniatures do nothing less than alter our sense of, and relation to time and space. Finally, and most strangely to me, miniatures are radically self-sufficient. The beings who inhabit fairylands, those elves and sprites, pixies and trolls, don't usually strive to be our pals. They're distant and go about their business. They don't need us. Their smallness is our problem, or intrigue, or desire. They don't need us, and thus we are drawn to them—as any smitten lover might be, to a beloved who remains so close and yet just out of reach."

Perhaps there are so many ways to describe flash fiction because of the many things it does. As the poet Mark Strand said, "It is condensed, even curt; its rhythms are fleeting, its languor quick, its majesty diminutive. It discredits accretions, honors reduction, and refuses to ramble. Its identity is exceptional, its appetite exclusive. It is refractory, rapid, runtish. It reverses, refutes, revises. It can do in a page what a novel does in two hundred. It covers years in less time, time in almost no time. It wants to deliver us where we were before we began. Its aim is restorative, to keep us young. It thrives on self-effacement, and generates statements, on its own behalf, that are shorn or short. Its end is erasure."

The beauty of a firefly's light is not how it illuminates the world, as the sun does, but in how it illuminates the darkness. Sometimes it takes the smallest of things to open up the biggest of spaces.

Grant Faulkner is the Executive Director of National Novel Writing Month (NaNoWriMo) and the co-founder of *100 Word Story*. He's published *All the Comfort Sin Can Provide*, *Fissures* (a collection of 100-word stories), and *Nothing Short of 100: Selected Tales from 100 Word Story*. He has also published two books on writing, *Pep Talks for Writers: 52 Insights and Actions to Boost Your Creative Mojo*, and *Brave the Page*, a teen writing guide. His stories have appeared in dozens of literary magazines, including *Tin House*, *The Southwest Review*, and *The Gettysburg Review*.

SPOTLIGHTED

***The Best Small Fictions* (Nathan Leslie):** Please talk a bit about the beginnings of *The Adroit Journal* and how *Adroit* has evolved over the years.

***The Adroit Journal* (Garrett Biggs):** The short version is that it was founded in 2010 by our editor-in-chief Peter LaBerge when he was in high school (!). Needless to say, the journal has grown from its high school years both in its taste and reach since then: Just recently, Adroit formally became a 501(c)(3) nonprofit, which will help considerably in our future growth. On a less technical note, I think our work has steadily become more ambitious over the years: more longform fiction, more experimental poetry, a more open aesthetic, etc.

BSF: On your website the following captures me: "We're looking for work that's bizarre, authentic, subtle, outrageous, indefinable, raw, paradoxical. We've got our eyes on the horizon." There is so much here to discuss. I especially like the focus on the future here. What inspired this focal point?

Adroit: I am pretty siloed to editing the prose section, so I'll speak to that: There's always discussion about who fiction and nonfiction writers write for: Should we aim to write something timeless? Should we aim to write for our generation? Future generations? It's a productive discussion. I think my two cents on the matter is that you can only really write for your own time—what you imagine the future of literature is in your specific moment. We may very well be wrong, but whatever. We can't promise anyone will care in twenty years, and we certainly can't put our work in a time capsule and send it backward. I think we're as interested in the *now* as we are the future.

BSF: How did you all manage the pandemic (and how are you still managing)? Did you see an influx of pandemic-lit or notable pandemic-related anxiety?

Adroit: The journal has always been entirely run remotely—our staff is located all around the globe—so it didn't really get in the way of operations. And yeah, we read quite a few pieces on the pandemic or pandemic-adjacent subjects. Some we even tried to publish, but we were beaten to the punch by other great journals. That's the kind of stuff people want to move fast on publishing, and I guess we've been slow to the draw.

BSF: I admire the eye that *Adroit* keeps on the up-and-coming writers. You award prizes to work emerging from secondary and undergraduate writers. Why is this important to your mission?

Adroit: We have quite a few educators on staff (myself included) and then there's the fact that Peter founded the journal when he was a young writer himself. It just feels natural for us, like it's really built into our DNA. More broadly though, I think young writers who take their work seriously (as they should) carry a bit of a chip on their shoulders: That attitude is useful. It makes the work more exciting. It makes them swing for the fences. We want to validate the energy behind young writers and their work.

BSF: *Adroit* publishes a wide range of poetry as well as prose and many interviews. You have a reputation in the flash world for publishing high-quality work. In your view, what are some of the traits that make for great small fictions?

Adroit: Thanks—I'm glad to hear we have that reputation, considering we are really selective about the microfiction we choose to publish. It's a difficult form. Harder than writing longform, if you ask me. There is less room to make mistakes, sure, but you're also working with a far more restrictive set of constraints. And in some ways, I think it's best to think of writing flash or micros as a separate craft from novel writing or short story writing altogether. A lot of treasured craft principles seem to not apply when you are writing stories under 1000 words. There's room for disagreement here, of course, but that's how I have always made sense of flash as a genre. So, what are we left then without a traditional sense of character or plot? I always look for remarkable work at the level of the line, and a story that feels like it's overflowing—as if there's somehow more in the story than its container can allow for, but it's there and it's exciting.

BSF: *Best Small Fictions* 2021 features several outstanding works from *Adroit.* In Kate Bernheimer's "Eagle Swallowing Girl" there is this collision of the mundane with the menacingly transcendent. Is this what drew you to this particular piece? Or was it perhaps the surprising humor?

Adroit: "Menacingly transcendent"—I love that. There's something transcendent about all of Kate Bernheimer's work, isn't there? I've been a fan of her writing going back years and honestly, I struggle to imagine a story of hers I wouldn't be drawn to. If I had to peg something here though that most compelled me, it would be a kind of bounciness to the narrator's voice: "I noticed something in the sky. An enormous eagle –way bigger than eagles are in real life. I told the mechanic, 'That's an eagle.' I began a conversation with him about how the eagle was a national symbol. Soon I became insecure that the eagle was a national symbol." The way repetition builds voice here is masterful.

BSF: Speaking of humor—"Balthazar" by John Elizabeth Stintzi also cultivates an odd sense of the unexpected, which sets me on the edge of my seat. I love the odd detail about walking the snake especially. What inspired you to nominate this particular story (which we also love)?

Adroit: There is a dark sense of longing here that I really latched onto: "The more I saw the scars, the more I wanted to have that effect on someone. I wanted to make a temporary mark. To play a role in a story that would, with time, fade away." This is what I mean earlier when I mentioned how I want a story to feel like it's overflowing: There's so much held in just those three lines. And then that ending: "I would sometimes bite him, too." On one hand, shiny. On the other, understated. It's the perfect button to end a micro with.

BSF: Jennifer Tseng's "Menemsha Hills Reservation" keeps the reader off-balance with its askew presentation of scene. The reader is placed within this milieu and must dissect what is really going on here. It's a wonderful flash. What is your take on this piece?

Adroit: For me, this one comes down to its sound and rhythm. Tseng is so careful with every line. One editor pointed out how this is the perfect example of a piece where you don't know what's going on at every single moment of the story, but the writer is so confident in their delivery, you don't care. I don't think that's something you can teach a writer to do, which makes this story all the more special. As a reader, you just sit back, and trust Tseng to take you where you need to go; and you do wind up there.

BSF: Since you mention the issue of the future—where do you see flash going aesthetically after 2021? Do you see any trends worth mentioning?

Adroit: I don't have a crystal ball, so I'll tell you where I want it to go: I really would love to read more flash that grapples directly with class dynamics. In some ways, it's the perfect form to do so. There's a lot of privilege in having the time to write a novel, and the ability to write flash on a tight schedule topples over some barriers to entry. I'd love to see more writers engage openly with that.

BSF: Who are some of the authors you admire but have not yet had the chance to publish in *Adroit?*

Adroit: Great question. Amelia Gray is the first that comes to mind. Ottessa Moshfegh is on my dream-list too. I know I just said I don't have a crystal ball, but if I did, I'm pretty certain it would say that her work will outlive this moment, and only gain more currency with time. She's as good as it gets.

BSF: Thank you for taking the time to chat. Really enervating small fictions, *Adroit.* Keep up the wonderful work!

Adroit: Thank you. We appreciate y'all supporting our authors!

The Best Small Fictions (**Michelle Elvy**)**:** This year, *BSF* includes four stories from *Gargoyle's* pages: 'Lighthouse' by Melissa Scholes Young, 'Get Bent' by A.A. Balaskovits, 'Sirens' by Marija Stajic and 'Animals with Wings' by Rosanna Staffa. Can you tell us what you find outstanding about each of these pieces? And do you think these are a fair representation of what's in *Gargoyle's* pages, generally, or are they of particular interest in a more specific manner, as shorter fictions?

Gargoyle (**Richard Peabody**)**:** I do love the Phantom Zone between prose poems and flash fiction. Melissa has a couple of indie chapbooks but is more widely recognized as a novelist. Her second is due out later this year. And of course she's taken over the "Grace and Gravity" series of writing by DC Area Women. A.A. Balaskovits has a blast twisting nursery rhymes and I've always considered *Gargoyle* the perfect home for anything "twisty." Her second book collection of stories is due from sfwp. Marija Stajic has a debut novel looking for a home but we've been printing her longer stories for a few years now. Something short is unusual from what I've seen of her writing. Rosanna Staffa is pretty new to me. I loved how she focused the story on an office cleaning lady and how she imagined the lives of the workers from their desks and photos. Plus how that impacts our fantasies and our dreams.

I like to mix up the page lengths of the stories. It works very well to hit the brakes for more traditional prose and then put the pedal to the metal in the shorter pieces. So, yes, that's the magazine these days. Long straightaway at Monaco followed by a chicane.

BSF: Notably, all four of these works are by women, dealing with fragments of self, with a sense of being alone—each offering a view of the individual and the other, and each exploring these themes with a strong sense of voice. Do you think voice is one of the most important things in storytelling?

Gargoyle: I believe a large percentage of readers are looking to identify with Voice. Old-school characters or a dynamic narrator—be they human, insect, or amorphous. Being a guy and after running the mag for 45 years, I can frequently predict where a male writer's going. But women writers continue to surprise me. I never seem to know what they're going to do.

BSF: Your own work often engages a sense of place – as these four stories from *Gargoyle's* pages do. Are you always grounded in place as a writer yourself?

Gargoyle: I don't think I am necessarily drawn to place. I do feed off some locales more than others, and as a DC native have always made an effort to represent the area. Whatever works.

BSF: Gargoyle dates back to 1976. Now, in 2021, you are publishing your 75th issue. How has the magazine changed since its early incarnation? Are some things still the same for you as an editor, or do you look at creative submissions with a different sensibility now, compared to 1976?

Gargoyle: Yikes. We started as a newsprint monthly that sold for a quarter, romped through a myriad of formats, shapes, sizes, learning what was possible as we quit and were then reborn finally in 1997 into our current look. For decades I said I would one day be assassinated by a crazed librarian because there was no way to bind our issues together.

I still have one foot in the 70s Small Press Underground, in that I knew so many of the Mimeo and Letterpress pre-computer folks who are now retiring or dying out. There are a lot more poets and writers these days and that is a mixed blessing in terms of sifting through submissions to find work that resonates for me. That said, there are so many fabulous writers right now. As the previous volumes of this anthology series have demonstrated.

BSF: You say *Gargoyle* is 'a scallywag magazine, a maverick magazine, a bit too academic for the underground and way too underground for the academics'—and we wonder about the blurring of lines and definitions. Do you see your magazine as subversive in a sense?

Gargoyle: Not as subversive for the times as the mags I idolized in my high school and college days were—*Evergreen Review, New American Review, Transatlantic Review, New Directions, Ambit, Oz, It, Antaeus, Wormwood Review, Ins & Outs, Truck, Little Caesar, Toothpaste.* Most were representative of an editor or editors and had style and substance that couldn't really be imitated. My first anthology collected work from three historic DC litmags—*Portfolio, Voyages,* and *Dryad.* My second was called Mavericks and featured reprinted interviews with small publishers—George Braziller, Maurice Girodias, David Godine, James Laughlin, John Martin,

James Boyer May, Barney Rosset, Alan Swallow, and Noel Young. Names worthy for a literary round table of movers and shakers.

BSF: Your own work as writer/ editor has covered important and iconic cultural topics from Barbie to James Dean to abortion. More recently, you've edited a series of collections of writing by Washington, DC women. How do you see today's creative writing reflecting our real world, in all its complicated layers? And what ideas or approaches to creative expression are you most interested in, as we move through 2021?

Gargoyle: There are aspects to Pop that provide a portal to universality. Love it or hate it, Fan Fiction has changed the literary universe. I tend to steer clear of Insta poems re: the day's disaster. It takes me close to a decade to process what happened today. Some are better equipped to tackle the immediate. Let them have at it. I welcome more voices, more diversity, more possibilities. But the past few years have been an ongoing nightmare, and threats keep mounting. Will anything we do matter a decade from now? Some days I give in to despair, and other days I try to write something that will matter. That's the best you can hope for.

The Best Small Fictions (**Claire Guyton**)**:** Your website's "About" page notes that you look for work that takes risks and challenges readers. Can you tell us more about that?

Hayden's Ferry Review (**Tucker Leighty-Phillips**)**:** Admittedly, our masthead experiences a bit more turnover than our "About" page, so I think our definition of risk changes depending on who our editors are, so I'm mostly speaking for myself here. My most pleasing experiences as a reader are when I find myself feeling overjoyed by a submission as soon as I see it on the page—this can mean a unique format, a daring title or opening line, or some other way that a submission can offer a more direct invitation to read it. Noa Covo's "Katya" was the first piece we accepted for our Haunted online issue, and it built trust with us from its first line: "The girls on the beach say Katya killed her twin sister in the womb." There's so much ground-setting happening in that line; we've got characters and characters in conflict and a premise that feels dangerous. The story only furthers itself from there.

I think more than anything, we want work that defamiliarizes; allows us to look at an old object or concept in a new way. I also like audible experiences. Sometimes when I'm reading submissions, I read aloud, because I like to get a feel for the language in my own mouth and ear. When a work is bold and playful, I think you can sense it on your tongue.

BSF: Given that a reader won't be asked to entertain a challenging conceit for long, is there more opportunity for successful risk-taking in very short work?

HFR: This is something I think about a lot! Look at Meredith Alling's "Other Babies," for example. If you haven't read that story, it's a great flash fiction that is essentially a list of different kinds of babies. That would be a hard novel to sustain, right? I don't know if there's more opportunity in short-form work, but I do think that maybe there's a different kind of permission. Shorter work can take an alternative approach without having to worry as much about tiring readers out or pushing them away. We, as readers, may be more willing to see it through to the end, even if we're still making sense of the conceit at the halfway point. You can't always say the same for a longer work.

BSF: What makes for a small fiction *HFR* wants to publish? Do you look for the same elements in all short fiction, or does the *very* short form have its own requirements?

HFR: For me, I want to see a repeating cycle where Concept becomes Story, where Story becomes Emotional Resonance, where Emotional Resonance is only possible in this specific Concept. Some writers are really good at building that over the course of twenty-five, thirty pages. Some can do it in a paragraph (although one is not more valuable than the other—both are their own kinds of lovely alchemy). Some writers can do both, and I wish they'd stop showing off so much.

Sometimes, I feel like great short-form fiction is similar to joke-telling—you build to a punchline that asks the reader to do a mental math equation of the story they just read, to feel the satisfaction of that closing moment solving a puzzle, capping (or perhaps uncapping) a bottle. With some writers, a great microfiction is inseparable from a joke and punchline, like Ana María Shua's fantastic and often-hilarious work.

BSF: What drew you to these three pieces selected by *BSF*—"Katya," by Noa Covo; "The Home for Problem Girls," by Emmilea O'Toole; and "Alvin," by Vincent Poturica?

HFR: This is a thrilling question! I am such a sucker for bragging on the artists I love. Let me try to answer collectively and then I'll speak to each individual piece, if that's alright. As a unit, these stories are all oozing with a sense of multiplicity and charm. All three take a concept, ramp its emotional energy, and use their separate unique tones and imagery to build something really cohesive and gorgeous.

As I mentioned earlier, "Katya" was the first piece we took for our Haunted online issue. We'd been reading submissions for a Haunted print issue simultaneously, and we were seeing lots of what you'd expect—ghosts and spirits and more literal plays on the theme. I wanted to find a story that was working as a crux for the issue, something to build around. Covo's story felt haunted in tone—there was something about it that stayed with me, forced a quick second and third read. It had a concept that I didn't think we'd see again in that specific call, and it was so heavy with emotion towards nostalgia and puberty and fear, all through the lens of this teenage birthday party, that I couldn't help but love it.

"Alvin" was, editorially speaking, the opposite. It was a story selected much later for that issue, one of the last pieces we took. There's a completely different kind of scrutiny for those last-ones-in; if you've only got room for one or two more pieces, you want those pieces to be fantastic, to round things out, to give the issue as a whole a sense of completeness. If your first acceptance for an issue is your crux, your last is the final puzzle piece—which is really the same metaphor, just existing in a different spatial area. Poturica's story was a welcome relief from some of the heavy themes in the Haunted submission queue; his story about a person living in the walls of a rental home was charming and funny. I think some of the really successful pieces from that call for submissions were the ones that acknowledged the relationship between humor and heartbreak, and found there is a special space for haunting between those walls. There's a line early in the story after the narrator catches Alvin, the titular person-in-the-walls looking in from a peephole. Poturica writes "Peephole—the word has such a nasty flavor. I'll call them vantage points from now on." I found this to be a charming piece of narration, and found the vantage point to be one of the really powerful aspects of this story; so much of it has been told in backstory, events leading up to a now, and the "now" in the story is an absence, of Alvin's removal of self from the story, and we as readers get a "vantage point" to see and feel how this loss has impacted the narrator.

As for O'Toole's story, which was featured in our print journal, it was working in similar ways to Poturica's—a creative concept, a strong toed-line between humor and sadness, and a gorgeous blend of creative images directed through those complex emotions. One of the early images in the story is a moment of sibling companionship presented through two sisters secretly going barefoot beneath the tables in their classroom. This story was initially found in the queue by Poetry Editor Rachel Reeher, and I asked her about it. She said she loved this story because it didn't just present a unique premise, but made her "crave the premise," and that O'Toole makes "nakedness a source of magic, a mystical thing."

BSF: Two of these selections ("Katya" and "Alvin") come from a special call for short-form work. Did the response to this call whet your appetite for more very short prose?

HFR: I've actually been a huge proponent of flash/microfiction for a while, and initially proposed the online short-form issue! *HFR* published a "long" issue a few years ago, which exclusively published longer-than-normal poems and stories, and when I arrived at *HFR*, our queue was primarily longer stories, twenty-five to forty pages. I thought an issue consisting of shorter work might speak to writers working in those forms, allow us to showcase more authors, and boost *HFR's* profile as a venue for such work. There are a lot of great magazines working exclusively in flash fiction, and with the academic literary journals, it can sometimes be a bit tricky to determine which are receptive to flash and micro. The online issue was not only a companion to our print journal, but was an expression of interest in shorter work. I'm glad to see it has resonated with readers!

The Best Small Fictions **(Caire Guyton):** The name of your magazine was inspired by Zora Neale Hurston's work in the 1930s turpentine camps in Florida's longleaf pine forests, where she documented folklore for the WPA. As you point out, Hurston demonstrated so beautifully that *everyone has a story*. Can you tell us more about how this belief shapes the magazine?

Longleaf Review **(Lilly Schneider):** If a longleaf pine tree falls in a forest and no one is around to hear it, does it make a sound? If a writer writes a piece of bold, innovative, exciting, and beautiful prose, and no one is able to read it, does it make a sound? *Longleaf* is a place where we celebrate experimental styles and aim to amplify the voices of those who have been systematically quieted.

(Stephanie Trott): There's no one "right" way for a tree to grow, just as there's no one "right" way to tell a story. Every submission we receive is unique because of the person who wrote it, and we want to celebrate and promote the diversity of the literary arts community while amplifying its weirder side. Just as trees provide oxygen, we want the stories we publish to give back to the reader in some way that sustains them and inspires them to write something of their own.

(Adelina Sarkisyan): "All of it weird" is how we describe the stories we publish at *Longleaf*. "Weird" meaning, "open to interpretation." Every story is unique because the voice behind it is unique, and at *Longleaf*, we aim to amplify voices that are authentic and unapologetic in who they are. In a forest of longleaf pines, no two trees look the same, grow the same, or communicate the same. We aim to publish work that redefines the way we tell our stories.

(Kate Finegan): We have an incredible team of generous, enthusiastic readers and editors who open each submission with a sense of wonder and possibility. We're not afraid to accept pieces that are a bit odd or rough around the edges. *Nothing* makes us happier in editorial meetings than declaring, "We've accepted this story, and it's the author's first publication!" We want stories that grow in unlikely soil, that might have come about as the result of a lightning fire or a controlled burn.

BSF: Flash fiction has been a prominent part of *Longleaf Review* since your first issue in 2018. What makes you so fond of this form?

Longleaf (LS): Flash is a high-wire trick. A great flash story hits like a lightning bolt and leaves you with a face full of ash and smoking hair.

(ST): I love flash that makes me feel something visceral and makes me want to read it another time through. I want to be like the little kid who flies fast and furious down the playground slide and runs back to climb atop it once more, yelling, "again, again!" Flash fiction should be just as high and just as quick. Even with quieter pieces that center more on something small, as a reader I really want to use my senses and slip easily into voice or scene.

(AS): Flash often feels like complete incompleteness (or vice versa!). It's a tiny window into a very large world, a literary Tardis if you will (any *Doctor Who* fans?). And the experience of reading flash is very different from reading poetry or longform prose, as are the voices who write them. *Longleaf* wouldn't be complete without this heart clenching experience.

(KF): We adore the big ideas that take up a tiny space. Adelina is absolutely right in calling flash a literary Tardis! Flash is ultra-compact and can do such interesting things with time. A moment can expand to fill a universe; the ocean can fit inside a shoebox. Flash can be audacious, surprising, and wonderful. It can also zero in on small details that might be skimmed over in a longer piece. It is a high-wire act, as Lilly said. When I read great flash, I feel that I've been suspended in time and space, and I don't want to come back down.

BSF: What drew you to the 3 pieces selected for *BSF*—The Farmer's Daughter," by Melissa Benton Barker; "The Space of Continuous Decline," by Mary Grimm; and "Boba Talk," by Andy Lopez?

Longleaf (LS): Every one of these stories demonstrates a consistent, alluring voice and a unique sense of tone and style on the sentence level. Each of these three voices seems to be telling a secret, deeply buried story, one that each of the respective first-person narrators have told to no one else in their fictional worlds; there's urgency, grief, and a kind of heartbreaking resistance there.

(ST): Each of these authors has a masterful sense of line balance; they're thinking about their work on both a micro and a macro level, how words become lines and then paragraphs and then a unified work, and they never lose track of the reader. There's a sense of authority and ownership from both the narrators and the authors, and I love the command that they display from a narrative and a craft standpoint. These are writers who know what they're about. I suppose the phrase I'd use is "unabashedly authentic."

BSF: In your FAQ about the workshops you offer, you talk about the importance of building a writing community. You've been doing these online workshops since 2020—how have the workshops contributed to the voice of the magazine?

***Longleaf* (LS):** Free admission to the workshops for contributors and staff is one of the ways we thank them for sharing their time and work with *Longleaf.* You don't have to apply to take the workshops or pay more than you can afford, and you'll be asked to be kind and respectful. Editors, members of our amazing reading team, past contributors, future contributors, fans of the magazine, and writers of all stripes meet as equals to learn from and be inspired by each other. *Longleaf* is more than just a magazine—it's a community where anyone who wants to be involved can find more than one way to engage.

(ST): We want to cultivate a space that's centered around equity and belonging, where writers can come as they are, have a comfortable seat at the table, and engage with their writing in a way that feels good for them. That philosophy is something we aim to emulate with our reading team as well: our readers come from a wide range of backgrounds and experiences, and they each have different tastes and preferences. At the core of our team, however, is the want to publish compelling fiction that sparks conversations and has the power to alter the reader's perspective (in a good way!). We look at everything we do as a conversation, where it's equally as important to listen as it is to contribute.

(AS): At *Longleaf,* we love exploring the before and after of being published. We created workshops, and a writing community, because we wanted to invest in and engage with content that writers don't usually explore together—all the nuances of a writing life. The community we've created is a space where writers can engage with their own writing, and the writing of their peers, safely, honestly, and with a ton of curiosity (and no pressure!). If anything, we want to create a community of writers and readers that continuously inspire each other.

(KF): The word I overuse in all the workshops is *play.* We embrace the wild mess of discovering a new idea or excavating a new layer in an existing piece. We want to break down the barriers between the pen and the page and allow writers to explore the possibilities of writing in a no-pressure atmosphere that is also intensely focused. We hope the compressed timeline of the workshop gives writers permission to connect with one another quickly in group discussions and enter a state of flow in the quieter moments when they're working independently. I want to show writers, including those who don't yet embrace that title, that they have so much to bring to the page.

BSF: 2021 is your fourth year. What's next?

Longleaf **(LS):** Continuing to publish great fiction from emerging and established authors. Expand the *Longleaf* family—contributors, readers of the magazine, staff, and workshop participants. We dream of in-person events. Our themed submission calls in 2020 have led to some incredible issues. We'll have two unthemed and two themed issues a year going forward and keep doing online mini-workshops leading up to our themed submission periods.

(ST): I'd love to see us branch out into deeper community with our contributors and readers. I love our 30-minute writing prompt sessions and would love to do more, and I hope we can get the editor-contributor interviews we've briefly discussed off the ground.

(AS): Find new ways to amplify our writers and their published pieces on our website, whether it's through interviews, or accompanying audio readings of their pieces. It'd be a dream to have some type of in-person event or meetup. But overall, continue to publish work that is exciting and weirder than ever. And continue creating community via workshops with our readers and contributors because that is as big a part of *Longleaf* as the stories we publish.

(KF): I often think of *Longleaf* as a creative incubator that publishes quarterly issues. Within our team of volunteers, we've started doing "staff draft readings" in which we get together on Zoom to read things we're working on, and the chat box is abuzz as we sing the praises of our fellow writers' rough drafts. Lots of exclamation points! It's really great to be a home for such amazing polished work in the quarterly issues, but I would love to provide a sandbox, as well. I want to be a place where people can bring their work and learn how to make it shine by polishing the magic that's already there. Building opportunities that are safe, inclusive, and rough-draft-friendly is one of my priorities for the volunteer team but also for our broader community of contributors and readers.

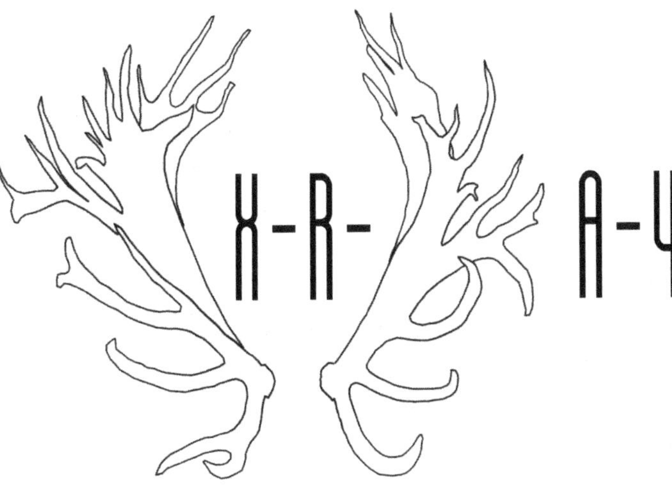

***The Best Small Fictions* (Nathan Leslie):** Let's start at the beginning. First of all, I would love to know about the genesis of *X-R-A-Y.* How and why was it founded and was there a particular literary void that you were trying to fill with *X-R-A-Y*?

***X-R-A-Y* (Jennifer Greidus):** I met Chris (co-founder, bf) online while he was in Houston and I was in Pennsylvania. Our initial correspondence contained a bunch of lit talk. Then, you know: love, love, etc. After a few months, I flew to Houston, and we drove back to PA to live together. We spoke about starting our own mag on that three-day trip.

Chris has had a much longer relationship with online publishing than I do. He also has stronger convictions about what he'd like to see happen with internet writing. But that's his story to tell.

I simply wanted a steady flow of stories in my inbox. I wanted to get to know who wrote what I liked to read, and the mag seemed the fastest and most pleasurable way for me to do it. Until that point, I had sheltered myself from a lot of news, social media, and so forth; before starting *X-R-A-Y,* most of my enjoyment came from physical books. In short, the particular literary void I was trying to fill was my own.

BSF: Tell me about the great name? *X-R-A-Y* is both imagistic and perhaps tells your readers something about the function of literature as well?

X-R-A-Y: The same reason Triple A picked AAA. Eyes go to the beginning of a list, then to the end, and then they scan the middle bits. We didn't want to be a middle bit.

BSF: Your mission statement reads: *"X–R-A-Y Literary Magazine's* vision is to publish uncomfortable, entertaining, and unforgettable prose that shines brighter than the skeleton in your body, prose that sees through the skin and reveals something deeper." Can you elaborate on *X-R-A-Y's* particular aesthetics? Is there such a thing as an *"X-R-A-Y"* piece?

X-R-A-Y: I hope we sometimes surprise readers with what we publish. Our archive contains stories about abuse, dog fashion shows, shitting in a box, loss and grief, pirates. We've published sentimental stories that make some of our readers groan; alternately, we can promote a streak of stories other readers find vulgar or unforgivable. We lose followers. We gain some. If we occasionally have a severe reaction, then we're doing something right.

On our social media posts, the first thing a reader sees is the instantly recognizable story art by Bob Schofield. At a glance, each of his creations is innocuous. If you spend another moment appreciating the graphic, however, you may find his delicate, neon sketch is a wild-eyed, hulking baby toting a flamethrower.

BSF: Is there something specific you look for in a great micro or work of flash? In other words, is there something that all great micros or works of flash have in common?

X-R-A-Y: If I'm still thinking about a story while I'm walking my dog, at work, or on the toilet, that's a great story.

BSF: How have you seen small fictions change/evolve over the years?

X-R-A-Y: I remember reading micro and flash in 2011-12, and I was often disappointed. I felt empty at the end, unmoved. I wonder if that was me being snooty about it. For me, the talent in the flash/micro category over the years has improved tenfold in both voice and variety of content. Now, I feel there's a greater chance I'll open a doc and find a tiny treasure.

BSF: "A Eulogy" by Michael Hendery makes some pointed, funny insights regarding the social media landscape. This flash is so fresh and revealing about our behavior in 2021. What drew you to this particular piece?

X-R-A-Y: The premise of an obit being a recount of every minute thing you've shared on social media is great. That story could have been hacky, but Michael pulled it off. I think we can ditch the "in 2021" from that question above. This is how it is now: We die, and barring celebrity and reproduction, few of us leave much more behind than a digital wrap-up.

BSF: In "Freak Deaths" by Aishwarya Mishra the image of a bruise reappears throughout. What do you make of this image as it pertains to the overall meaning of the flash?

X-R-A-Y: In the first line, the author mentions the characters seeming "more mirage than matter." For me, that summed up the tone of the entire story. The mentions of the bruises served to ground me before I became lost in the abstract.

Jo Varnish, *X-R-A-Y's* CNF editor and the other reader for this piece, loved the use of the plural first person. She felt it gave the piece a conspiratorial air, into which the reader is invited.

The language is both beautiful and unexpected—"Our mothers mumble on the terrace as they lay out the pickles to dry"—the imagery of the bruise is sinister, its repetition a reminder of the omnipresent threat of violence. Mishra's ending satisfies, and begs one to reread from the beginning immediately.

BSF: Meg Tuite's "Spree" offers an askew vision with askew language--it's a great piece, and perhaps it goes back to that "uncomfortable and unforgettable" phrase in your vision statement. What drew you to this particular flash?

X-R-A-Y: *X-R-A-Y's* readers/editors admired this one. I read it several times upon first open. For me, beyond Meg's colorful, tight storytelling, the premise hit hard. There is an appreciable similarity to my own mother/daughter dynamic, a sort of dysfunctional heist movie. Although the imagery provides plenty of detail about the daughter's physical presence, to me she feels almost as invisible as she seems to the mother. It was an uncomfortable and unforgettable read, and I enjoyed every line of it.

BSF: Do you have additional future goals for *X-R-A-Y* as we move into 2022 and beyond? How do you see *X-R-A-Y* progressing?

X-R-A-Y: We're thinking about micro-novels. Our inbox is always open for a pitch, something we haven't tried yet.

BSF: It seems like *X-R-A-Y* has flourished this past year. What's the biggest contributor to that success?

X-R-A-Y: It's a group endeavor. We have such a strong team. Since you asked for the main influence, though, it's our Managing Editor, Crow Jonah Norlander. He is the key to X-R-A-Y's growth this past year. Not only has he streamlined our processes and redesigned our site, he keeps everything going with no or few hiccups. Deadlines, issues, newsletters, contests. He's on it. It seems like every day he's tweaking this or that, all while editing and helping each of us with our nitpicky tech questions. If it weren't for Crow, it would still be Jo (Varnish) and me, toiling over our little spreadsheet, and comparing notes at one a.m. on a Tuesday. I could gush some more, but it would be annoying to read. I know all you mags out there have your eye on Crow. Back off.

EDITOR BIOGRAPHIES

Rion Amilcar Scott is the author of the story collection, *The World Doesn't Require You* (Norton/Liveright, August 2019), a finalist for the PEN/Jean Stien Book Award and winner of the 2020 Towson Prize for Literature. His debut story collection, *Insurrections* (University Press of Kentucky, 2016), was awarded the 2017 PEN/Bingham Prize for Debut Fiction and the 2017 Hillsdale Award from the Feelowship of Southern Writers. His work has been published in places such as *The New Yorker, The Kenyon Review, Crab Orchard Review, Best Small Fictions 2020* and *The Rumpus,* among others. His story, "Shape-ups at Delilah's" was published in *Best American Science Fiction and Fantasy 2020.* He was raised in Silver Spring, Maryland and earned an MFA from George Mason University where he won the Mary Roberts Rinehart award, A Completion Fellowship and an Alumni Exemplar Award. He has recieved fellowships from Bread Loaf Writing Conference, Kimbilio and the Colgate Writing Conference, as well as a 2019 Maryland Individula Aritist Award. Presently he teaches Creative Writing at the University of Maryland.

Nathan Leslie's ten books of fiction include *Three Men, Root and Shoot* and *The Tall Tale of Tommy Twice.* Nathan's poetry, fiction, essays and reviews have appeared in hundreds of literary magazines including *Boulevard, Shenandoah* and *North American Review.* Previously Nathan was series editor for *Best of the Web* anthology 2008 and 2009 and he edited fiction for *Pedestal Magazine.* He was also interviews editor at *Prick of the Spindle.* Nathan's latest work of fiction, *Hurry Up and Relax,* was just published by Washington Writer's Publishing House after winning its 2019 prize for fiction. He is the founder and host of the monthly Reston Readings Series and he teaches in Northern Virginia. Find Nathan on Facebook and Twitter as well as at Nathanleslie.net.

Michelle Elvy is a writer, editor and manuscript assessor. Her online editing work includes *52|250: A Year of Flash*, *Blue Five Notebook* and *Flash Frontier: An Adventure in Short Fiction.* In 2018, she co-edited *Bonsai: Best small stories from Aotearoa New Zealand.* She was also an associate editor for *Flash Fiction International.* Her poetry, fiction, travel writing, creative nonfiction and reviews have been widely published and anthologized. Her new collection, *the everrumble,* is a small novel in small forms, launched by Ad Hoc Fiction at the UK Flash Fiction Festival in June 2019. Find Michelle at michelleelvy.com.

Claire Guyton is a transplanted southerner very happy to be living in Lewiston, Maine, where she works as a full-time writer and editor; and a part-time librarian. Her short fiction appears in *Crazyhorse, Mid-American Review, Vestal Review, River Styx, Sliver of Stone Magazine,* and many other journals, as well as the Maine anthology *Summer Stories.* She has been a Maine Arts Commission Literary Fellow and a finalist for the Maine Literary Award, and her work has been selected for the *Best Small Fictions* anthology and nominated for a Pushcart. She is currently revising a collection of linked stories, and a researching a novel inspired by five real women of 1890s Central Maine.

CPSIA information can be obtained
at www.ICGtesting.com
Printed in the USA
BVHW010111131022
649159BV00027B/306

9 780999 750155